4·14·22

FORMATION
EVALUATION

HARPER'S GEOSCIENCE SERIES

Carey Croneis, Editor

FORMATION EVALUATION

Edward J. Lynch

Assistant Professor of Petroleum Engineering
Stanford University

HARPER & ROW, PUBLISHERS   NEW YORK, EVANSTON
AND LONDON

This book is dedicated to

JOHN AND ELIZABETH LYNCH

Contents

Editor's Introduction

The author of *Formation Evaluation* begins the Introduction to this book with the flat statement that "there is no instrument available for indicating the presence of oil underground." In the strictest sense Dr. Lynch is entirely correct. Nevertheless, he ably utilizes the remaining pages of his pioneering text and reference work in describing and evaluating the various ingenious instruments, materials, and procedures which have been developed to make the extraordinarily expensive exploration for oil and gas a little more scientific and thus less costly. Furthermore, Dr. Lynch has paid equal attention to all of the advances in petroleum engineering which increase the efficiency of the production of hydrocarbons once they are discovered.

Formation Evaluation presents in Chapter 2 a short, but nevertheless complete picture of the complex problems growing out of the nearly universal use of drilling fluids in the modern search for oil. Although, as the author points out, mud is not normally thought of as a prime factor in the evaluation of subsurface conditions, all of the various well operations, including logging and testing, are influenced to some degree by the nature of the drilling fluid.

Chapter 4, which is entitled "Drilling Fluid and Cuttings Analysis Logging," underscores the validity of the inclusion of the subjects discussed in Chapter 2. Dr. Lynch also presents a complete picture of coring and core analysis in Chapter 3. His chapter on electric logging is unusually complete and should prove valuable alike to beginners and "old timers" in a technique which has been of tremendous importance in the development of the petroleum industry. The sixty-two well-selected references at the chapter's end in a small measure demonstrate the importance of the subject.

Radioactivity logging and acoustic velocity logging represent somewhat newer and developing fields which are described in significant chapters. Drill Stem Testing, which is so important in any evaluation of subsurface situations of geological or engineering import, also merits, and receives, full consideration in a chapter in Dr. Lynch's volume.

Chapter 9, entitled "Other Evaluation Methods," includes full descriptions of various secondary tools for formation analysis, such as temperature logging, nuclear magnetism and section gauge logging. In addition, there are included descriptions of the various methods currently employed in the determination of the dip of subsurface formations.

"Well Completion," Chapter 10, which is presented in synoptic form, should prove particularly valuable to producers as well as students. It includes in outline a digest of recommended procedures for the various well completion methods which have been found to be the most successful. Chapter 11, which is designated "The Formation Logging Program," is an equally practical presentation of an important subject which is not commonly treated so fully either in textbooks or in reference works.

There are also four valuable Appendixes. Of these the one on log quality control checks is an extended and detailed guide for well procedures. It includes practical suggestions for the preparation for a logging run, and a check list for all types of logs, which should be of interest to every petroleum geologist and production engineer. The professional workers in the various divisions of oil and gas technology should also appreciate the inclusion of the Appendix on pressure-temperature ratings of downhole tools and hole-size limitations. This material has been made available through the courtesy of Schlumberger Well Surveying Corporation.

Formation Evaluation has been illustrated with many figures of diverse type. The schematic and diagrammatic representations should be helpful both to students and to teachers; and the generous use of illustrative materials—there are 108 figures in the chapter on electric logging alone—should make "Lynch on Formation Evaluation" a much appreciated addition, as well as an adjunct, to the presently scattered literature on the subject.

Dr. Edward Joseph Lynch is a native of New York State, who received his bachelor's degree in chemical engineering from Pratt Institute. His doctorate in the same field was conferred by the University of California. Professor Lynch has had experience with the purification of fissionable materials while working at Los Alamos, and he has also served as a Research Associate at the Radiation Laboratory of the University of California. He joined the faculty of Stanford University, Department of Petroleum Engineering, in 1954. For a number of years he has served as an adviser to organizations engaged in the production of oil and gas, notably as a consultant to the Standard Oil Company of California. His richly diversified research, academic and professional background is brightly reflected in the present volume.

CAREY CRONEIS

Rice University

Preface

The ultimate tool in the search for new sources of petroleum is the exploratory well. The methods of geology and geophysics can suggest the most probable geographical locations and geological time periods in which oil is likely to be found in significant accumulations; but it is the exploratory well that determines whether the estimates made from surface measurements will be borne out in fact.

Good drilling practice dictates the use of methods that are designed to make drill hole, and in so doing frequently obscure the presence of oil in the formations penetrated by the bit. It then becomes the duty of the wellsite geologist or engineer to locate those formations that contain hydrocarbons and to evaluate their commercial significance. This process of location and appraisal comprises the field known as *Formation Evaluation*. It is the purpose of this text to study the methods and the tools that are available for this very important task, to review their theory and principles of operation, to point out their uses and limitations, and finally to show how they may be used to complement one another in providing a useful and coordinated system of evaluation at a reasonable cost.

Included in the formation evaluation methods are logging from drill returns, coring and core analysis, formation testing, and various wireline services that come under the general headings of electric logging, radioactivity logging, and acoustic velocity logging. As far as is practical, each topic is divided into theory, description, and operation of the logging tools, and practical application of the logs for the determination of porosity, permeability, and hydrocarbon saturation. There is much information available in the literature on most of these topics; it is unfortunately disorganized, sometimes unduly biased, and rarely coordinated with other logging methods.

This text is designed primarily for those who are completing their training in petroleum engineering or geology and anticipate a career in the oil industry in exploration and development work. It should be useful for practicing exploration engineers and geologists whose academic training was completed before much of this material was available, and for reservoir engineers whose source of information about the reservoir that they are studying is all too often only the logs obtained during the drilling and completion operations.

Logging is a field that depends heavily on experience factors. It is not possible to provide the answers to all questions that may arise in practice in a text of this type. The emphasis here will be placed on theory, in the hope that a solid grounding in fundamentals will provide the necessary foundation which may later be tempered by individual experience.

Many people have directly and indirectly contributed their time and talents to the preparation of this book. Mr. John E. Walstrom of the Standard Oil Company of California was responsible for the initiation of this course at Stanford, and has been very helpful in many ways through the years. His counsel and encouragement were responsible in a large measure for my decision to write the text. Mr. Albert A. Brown of the California Standard Company of Canada has been very helpful in reviewing the manuscript and suggesting corrections and changes that have always been improvements. To Al Brown must go the credit for the system used for classifying carbonate rocks. He has also been responsible for many of the illustrative logs that are to be found throughout. Mr. Frank Campbell of the California Oil Company reviewed the chapter on Drilling Fluid and Cuttings Analysis Logging. Mary Dowden did the typing of my class notes and managed to keep some order among the myriad of papers that went into the final compilation. Myra Campbell and Walter Zawojski were responsible for the typing and drawings that went into the final manuscript.

In addition to these individuals, there were others whose contributions are not so easily specified, but whose help was nevertheless important. Among these are my wife and family, my colleagues at the university, and my students. To all of them I would like to express my heartfelt thanks.

Special thanks are also due to those companies that have contributed materially to the preparation of illustrations and tables in the text. These include Schlumberger Well Surveying Corporation, Halliburton Company, Lane-Wells Company, Baroid Division National Lead Company, Magnet Cove Barium Company, Welex, Johnston Testers, and Core Laboratories, Inc. Particular thanks is extended to the Standard Oil Company of California, with whom the author has worked as a consultant, for permission to attend and participate in numerous meetings and seminars on this subject.

EDWARD J. LYNCH

Stanford University
July, 1962

FORMATION
EVALUATION

1

Introduction

There is no instrument available for indicating the presence of oil underground. This is a cold fact of the oil business for which the oil companies pay dearly, since only about one exploratory well in forty taps a commercially productive reservoir; and this current $2\frac{1}{2}$ percent discovery rate is constantly declining. Thus far, geological and geophysical methods have been found to be the most satisfactory for locating oil, but these are indirect methods. They indicate only the structural and stratigraphic locations where oil might be found. They give no evidence whatsoever as to whether there might be a significant accumulation at a depth of one, two, three, or even four miles below the surface of the earth. The only method that is available for answering this critical question is the exploratory well.

At the time of drilling a well, the most important thing to those who are directly concerned with the drilling operation is to make a straight, true-gage drill hole as quickly and safely as possible at the specified location and to the specified depth. The drilling practices that are necessary for the accomplishment of these ends always act as a barrier to the discovery of hydrocarbons. For example, it is essential that the pressure created by the weight of the drilling fluid in the hole should be sufficient to overcome the pressure of fluids in the formations; the alternative is a costly and extremely dangerous blowout. Yet this same overpressure causes filtration of the drilling fluids into the formations and pushes the formation fluids away from the wellbore, so that their composition and concentration can be determined only with difficulty. In exploratory drilling, therefore, it is necessary to have available a group of methods and tools that are capable of locating and evaluating the commercial significance of the sedimentary rocks penetrated by the

1

drill bit, and to do so under frequently adverse conditions. The use and interpretation of these methods we call *Formation Evaluation*.

The costs of drilling are high and increasing. Current drilling costs in the United States are at least $50 per hour. (An offshore, foreign venture may be ten times this amount.) On this basis a well that requires three months of drilling would cost about $100,000. If this were an exploratory well, about $20,000 or 20 percent of this would represent formation evaluation costs; for a development well, about $7,000 or 7 percent would be spent on formation evaluation. When it is considered that there are 40,000 to 50,000 wells drilled each year at an average cost of about $18,000 per well, the cost of evaluation becomes quite impressive. In addition, drilling of an exploratory well is the final step in a much larger program that entails costs for land acquisition and geological and geophysical studies that may run into hundreds of thousands of dollars. Certainly, the need for effective evaluation is absolutely essential to the success of a major oil company.

The value of an oil reservoir is defined by its areal extent, its thickness and permeability, its fractional porosity, and the fraction of the porosity that is saturated with oil. The objective of good formation evaluation is the quantitative determination of these items. Within an individual well, and under the proper circumstances, each of these (except the areal extent) may be determined with reasonable accuracy for any formation by use of the proper tools or combinations of tools. In order to select the proper methods to achieve these ends, however, it is necessary to have a thorough understanding of the fundamentals which govern their use. When the problems of the individual methods are understood, then they may be combined into an effective evaluation program. The study of these problems will be the concern of the following chapters.

Formation evaluation methods can be classified broadly according to whether they are used as drilling is in progress, or whether they are used after the hole, or at least a portion of it, has been drilled. In the first classification are the methods of Coring and Core Analysis, and Drilling Fluid and Cuttings Analysis Logging. In the second classification are the wireline logs, such as Electric Logging, Radioactivity Logging, and Acoustic Velocity Logging. Drill Stem Testing, which is the final step in the evaluation program, may be used either as drilling progresses, or after extensive sections of hole have been opened.

Coring requires drilling with a special bit which will permit the recovery of a section of the rock that is being penetrated. On this sample, measurements can be made of porosity, permeability, and the saturations of oil, water, and gas. Core analysis is a fundamental method that serves as a basis for calibration of all other logging tools. It is slow, usually expensive, and other methods are used as substitutes whenever possible. In addition to cores taken in the usual manner with the drill bit, small rock samples can be recovered from the sidewall of the bore hole with devices run on logging cable. Samples obtained in this manner are generally much less diagnostic.

Logging from drill returns is a fairly recent addition to the evaluation field. Although it was first introduced in 1938, its major development and use followed World War II. It is a method which takes little, if any, additional rig time over straight drilling, but it is still fairly expensive because it requires the constant services of trained technicians to do the logging and operate the equipment. This method looks directly and continuously for evidence of hydrocarbons in the mud and in the rock cuttings. In addition, a mud logging service company will keep a record of lithology, porosity, drilling rate, mud properties and the bit changes. Sometimes a complete core analysis service is also available. Logging from drill returns is particularly important on exploratory wells where the objective zones may not be clearly defined and the lack of experience with other logging tools may result in misinterpretation of the measurements. The recent introduction of automatic recording equipment promises to bring down considerably the cost of this service.

After a section of hole has been drilled, it is customary to run one or more of the wireline logging tools, depending on the complexity of the interpretation problem. These devices may measure the electrical, magnetic, radioactive, or acoustic properties of the formations. The measured information is displayed continuously as a function of depth on a strip chart or log. Six thousand feet of hole can usually be logged in an hour's time.

Electric logging is the backbone of the wireline services. First introduced in 1927 as a simple resistivity survey, the term now encompasses about eight different types of logging devices. Probably the widest use of electric log surveys is in correlation of structure from well to well. In formation evaluation it is used for estimating porosity, water saturation, and, in some cases, permeability. A variation of electric logging may also be used for determining the angle of dip of the formations.

Radioactivity logs in common use today comprise two surveys, one of the natural radioactivity of the subsurface rocks and one of the response of the rocks and their fluids to bombardment with neutrons. The natural radioactivity survey serves primarily as a lithology device, while the neutron curve is used to measure porosity. There is wide experimentation under way at present with tools utilizing other radioactivity techniques. These are directed toward measurements of the formation density, and spectral measurement of the various elements that are present. It is still too early to tell if they will prove to be widely applicable in field measurements.

Acoustic velocity logging, introduced but a few years ago, has already made a place for itself as the standard wireline tool for estimating porosity. This device measures the acoustic velocity of a sound wave traveling through the formations. A variation of this logging method that measures the intensity of the signal picked up by the receiver has been highly successful as a "cement bond log" for determining the effectiveness of a cementing job in isolating the various formations behind the casing.

If a formation looks promising according to the results of one or more of these evaluation methods, then a drill stem test is made. If it is possible, this is done before casing is cemented in the hole. The test is made by running a packer and valve assembly on the end of the drill pipe. The packer is set so as to isolate the test interval from the mud column and from other formations. Fluid can then be produced into the empty drill pipe by opening the valve. This dynamic method of evaluation simulates the conditions that will prevail when the well is completed, and so it is the deciding factor in determining whether the production will be adequate to justify the additional cost of completion. In addition to the packers and valve assembly, it has been customary, since 1934, to include a pressure recorder in the test string. This pressure record made during the test will indicate whether the test has been successful; it can also be used to determine the reservoir pressure and the permeability of the reservoir rock; in some cases it may be used to indicate the presence of faults or other features which will limit the areal extent of the reservoir.

Before a well is spudded, a thorough study should be made of the electric logs, drill stem tests, drilling time logs, and other geological and geophysical information as may be available in the area. On the basis of this information and other experience factors, a formation evaluation program can be outlined. This program establishes the general procedure that is to be followed to give an adequate and yet economic evaluation. It covers such things as when cores should be taken, how often the electric log should be run, and whether a mud logging unit is to be used on all or part of the hole. This program is then incorporated as part of the drilling program for the well. The flexible application of this program as drilling proceeds is the responsibility of the wellsite geologist, and on him rests the success or failure of the venture.

2

Drilling Fluids

The discussion of drilling fluids can hardly be classified as formation evaluation, but in a sense it is very appropriate that this subject should introduce a book of this type. Every operation that is performed in the hole, whether it is drilling, coring, logging, or testing, is in some manner dependent on the nature of the drilling fluid. In order to get a proper background for the discussion of the various evaluation operations, a brief survey will be made here of the theory of drilling fluids and of the nature and properties of some of the more common fluids in use today. It is not intended that this should serve as more than an outline. For a more complete discussion of this subject, the reader is referred to books by Rogers (11), Grim (7), and the University of Texas Extension Service (3), and the numerous publications that are distributed by drilling mud supply companies.

The primary purpose of a drilling fluid is the removal of cuttings from the well. When hydrocarbon accumulations are encountered, the well fluid must be able to exert sufficient pressure to prevent the entrance of these substances into the well bore. Drilling fluid also has other purposes, such as cooling the bit, lubricating the drill pipe, suspending solids, plastering the walls of the hole to prevent the loss of fluids, controlling the disintegration of certain types of sedimentary rocks, and providing a contact medium for many logging operations. The American Petroleum Institute has set up standards (API RP 29 (2) for a series of tests which are designed to indicate whether the mud is capable of performing these functions adequately. Since the effectiveness of a mud is determined by these tests, the discussion of drilling fluids is probably best introduced by a review of some of these testing methods.

MUD PROPERTIES

The most important properties of a mud are the density (or mud weight), the viscosity and gel strength, and the filtration rate.

Density

The standard API instrument for measuring density is the mud balance shown in Fig. 2-1. A fixed volume of mud is put into the cup,

Fig. 2-1. Balance for determining the density of drilling fluid. (Courtesy of Baroid Division, National Lead Company. Reproduced by permission from API RP 29: Standard Field Procedure for Testing Drilling Fluids.)

and the rider on the balance arm is then adjusted so that the arm is level. The mud weight can be read directly from the balance as pounds per gallon, pounds per square inch per 1000 ft of depth, pounds per cubic foot, or specific gravity. Mud weights are usually expressed in pounds per cubic foot in California and pounds per gallon elsewhere in the United States. Control of the mud weight can be of critical importance in many instances. The pressure in the mud column at the bottom of the hole is a direct function of the mud density (see Fig. 2-2), and this pressure must be adequate at all times to prevent the flow of formation fluids into the mud column. (Formation pressures are usually slightly less than the pressure that would be created by a column of salt water extending to the surface.) This is particularly important for the gaseous hydrocarbons, which can quickly reduce the density of the mud column to such a point that a blowout will occur. On the other hand, it is not possible, nor economic, to make the mud weight too high. Excessive mud weights result in fracturing of weak formations with the consequent dangerous and expensive loss of drilling fluid in a condition known as "lost circulation."

Mud weights up to about 11 lb per gallon can be achieved by the addition of clay, or powdered limestone to the mud. Higher mud weights require the addition of finely ground materials of higher density such as barite ($BaSO_4$) or galena (PbS).

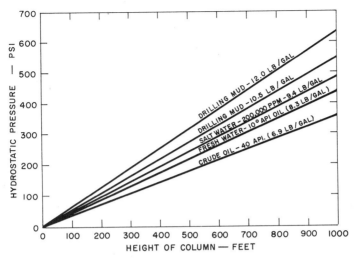

Fig. 2-2. Hydrostatic pressure of a fluid column.

Viscosity and Gel Strength

The resistance to deformation exhibited by a real fluid is called its consistency. For simple Newtonian fluids, such as air or water, the shear rate, or the rate of deformation, at low flow rates, is directly proportional to the shear force that is causing the fluid to flow. The constant of proportionality between the shear stress and the shear rate in this special case is called the viscosity. The unit of viscosity is the centipoise (cp). The stress-strain curve for a simple fluid is shown in Fig. 2-3 as a straight line passing through the origin.

Many materials, among which are drilling muds, do not show this simple relationship. Instead, no flow takes place until a finite shear stress has been created (yield point). At slightly higher stresses, a condition known as plug flow is in evidence, with the shear taking place only at the walls of the container while the center of the fluid remains relatively motionless. Finally, the stress becomes sufficiently high so that viscous flow occurs, and thereafter there is an approximately linear relationship between the stress and the shear rate. Because of the similarity of this last part of the curve with the simple Newtonian curve, the slope of the straight line is called the Bingham (or plastic) viscosity. Materials that demonstrate this type of a stress-strain relationship are known as pseudoplastic (non-Newtonian) fluids.

Viscosity is defined as the ratio of the stress to the shear rate. The apparent viscosity of a pseudoplastic fluid is therefore changing with every change in shear stress. An example of the apparent viscosity is

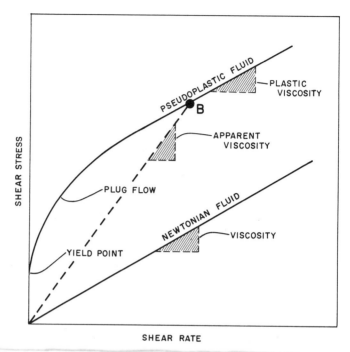

Fig. 2-3. Consistency curves for Newtonian and pseudoplastic fluids.

shown on Fig. 2-3 for the point B. In order that an apparent viscosity may have some meaning, then, it is necessary to specify the manner of measurement and the shear rate at which the apparent viscosity is given. The API has specified that a rotational type of viscometer, like the Stormer shown in Fig. 2-4, should be the standard of measurement for drilling muds, and that the apparent viscosity should be measured when the bobbin is rotating at 600 rpm. If the plastic viscosity is desired, a second measurement is made at 300 rpm. This same instrument can be used to find the gel strength (yield point) by determining the minimum force necessary to start rotation of the spindle from a stationary position. Because of the thixotropic nature of drilling muds, gel strengths are measured immediately after agitation of the mud and also after the mud has been quiescent for a period of 10 minutes.

The viscosity and gel strength are among the most important properties of drilling muds because they govern the ability of the mud to lift and suspend the cuttings. Muds which are too thin permit the cuttings to settle around the drill collars and bit, whereas very thick muds require excessive power on the mud pumps, cause unnecessarily high pressures in the hole, and do not drop fine cuttings in the mud ditch or release entrained gas at the shakers and in the pit. Good gel strength is necessary to suspend the cuttings in case circulation of mud should be stopped. The mud must have thixotropic properties so that as soon as it stops moving a gel will develop which will hold the cuttings where they are in the hole and not permit them to settle around the bit. Again, gel strengths which are too high are undesirable because they prevent

Fig. 2-4. Stormer visco-meter. (Courtesy of Baroid Division, National Lead Company. Reproduced by permission from API RP 29: Standard Field Proce-dure for Testing Drilling Fluids.)

release of hydrocarbon and cuttings at the surface, and because they promote a swabbing action (which could result in a blowout) every time the pipe is moved in the hole. Gel strengths, or shear strengths, are usually expressed in pounds per square feet. Drilling muds ordinarily have gel strengths between 1 and 50 lb per 100 sq ft.

Filtration Rate

The general equation for the flow of fluid in a porous meduim is Darcy's law. (See Chapter 3, page 36.) According to Darcy's law, the rate of filtration of fluid through a mud cake is given by

$$Q = \frac{KA}{\mu} \frac{\Delta P}{x} \tag{2-1}$$

where Q is the flow rate, K is the permeability of the cake, A is the cross-sectional area, ΔP is the pressure differential, and x is the thickness of the cake in the direction of flow. Over a period of time the total amount of filtrate that passes through the cake is

$$V = \int_0^t Q \, dt = \int_0^t \frac{KA}{\mu} \frac{\Delta P}{x} \, dt \qquad (2\text{-}2)$$

During a filtration operation the pressure differential is usually constant, but the thickness of the filter cake increases with time. If C is the volume of filter cake formed by the solids from a unit volume of filtrate, then the thickness of the filter cake at any time is CV/A and the equation for the total volume of filtrate is

$$V = \left(\frac{2KA^2 \, \Delta Pt}{C\mu}\right)^{1/2} \qquad (2\text{-}3)$$

This equation indicates that the filter loss of a mud should be proportional to the square root of time, the square root of the pressure, and the square root of the permeability of the mud cake, and inversely proportional to the square root of the viscosity. In practice, it is found that the relations between V and K and ΔP are not valid, and the relation between V and t is only approximate. The reasons for this will be discussed later.

The standard procedure for testing the filter loss character of a mud specifies that the sample must be filtered through a hardened filter paper under a differential pressure of 100 psi for a period of 30 minutes. (See Fig. 2-5.) The filter paper is 3 in. in diameter. Untreated drilling muds give between 8 and 15 cc of filtrate under these conditions. An effort is generally made to keep the filter loss of a mud below 10 cc. If the filtrate exceeds 15 or 20 cc, the mud is in poor condition and some remedial treatment is indicated. Special muds may run between 2 and 6 cc, and most oil base muds have filter losses of less than 1 cc.

Control of the filtration rate is necessary for two major reasons. First, excessive filtration results in excessive filter cake. This reduces the diameter of the hole, thereby increasing the possibility of sticking the drill pipe or of swabbing the hole when pulling the pipe. Thick filter cakes also complicate the problem of interpreting wall resistivity electric logs. Second, high filter loss causes deep invasion. Deep invasion makes it extremely difficult, and sometimes impossible, to interpret electrical resistivity logs. Deep invasion also introduces a large quantity of foreign water into the formation, and this may result in severe reduction of the permeability of the formation to the flow of oil. The water may also cause swelling and sloughing of the formation.

Fig. 2-5. Filter press for measuring the filtration rate of drilling fluids. (Courtesy of Baroid Division, National Lead Company. Reproduced by permission from API RP 29: Standard Field Procedure for Testing Drilling Fluids.)

DRILLING FLUIDS IN FIELD USE

The drilling fluids that are available today may be classified into three broad types: (1) single-phase fluid with solid additives of which the common water-clay muds and oil base muds are the two important subdivisions; (2) two-phase fluid with solid additives, made up of the emulsion muds; (3) air or gas. This last class is used in special circumstances where shallow zones of lost circulation are encountered and where surface water is not readily available and little subsurface water is present. The problems in the use of gas or air lie outside the scope of this discussion.

Water-Base Drilling Fluids

The first fluid used for rotary drilling was water. However, it is not possible to drill for any distance with water without dispersing shale in it and forming mud. The superiority of mud over water as a drilling fluid was soon recognized, and native clays were added to the drilling water to form mud at the start of the drilling operation. Clay-water suspensions account for the majority of drilling fluids in use today. In order to understand these fluids, it is necessary to consider first the physical and chemical nature of the clays that are used in making them.

The term clay designates a finely ground (between 2 and 100 microns) earth material which is plastic when wet and which is composed of hydrated aluminum silicates. Clays are formed by weathering of feldspar, serpentine, and other basic igneous rocks. Because of the size of the particles, many of them are classified as colloids (particles whose diameter is about 0.000005 mm), and possess the reactive properties of this class of materials, e.g., hydration and high degree of dispersion. Not all clays exhibit the same properties, and only a few are of interest to the petroleum industry. There are four primary classes of clay minerals: kaolin, bentonite, hydrous micas, and attapulgite. The kaolin group of clays includes the minerals kaolinite, halloysite, dickite, nacrite, and endellite. These minerals possess the general chemical formula $Al_2O_3 \cdot 2SiO_2 \cdot nH_2O$, where n has a value of 2 or 4. They are plastic when wet, but they do not have the properties of base exchange or of ultimate particle hydration. In drilling muds they act as inert solids which impart weight and high viscosity to the mud, but little else of interest. This is also true of the hydrous micas, which are represented by the minerals bravaisite and illite. They also possess no base exchange and little ultimate hydration.

The bentonite group, consisting of montmorillonite minerals, possesses both base exchange properties and ultimate hydration. The combination of these two properties gives the bentonites a range of physical characteristics which, when properly controlled, are particularly suitable for the requirements of rotary drilling muds. The name *bentonite* was first applied to a bed of highly colloidal clay found near Fort Benton, Montana. It is composed of a mixture of minerals, but it is primarily the mineral montmorillonite. The structure of this material is complex, and can best be understood by starting with a discussion of the mineral pyrophyllite, which furnishes the base structure.

All clays are formed basically from combinations of SiO_2, and hydrated Al_2O_3. The mineral *pyrophyllite*, shown structurally in Fig. 2-6, is composed of two layers of SiO_2 with a single layer of $Al_2O_3 \cdot H_2O$ in between. These three layers form a crystal that extends for an indefinite distance in width and depth but which is limited in thickness by the

Fig. 2-6. Diagrammatic representation of the structure of pyrophyllite. (After W. F. Rogers, *Composition and Properties of Oil Well Drilling Fluids*, second edition. Copyright 1953, Gulf Publishing Company.)

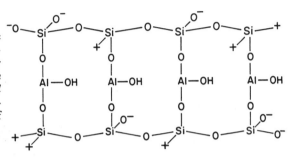

crystal structure as shown. (It has the appearance of a sandwich made of aluminate spread between two slices of silicon dioxide.) Clay particles are composed of many thicknesses of these platelets stacked on top of one another. The crystal itself has great strength in all three directions, but the platelets are easily separated from one another where the two silicon dioxide surfaces are in contact. The pyrophyllite crystal is electrically neutral, with only the edge valences remaining unsatisfied where the crystal has been broken. It has no base exchange properties, does not swell in water, and in general is inert.

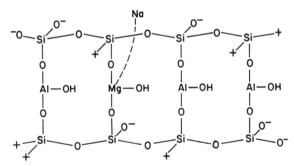

Fig. 2-7. Diagrammatic representation of the structure of montmorillonite. (After W. F. Rogers, *Composition and Properties of Oil Well Drilling Fluids*, second edition. Copyright 1953, Gulf Publishing Company.)

Consider now the structure shown in Fig. 2-7 for *montmorillonite*. It is essentially the same sandwich arrangement, with the single exception that the element magnesium occupies some of the internal lattice sites that are completely occupied by aluminum in the pyrophyllite. This substitution in the structure results in a net negative charge on the

CRUDE BENTONITE

CRUDE BENTONITE
AFTER 24 HOURS IN WATER

Fig. 2-8.   Example of swelling of bentonite.

crystal (Substitution of Mg^{++} for Al^{+++}). The negative charge can be balanced by the addition of another positive ion, but since there is no room for the additional atom within the crystal lattice, this extra atom must occupy a surface location. In the diagram the element sodium is shown in this external position. Being external to the crystal, this atom is relatively free to move, and when the montmorillonite is placed in water, the sodium goes into solution. The remaining charged platelets of montmorillonite tend to repel one another, while attracting the polar solvent, water, to their surfaces. In this manner it is possible for a sodium bentonite to increase its volume by eight or ten times. Figure 2-8 is an example of this.

If the sodium bentonite of Fig. 2-7 is washed by a solution containing an excess of calcium ions, the calcium will replace the sodium from its position as part of the clay, and form a calcium bentonite. This process is called "ion exchange," and the extra atom associated with the clay lattice is called the exchangeable ion. The order of exchange replacement among the common ions is

Na, K, Mg, Ca, Ba, H

Each of the listed elements will be replaced on the clay by any of those following it. The more strongly the element is attached to the clay lattice, the more difficult it is to remove it by ion exchange. Elements on the right end of the exchange series, therefore, have less tendency to separate from the clay lattice as ions when the clay is placed in water. Clays of the calcium type, for example, do not exhibit the very high degree of hydration, with the associated physical properties, that the sodium clays do.

When sodium bentonite is mixed with water to form a mud, the interlayer adsorption of water becomes so great that the individual sheets literally float away from one another. Each of these sheets has a large quantity of adsorbed water which is fixed firmly to the surface. This has the effect of increasing the size of the particle, while decreasing the amount of free water that is left between the particles. The result is a very marked increase in the consistency of the suspension. Not only is this hydration thickening of the mixture observed, but if the suspension is allowed to stand for even a very short period of time, there is evidence that some type of fixed structure tends to form in the mud which gives it a gelatinous appearance. Hauser (8) has proposed the following attraction-repulsion theory to explain this latter effect.

Ionization of the bentonite salt produces surface charges on the clay platelets which cause the platelets to repel each other. The unsatisfied edge valences where the platelets have been broken, and the normal van der Waals forces cause an attraction between the particles. When these two sets of forces are in balance, the particles line up in a series of equilibrium positions that give the water-clay suspension a weak but definite structural arrangement. The longer the mud is quiescent, the more developed this structure becomes, and the gel strength increases. If the mud is agitated, the particles are moved from their equilibrium gel positions and the mud becomes much more fluid. This ability of the bentonitic muds to change their consistency according to the amount of stirring action is known as thixotropy.

A reduction in gel strength may also be accomplished by any means that changes the equilibrium structure through a reduction of the forces involved. Thus, changing from a sodium form to a calcium form of clay reduces the repulsive charge between the platelets; large additions of salt to the mud accomplish the same thing by destroying the ionic atmosphere surrounding the particles; adding materials that satisfy the edge valences reduces the attractive forces. All these changes cause a reduction of the gel strength and the viscosity of the suspension.

In addition to having good viscosity and gel characteristics, the Wyoming bentonites also have very desirable filtration properties. This

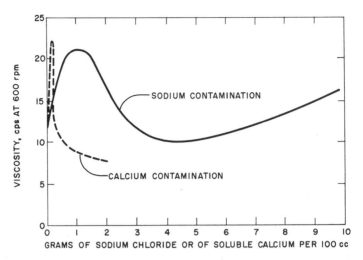

Fig. 2-9. Effect of sodium and calcium contamination on the viscosity of a bentonite mud. (After W. F. Rogers, *Composition and Properties of Oil Well Drilling Fluids*, second edition. Copyright 1953, Gulf Publishing Company.)

is partially the result of the very high degree of dispersion of the particles. Bentonite particles are of colloidal size, and when they are formed into a filter cake, the cake has a very low permeability, and therefore the mud has a low filter loss. In addition, the shape of the particles is flat. Under high-pressure differentials, these flat plates pack together more tightly and reduce the cake permeability. It has been found in tests of highly colloidal muds that the rate of filtration is almost completely independent of the pressure differentials across the cake; the reduction of the permeability term in equation 2-3 exactly counterbalances the increase in the pressure term. This is the reason that the square root proportionality is not observed between V and K or V and ΔP.

Changes in the mud system that cause a reduction of the repulsive force between the particles, as for example through the addition of calcium, cause the particles to flocculate or agglomerate into larger particles. These, in turn, form a more permeable mud cake and cause the mud to have a greater filter loss. When contamination of the mud causes flocculation, it is usually necessary to add some prepared material such as starch or carboxymethyl cellulose to restore the filter loss properties to their original level. If starch is used, it is also necessary to add formaldehyde to prevent bacterial fermentation of the starch. In high pH muds this additional treatment is not necessary.

High temperatures cause a reduction in the viscosity of the mud filtrate, and so it might be expected that the filter loss would go up moderately as the temperature increased. The loss at high temperatures is usually much greater than would be indicated by use of a lower viscosity in equation 2-3, however, because most drilling muds will flocculate to some extent at high temperatures. This may cause such a large increase in the filtration rate that some filter loss additives may be necessary. In addition, if the clay is in the calcium form, as in lime muds, high temperature may cause solidification of the mud into a cement-like material. In carbonate areas this solidification can occur in the vugs and fractures that form the normal flow channels for production of reservoir fluids into the well. Drill stem testing under such conditions becomes difficult or impossible.

Figures 2-9 and 2-10 show the general effect of contamination with sodium and calcium on the viscosity and filter loss of a bentonite mud. Additions of NaCl up to 1 percent cause an increase in gel strength and viscosity, but above this value there is a marked decrease in viscosity as the mud flocculates. Correspondingly, the filter loss remains fairly good until this 1 percent concentration level is reached; above this amount the filter loss increases rapidly. One percent is therefore the dividing line between the use of fresh- and salt-water clays. The effect of calcium contamination is much more marked. Less than 0.1 percent calcium is sufficient to cause the high viscosity peak, and this is immediately followed by a large reduction in viscosity and increase in the filter loss as the clay is partially converted to the calcium form and becomes agglomerated.

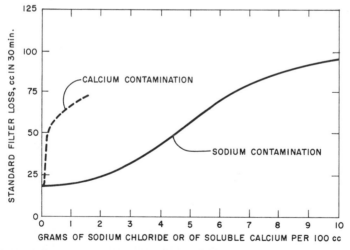

Fig. 2-10. Effect of sodium and calcium contamination on the filter loss of a bentonite mud. (After W. F. Rogers, *Composition and Properties of Oil Well Drilling Fluids*, second edition. Copyright 1953, Gulf Publishing Company.)

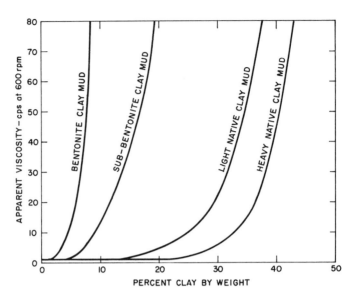

Fig. 2-11. Yield of various types of drilling clays. (Courtesy of Baroid Division, National Lead Company.)

Sometimes a mud will become too viscous through the addition of drilled-up shale or through minor amounts of contamination. Thinning of the mud in this case can be effected by the addition of water. In cases where this procedure is not practical, chemical thinners such as quebracho or the sodium polyphosphates may be added to the mud. The function of these materials is to satisfy some of the broken edge valences which normally cause an attractive force between adjacent particles. This reduces the gel structure contribution to viscosity. It also reduces the tendency to agglomerate, so that thinners will usually improve the filter loss characteristics as well.

In addition to the Wyoming bentonites, there are sub-bentonites and native clays that are used for making drilling muds. The sub-bentonites are similar in structure to the bentonites, but they are principally in the calcium and magnesium forms. The bentonitic character of these clays can be improved by treating them with soda ash (peptizing), thereby converting them to the sodium form. Peptized clays are about 90 percent as good as the bentonites for development of gel and viscosity, but they do not respond to chemical treatment in the same manner, and, in fact, lose much of the peptizing value when so treated.

The term native clays is a general one referring to any local accumulation of clay material. In composition they may be almost anything from pure kaolin to pure bentonite. Most native clays do not hydrate appreciably, however, and merely add solids to the mud. Unless an attempt is being made to increase the weight in this manner, the native clays might more often be considered harmful rather than beneficial to the system. Proper viscosity control with native clays is usually difficult.

Figure 2-11 shows the relative yield of various drilling clays. For a mud having a viscosity of 15 cp, 100 bbl of mud can be made from a ton of bentonite, 50 bbl from a ton of sub-bentonite, and 13 to 17 bbl from a ton of native clay.

When drilling through salt accumulations, or where salt-water flows are encountered, the bentonite type clays lose all of the desirable properties that they ordinarily possess in a fresh-water mud. In this situation it is customary to switch to the clay *attapulgite* as the base mud material. Attapulgite does not exist as platelets, but rather is in the form of needle-shaped crystals. Chemically it is a hydrous magnesium aluminum silicate. The crystals are of colloidal size, and because of their shape,

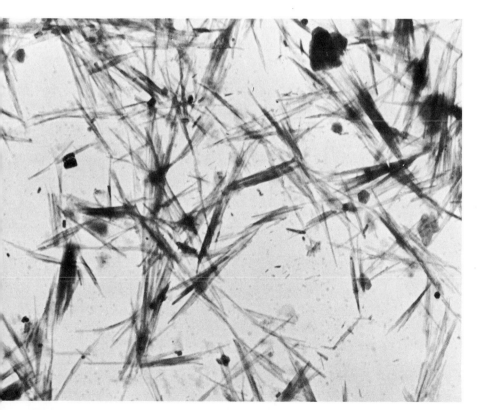

Fig. 2-12. Photomicrograph of attapulgite. (Courtesy of Magnet Cove Barium Corporation.)

they tend to form into a "brush heap" type of structure as shown in Fig. 2-12. This structure prevents the loss of surface water and maintains the colloidal properties of the particles. The mud therefore remains stable even in the presence of high electrolyte concentrations. Although the physical structure of attapulgite is adequate for viscosity and suspending qualities, it will not provide the necessary degree of control over filtration loss. It is customary to add gelatinized starch or a natural gum material for this purpose.

Although there is a wide variety of possible types and treatments of water base drilling muds, there is a fairly limited group of muds which have been found satisfactory for drilling. These are described below.

Natural Muds.   These are commonly used for surface drilling and drilling under the surface pipe. Muds are made from drilled-up shales, and the viscosity is controlled by watering back. Sometimes the mud is enriched with a little bentonite or the viscosity is controlled with caustic and quebracho. If the surface make-up water contains calcium, the calcium may first be removed by treatment with soda ash. Electrical resistivities may run between 0.7 and 5 ohm-meters at 75°F.

Drilling can sometimes be done with water alone when drilling impermeable formations that do not make mud.

Low pH, Caustic-Quebracho.   This is a very stable mud with a pH of 8.5 to 9.5 that is made by treating a natural mud with some bentonite, and a solution of quebracho and caustic (2 lb of quebracho per pound of caustic) to control the viscosity. If no mud is made from drilled shales, all bentonite is used. This mud is used where there is only a limited amount of mud-making shale because of the difficulties that are frequently encountered in drilling hydratable shales with fresh mud, i.e., enlarged hole size, high viscosity, sloughing.

High pH, Caustic-Quebracho.   This mud is similar to the previous mud except that the caustic and quebracho are added in a 1 to 1 ratio. The pH is 10.5 to 11.5. This mud has a low viscosity and gel strength, and will withstand some salt contamination. If some starch is used to help control the filter loss, it is not necessary to use a preservative because of the high pH.

Phosphate-Treated Muds.   If good soft water is available, the sodium polyphosphates may be used as thinners when drilling through mud-making shales. Very small quantities of phosphates should be used since large amounts have an adverse effect. There is a danger in trying to convert this type of mud to a lime mud because calcium precipitates the polyphosphates and this causes extreme thickening.

Lime Muds.   This is a very popular type of mud made by adding lime to a natural mud or a bentonite mud. The lime flocculates the clay, and this results in a high gel strength and a high water loss. Deflocculation is accomplished through additions of caustic and quebracho, and starch or carboxymethyl cellulose is added to control the filter loss. This mud can be used to drill through hydratable clays without thickening. It is insensitive to calcium contamination because calcium is already present. It will also stand salt contamination up to about 5 percent (50,000 ppm). Lime muds may have electrical resistivities as low as 0.1 ohm-meter at 75°F. The one major problem with lime mud is its tendency to solidify at temperatures of about 250°F (6).

Making lime mud requires about 4 to 8 lb of lime, 2 to 4 lb of thinner, 1 to 3 lb caustic, and $\frac{1}{2}$ to $1\frac{1}{2}$ lb of starch per barrel of mud. Pilot testing of the mud is always done before making any additions. In making the mud, the thinner is added first, then the caustic, then the lime, and finally the necessary starch to control the filter loss.

Gypsum Muds.   These muds were first developed and are primarily used for drilling through anhydrite sections in the Williston basin and in the Canadian plains. The mud is made by adding 3 to 4 lb of starch, $\frac{1}{2}$ lb of preservative, 3 to 4 lb of gypsum, and $\frac{1}{2}$ bbl of water to each barrel of clay mud. This gives a mud with a high flat gel strength which is controlled through the addition of water.

Salt-Water Muds.   For small salt concentrations, a lime mud may be used successfully, but where extensive drilling of salt is to be done, it becomes uneconomical to try to use a bentonite type of clay and then control its properties chemically. In such situations it is customary to change to an attapulgite clay. This provides the necessary suspending properties, and the filter loss is controlled through the use of gelatinized starch or natural gums. Carboxymethyl cellulose is not good in salt mud. The mud is made by adding 125 lb of salt, 28 to 30 lb of clay, and 4 to 10 lb of starch per barrel of fresh water. This will give a mud weight of about $10\frac{1}{2}$ lb per gallon. Barite is used where it is necessary to build up the weight.

Oil-Base Drilling Fluids

About twenty-five years ago it was recognized that the filtrate from a water-base drilling mud could cause swelling and plugging of shaly

TABLE 2-1. COMMON DRILLING MUD ADDITIVES

Products and Companies

	Magcobar	Baroid	Milwhite	Identification
Weighting Materials				
1.	Magcobar	Baroid	Milbar	Barium sulfate
2.	G-7 Super Weight	Galena		Special high-density material
Clays				
3.	Magcogel	Aquagel	Milgel	Wyoming bentonite
4.	High Yield	Baroco	Greenband	High-yield clay
5.	Salt Gel	Zeogel	Salt Water gel	Attapulgite clay for salt-water muds
6.	Kwik-Thik	Quik-Gel	Super-Col	Extra-high-yield clay
Thinners				
7.	Q-X Quebracho	Tannex	Tanco	Quebracho compound
8.	M-C Quebracho	Quebracho	Mil Quebracho	Quebracho
9.	Tann Athin	Carbonox	Ligco	Lignite
10.	Spersene	Q-Broxin	Uni-Cal	Modified lignosulfonate
11.	Kembreak	Lignox	Kembreak	Calcium lignosulfonate
12.	Magcophos	Barafos	Oilphos	Sodium tetraphosphate
13.	SAPP	SAPP	SAPP	Sodium acid pyrophosphate
14.	Alkatan	Hydrotan	Natan	Caustic/tannin compound
15.	Emulsite	Hydrocarb	Super Ligco	Caustic/lignin compound
16.	Rayflo	Rayflo	Rayflo	Hemlock extract
Fluid Loss Control Agents				
17.	My-Lo-Jel	Impermex	Milstarch	Pregelatinized starch
18.	Driscose	Driscose	Driscose	Sodium carboxymethyl cellulose

No.				Description
19.	Driscose T.G.	Driscose T.G.	Driscose T.G.	Tech Grade carboxymethyl cellulose
20.	Dupont CMC DM	Dupont CMC DM	Dupont CMC DM	Tech Grade carboxymethyl cellulose
21.	Cypan			Sodium polyacrylate

Lost Circulation Materials

No.				Description
22.	Mud fiber	Fibertex	Milfiber	Blended cane and wood fiber
23.	Fiber-Seal			Blended fiber product
24.	Cell-O-Seal	Jel Flake	Milflake	Shredded cellophane flakes
25.	Leather-Floc	Leather-Seal	Leath-O	Leather fiber product
26.	Magco-Fiber		Palco-Seal	Shredded wood fiber
27.	Magco-Mica	Micatex	Mil Mica	Graded mica
28.	Nut Plug	Tuf-Plug	Tuf-Plug	Ground walnut shells
29.	FormAplug			Time setting clay product
30.	Bridge Bag	Krevice Klog		Graded aggregate product
31.	Chip-Seal	Plug-Git	Milseal	Shredded wood fiber

Oil Mud and Emulsion Products

No.				Description
32.	Jel-Oil[a]	Driloil		Straight oil-base mud
33.	Jel-Oil "E"			Compound for oil-water emulsion muds
34.	Speedy-Drill	Secco Mul	Olox	Soap type emulsifier
35.	Magconate			Petroleum sulfonate emulsifier
36.	No-Blok	Invermul	Therm-Oil	Concentrate for invert emulsion
37.	Drilling Milk	Trimulso	Atlosol	O/W emulsifier for low solids mud

Miscellaneous

No.				Description
38.	DMS	DMS	DMS	Nonionic drilling mud surfactant
39.	DME	DME	DME	Nonionic drilling mud emulsifier
40.	HS-400 Special			Nonionic fluid loss supplement
41.	D-D	Con-Det		Low solids mud additive

[a] Black Magic is a straight oil-base mud distributed by Oil Base, Incorporated.

TABLE 2-1 (*Continued*)

Products and Companies

Magcobar	Baroid	Milwhite	Identification
42. Bit Lube	E.P.Mud Lube	Lubri-Film	Extreme pressure lubricant
43. T-8 Compound	Shale Ban	Caltrol	Shale control mud additive
44. Lube-Kote	Graphite	Mil Graphite	Drilling mud graphite
45. My-Lo-Jel Preservative	Impermex Preservative	Preservative	Starch preservative
46. Afrox	Afrox	Afrox	Foaming agent for air drilling
47. Barium carbonate	Anhydrox		Barium carbonate
48. Sodium bicarbonate	Sodium bicarbonate		Sodium bicarbonate
49. Soda ash	Soda ash	Soda ash	Sodium carbonate
50. Magconol		Anti-Foam	Higher alcohol defoamer
51. Magco-Defoamer E-150	Kero-X	Defoamer	Defoamer for salty muds
52. Magco-Defoamer A-40	Baroid Defoamer 23		Defoamer for saturated salt muds
53. Magco-Defoamer S-10			Defoamer for low pH muds
54. Magco-Aluminum Stearate	Aluminum stearate	Aluminum stearate	Defoamer for T-8 and gyp muds
55. Flowit	Barafloc	Separan	Drilling mud flocullant
56. Blok Buster			Well stimulant

SOURCE: Courtesy of Magnet Cove Barium Corporation.

sandstones, with a consequent reduction of the production potential of the formation. This led to the use of crude oil as a "drilling-in" fluid which obviously could not damage the potential of an oil-bearing sand. There are, however, serious disadvantages to using crude oil for drilling over any extended interval. The viscosity is limited to the available crudes. The absence of gel strength makes it impossible to add weighting material, and so the mud weight is limited to about 7.5 lb per gallon. Drilled-up solids do not form a good filter cake because they do not hydrate. Finally, crude oil often contains volatile compounds which create a fire hazard.

There are available specially compounded oil-base muds which meet all these objections. The base material is usually refined diesel oil. To this is added blown asphalt to provide the necessary viscosity and filtration properties; organic acids and alkalies are added to form unstable soaps which impart the necessary gel strength and provide control over the fluid properties during drilling; and weighting material, such as barite, can be added to make the mud weight as much as 20 lb per gallon. The filter loss of a properly prepared oil-base mud is less than 1 cc in 30 minutes, and in the standard test usually no filtrate is evident. The difficulties with oil-base mud come largely from the unpleasant handling conditions and from the high cost.

Formation evaluation becomes much more difficult when drilling with oil-base fluids. Cores and ditch cuttings will contain oil from the drilling fluid that will mask the presence of formation hydrocarbons. Wireline logging is limited to those tools that do not require electrical contact with the formations, e.g., induction log, radioactivity logs.

Emulsion Muds

Improvement in the lubricating properties of clay muds can be accomplished by emulsifying 10 to 20 percent by volume of oil into the mud. This results in a longer bit life and a lessened chance of stuck drill pipe. Crude oil should not be used for this purpose, particularly on exploratory wells, because it imparts a fluorescence to the mud that makes it difficult to detect oil shows. It is also essential that a stable emulsion should be formed, or else the oil may appear as free oil in cores and cuttings. The continuous phase of an oil-in-water emulsion mud is water. The mud is therefore electrically conducting, and the usual logging tools may be used. The filtrate from the mud is also water, as the emulsified oil remains in the filter cake.

Water-in-oil emulsion muds are also used, primarily to reduce the cost of the oil-base mud. As much as 40 percent water may be emulsified in the fluid. Again it is necessary to maintain a stable emulsion if the desirable properties of the oil-base mud are to be maintained. Free water will make the formation evaluation problem very complicated. The filtrate from an oil-base emulsion mud is oil, and the logging problems associated with oil-base mud are still present.

REFERENCES

1. Anderson, Francis, M., Oil-base drilling fluid: *Oil Weekly*, v. 126, June 30, 1947, p. 43.
2. *API RP 29: Standard Field Procedure for Testing Drilling Fluids:* American Petroleum Institute, Division of Production, Dallas, Texas, 1957.
3. API Southwestern District Study Committee on Drilling Fluids, *Principles of Drilling Mud Control*, Petroleum Extension Service, University of Texas, tenth edition, 1955.
4. Chaney, P. E., Oxford, W. F., and Chisholm, Fred., The chemical treatment of drilling fluids: *World Oil*, v. 138, January and February, 1954.
5. Goins, W. C., Jr., How to combat lost circulation: *Oil and Gas Jour.*, June 9, 1952, p. 71.
6. Gray, G. R., Neznayko, M., and Gilkeson, P. W., Some Factors affecting the solidification of lime treated muds at high temperatures: *World Oil*, v. 134, March, 1952, p. 101.
7. Grim, Ralph E., *Clay Mineralogy:* McGraw-Hill Book Company, Inc., New York, 1953.
8. Hauser, Ernest A., *Proceedings of the 1939 Colloid Sumposium:* School of Petroleum Engineering, University of Oklahoma, Norman, Oklahoma.
9. Lummus, J. L., Multipurpose water-in-oil emulsion mud: *Oil and Gas Jour.*, December 13, 1954, p. 106.
10. Prokop, C. L., Radial filtration of drilling mud, *Trans. AIME*, v. 195, 1952, p. 5.
11. Rogers, Walter F., *Composition and Properties of Oil Well Drilling Fluids:* Gulf Publishing Company, Houston, Texas, revised edition, 1953.
12. Schremp, F. W., and Johnson, V. L., Drilling fluid filter loss at high temperatures and pressures: *Trans. AIME*, v. 195, 1952, p. 157.
13. Van Dyke, Orien, Oil Emulsion drilling mud: *World Oil*, November, 1950, p. 101.
14. White, R. J., Bottom-hole pressure reduction due to gas cut mud: *Trans. AIME*, v. 210, 1957, p. 382.

3

Coring and Core Analysis

Probably the earliest of the formation evaluation methods to be used was coring, and, in fact, the process dates back almost to the Drake discovery well. Its companion, core analysis, had its beginning at the time of the Spindletop era when cores were described according to odors, stains, and salt taste; core analysis methods as they are known today were not common until the middle of the 1930's. Coring was expensive, and still is; and yet coring has never been successfully replaced by any other evaluation method. In many cases it has actually grown in scope, thanks to better coring tools. Probably the greatest difficulty with the method is knowing when to core.

The geologist or petroleum engineer uses coring to obtain samples of subsurface formations for a detailed lithologic examination. Measurements made of the porosity and permeability of the rock, and the amount of oil, water, and gas in the pore space can be interpreted in terms of probable production, reserves, and productivity. Oil-water and gas-oil interfaces may be located with some accuracy. Core data are also important in evaluation work because they serve as a basis for calibrating the response of the wireline devices which measure some of these same properties.

In order to have a proper understanding of the core data and their relation to conditions as they exist in the reservoir, it is necessary to understand how cores are cut and handled prior to the analysis. The subject will be introduced, therefore, with a brief discussion of coring methods.

CORING METHODS

The coring method that is selected for a particular situation will depend on a number of factors that vary from one area to another, and in some cases even from one point in the stratigraphic column to another. These factors are cost, formation hardness, core size desired, fractional core recovery required, the drilling depth and hole conditions. There are four major methods to choose from: conventional, diamond, wireline, and reverse circulation. In addition, small cores may be obtained from the sidewall of the hole by devices run on drill pipe or wireline.

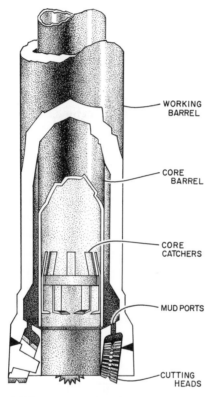

WORKING BARREL

CORE BARREL

CORE CATCHERS

MUD PORTS

CUTTING HEADS

Fig. 3-1. Conventional rotary core drill (schematic).

The conventional core bit is shown schematically in Fig. 3-1. The cutters are arranged to cut around the periphery of the hole while leaving a central stub of rock which will become the recovered core. As coring proceeds, the bit moves down over this stub, and the core moves into the inner core barrel. This inner barrel rolls on ball bearings so that it can remain relatively stationary while the outer barrel and bit are rotating. The top of the barrel is closed by a check valve which permits fluid flow only in the upward direction. The core is thereby freed from any abrasive action of the barrel but it is still protected by it from the scouring and continued flushing action of the mud passing down the drill pipe on the way to the cutting head. When sufficient core is cut, the weight on the drill is reduced and the speed of the rotary table is increased for a few minutes time; this will usually result in breaking off the core stub at the base. As the core barrel is withdrawn to the surface, the core catchers at the bottom of the barrel keep the core from sliding out.

The conventional coring method will cut a large core for a given size hole, and will recover a large proportion of the core that is cut. Cores range in size from $2\frac{3}{8}$ in. to $3\frac{9}{16}$ in. The method is readily adaptable to most formations and requires no special surface equipment. Its principal disadvantage lies in the fact that in most formations it is not possible to cut any more than 20 ft of core at one time, and in order to recover the core, it is necessary to pull all of the drill pipe. A round trip must be made, therefore, for every 20 ft drilled; if much coring is anticipated, the method can be very expensive, particularly if the coring is being done at great depths.

Fig. 3-2. Photograph of a diamond core bit. (Courtesy of Hycalog.)

Diamond coring is essentially the same as conventional coring, except that the inner core barrel and its supporting bearings are more finely machined, and the conventional rock bit is replaced by a solid casting of powered tungsten alloy set with diamond chips. (See Fig. 3-2.) This bit is brazed on to a steel shank. There is no hammering or chipping action with this type of bit, but only an abrasive rubbing action.

In hard sedimentary rocks it has been found that diamond coring can be done as fast as conventional drilling. High drill weights are avoided as they tend only to fracture the diamond surfaces while adding little to the drilling rate. Cutting rate does increase with rotary speed, so that somewhat higher rotation rates might be used. Pump pressure and mud velocities are usually kept low to reduce the scouring of the bit. With proper care cores up to 90 ft long can be cut by this method. The cores are large, ranging in size from $2\frac{7}{8}$ in. to $4\frac{7}{8}$ in., there is a high percentage of recovery, a long bit life, and in hard rock areas the method is economical. Diamond drilling has the disadvantages of using expensive bits and core barrels and requiring proper operating conditions, frequently under supervision of a diamond coring expert. For many cases it is more expensive than other types of coring.

The major source of expense in conventional coring comes from having to make a round trip to recover the core. To alleviate this condition, wireline coring was introduced. In this system, the inner core barrel can be retrieved with an overshot run on a wireline, the core removed, and the barrel placed back in the pipe and pumped to the bottom where it latches in place. When straight drilling is desired, the core barrel can be replaced by a solid plug that drills out the center of the hole. Thus, the system can be used for taking successive cores, or for alternately coring and drilling. Although lower coring costs can be realized by this method, it does have several disadvantages. In the first place, additional equipment is needed at the surface to run the wireline. Secondly, special subsurface equipment is needed in the form of a special drill collar, bit, core barrel, wireline guide, and overshot. The system works well only in soft formations, cuts smaller cores, and usually results in lower core recovery. Core sizes range from 1 in. to $2\frac{3}{16}$ in. In general, cores of 20 ft in length can be obtained.

In certain cases it is possible to recover core by pumping mud down the annulus and forcing the core up through the drill pipe in a reverse circulation procedure. Core sections brought to the surface by this method are caught in a special surface core barrel which may be opened intermittently to remove the core. If the cores are consolidated, excellent recovery can be obtained in this way with continuous coring. The method has the distinct disadvantages of requiring internally flush drill pipe and having a lower penetration rate because of the loss of the jetting action of the mud. Having high mud pressures in the annulus also increases the chance of lost circulation so that it may be necessary to set casing almost to the interval to be cored. Strato Drill, Inc., has recently proposed a method of reverse circulation coring that avoids this problem by using a dual pipe drill string (10). In their method, which is useful for coring at depths up to 5000 ft, the mud is pumped down the annulus between the two pipes, and the core pieces and cuttings return to the surface through the center pipe. Core sections are caught at the shakers.

It often happens that after the electric log is run there are zones indicated on which core data would be desirable for the proper inter-pretation of the electric log or to confirm the log interpretation. At this time, of course, it is no longer possible to take a core sample by any of the usual coring methods. To fill the gap, wireline coring devices were developed; these can take a core sample from the sidewall of the hole.

By far the most common type of sidewall sampler is the percussion type offered as a service by the electric logging companies. This device is pictured in Fig. 3-3. It is run on a logging cable and contains an SP electrode as well as the samplers so that it may be positioned in the hole to sample at the proper depth. The small cylinders shown in the gun body can be fired individually by electrically ignited powder charges. The cylinder penetrates the formation and cuts a cylindrical plug. The bullet remains attached to the gun by two heavy wires, and after the sample has been cut, it is broken from the surrounding rock and recovered by an upward pull on the gun.

As many as thirty shots can be made on one trip with a large coring gun. The core samples are of the order of $1\frac{1}{4}$ in. diameter by $2\frac{1}{4}$ in. in length for soft formations and $\frac{3}{4}$ in. diameter by $2\frac{1}{4}$ in. in length for hard formations. The hole size required for such a gun is $7\frac{1}{2}$ in. minimum. Smaller guns are available which may be run in holes as small as $5\frac{1}{2}$ in., but these will also cut smaller cores. The recovery efficiency of the electric sidewall sampler depends on the formation, but averages about 70 per-cent. In very hard formations the bullets may be smashed, and the recovery efficiency is lower. Sidewall cores in these formations may be recovered by an electrically driven sidewall diamond drill. It is also possible to use other types of samplers that are run on drill pipe and take samples by a drilling or stamping action. These more elaborate sampling methods are expensive, and therefore are used only when no other method will suffice.

Sidewall sampling with the percussion type device has the advantage of being quick and easy to run and, consequently, inexpensive. The disadvantages are that the sample is small, it is from a region that has been subjected to extensive flushing with mud filtrate, and the impact of the bullet tends to compress the formation and thereby distort the porosity and permeability. Below about 20 md, the permeability of a

Fig. 3-3. Percussion type of sidewall sampler. (Courtesy of Schlumberger Well Surveying Corporation.)

sidewall core will usually be considerably higher than a conventional core cut from the same level. This is undoubtedly the result of fracturing from the bullet impact. Above 20 md, the permeability of the sidewall core will usually be lower than a conventional core. This is probably due to compaction of the core plug and to invasion by mud solids.

Water saturations measured on sidewall samples are almost invariably higher than those found in conventional cores.

CORE SAMPLING

When the core arrives at the surface, the core barrel is sometimes "flashed" to see if it contains any combustible hydrocarbon gases. ("Flashing" is a procedure whereby an open flame is held at the end of the core barrel; if there are hydrocarbon gases trapped in the barrel, they will burn. It is dangerous, and it is prohibited in some areas.) The core should then be removed as gently as possible from the core barrel and placed in appropriately marked trays in the same sequence in which it was cut. The core can usually be slid from the barrel by raising one end, and by pushing or tapping it lightly. If this does not succeed, it may be pumped out with mud fluid, but it should be remembered that this probably will alter its fluid content if high pump pressures are used. Heavy pounding of the core barrel or the core should be avoided as this will result in an alteration of the rock structure, particularly if it is a soft sand.

As soon as the core has been laid out in the trays, it should be measured to determine the amount of recovery. If some of the core is missing, an effort should be made to determine the location of the missing section (see page 55). It is most likely that any lost recovery will be from the bottom of the core since this section is most likely to fall out of the core barrel if the core is soft sand, or to remain in the hole as a stub if the rock is well consolidated. Consequently, if the position of the missing footage is not obvious, it is usually assigned to this location. When measurements of the core have been completed, the core should be inspected to determine the proper locations for sampling. Samples should be about 6 in. in length and should be taken so as to be representative of the total core. In thick, fairly uniform sands, sampling should be every 2 ft. Sample frequency should be increased as the sand becomes more heterogeneous. In sandwiches of sand and shale, all sand members over 2 in. in thickness should be sampled.

A complete description of the core should be made, noting the type of rock matrix, texture, faults, cavities, dip, and any hydrocarbon staining. The selected core samples should then be packaged for shipment to the laboratories for analysis. Since the cores will be analyzed for fluid saturation, precautions should be taken to see that the fluids in the core when it arrives at the laboratory will be nearly identical with those in the core when it was first removed from the core barrel. Cores should not be washed with either oil or water before they are packaged; mud cake can be removed by either wiping or scraping it off. To minimize evaporative loss of fluids, core samples should be packaged by wrapping them in aluminum foil or polyethylene bags. Tests have shown that as little as one-half hour exposure can result in a 10 to 25 percent fluid loss. If more than 24 hours will elapse before analysis, consideration should be given to additional packaging, such as canning, wax coating, freezing, etc. Core samples should also be accompanied by as much information as is known about things that might influence the interpretation of the data, as, for example, the type of drilling mud, filtration loss rate, type of oil that might be anticipated in the zone, driller's log, and well logs if they are available. In the laboratory the core samples will be sampled again to obtain plugs for the measurement of porosity, permeability, and oil and water saturations. Core laboratories will usually supply a value for each of these items, plus a description of the core, and perhaps an interpretation of the probable fluid production from that depth at which the core was taken. Measurement of relative permeability and capillary pressure may also be made, but these are much more difficult and time-consuming than the other measurements, and many laboratories are not equipped to make them.

CORE ANALYSIS

The material of which a petroleum reservoir rock may be composed can range from a very loose, unconsolidated sand to a very hard, dense sandstone, limestone, or dolomite. Most of the granular material in sandstone is quartz. The grains may be bonded together with a number of materials, the most common of which are silica, calcite, or clay. Sandstones containing more than 5 percent of clay material are classified as dirty or shaly. The amount of shale present greatly influences the interpretation given to the results of a core analysis, as well as to the results of most other types of formation evaluation methods. Carbonate rocks may exhibit porosity that is oolitic, vuggy, fracture, or intercrystalline. Most production is from rocks with an intercrystalline porosity. The problem of shale in carbonates is not very important, since there are practically no known shaly carbonate reservoirs.

The procedures for analyzing core samples for porosity, permeability, saturations, and other properties will be discussed briefly in the following sections. For a thorough discussion of core analysis procedures, the recent bulletin of the API (1) on this subject should be consulted.

Porosity

The porosity of a rock is a measure of the amount of internal space that is capable of holding fluids. It is important because it represents a potential storage volume for hydrocarbons; a porosity of 1 percent is equivalent to a volume of 77.58 bbl per acre-foot. A commercial oil-bearing sandstone should contain at least 8 to 10 percent porosity. In granular limestones it is possible to have as little as 4 to 6 percent porosity associated with commercial production. Sedimentary rocks rarely contain more than 35 percent pore space.

Quantitatively, the porosity of a rock is the ratio of the volume of void space to the total volume of void space plus rock matrix. The porosity depends on the shape, surface texture, angularity, orientation, degree of cementation, and size distribution of the grains which make up the rock. Theoretically, there is no dependence of porosity on the absolute size of the grains. For example, if a rock were composed of uniform spherical grains arranged in a cubical packing, it would exhibit a porosity of 47.6 percent regardless of how large or small the spheres were. If the grains were of unequal size, however, the smaller ones could fit into the interstices between the larger ones and thereby reduce the void space. This is why shaly or silty material in a sandstone results in a lowered porosity.

In measuring the porosity, the field core is sampled to obtain a regularly shaped piece approximately 1 in. long by 1 in. in diameter. (With limestone exhibiting secondary porosity, measurements are often made on full-sized cores.) This sample is extracted with toluene, or some other solvent, and dried. The total volume is then obtained by a direct measurement of the dimensions or by measuring the displacement volume of a nonpenetrating fluid such as mercury. The void volume can be determined by evacuating the core and then saturating it with a wetting liquid. The increase in weight divided by the liquid density is the pore volume. A more common method of measuring pore space is with the Boyle's law porosimeter. This method determines the volume of air within the dried sample by expanding the air isothermally and measuring the increase in the volume during the expansion. Because of experimental problems, it is easier to measure the grain volume by this method, but the void volume is easily found once the grain volume and total volume are known.

Either of the above methods measures the interconnected or effective porosity. The total porosity of the rock, which is of little commercial interest, includes also those pores that are completely sealed off from all the pores around them. Some logging instruments measure the total porosity, however, so the distinction should be borne in mind.

The porosity of a sandstone, like the permeability, represents the contribution of a large number of pores of different size and shape. Although the individual pores differ, a statistical treatment of a large number of pores imparts consistent mass properties to the rock as a whole. This condition is not true for carbonate rocks. Porosity can vary widely from point to point. The presence of vugs and fractures can change the permeability tremendously over a very short distance. Whole core analysis attempts to circumvent this problem by taking a larger sample, but even this size is sometimes insufficient to represent average conditions.

Permeability

The permeability of a rock is a quantitative measure of the ease with which it will permit the passage of fluids through it under a potential gradient. Like the porosity, it is dependent on the several rock grain properties of shape, surface texture, angularity, orientation, and size distribution. In addition, it is very strongly dependent on the size of the grains, whereas the porosity is theoretically independent of this factor. The smaller the size of the grains, the larger will be the surface area exposed to the flowing fluid. Since it is the drag on this surface area which limits the flow rate, a small grain size will result in a low permeability. As might be expected, then, shales have practically zero permeability, and for most purposes they can be considered to be impermeable. (Measurements of the permeability of a number of shales were made by Gondouin and Scala (8). The permeabilities were in the range of 4×10^{-3} to 2×10^{-6} millidarcys.) The presence of shale in shaly sands usually results in very large permeability reductions.

Quantitatively, permeability is defined by an empirical relation known as Darcy's law.

$$\frac{Q}{A} = \frac{K}{\mu} \frac{\Delta P}{L} \tag{3-1}$$

Where Q is the flow rate (cubic centimeters per second), A is the cross-sectional area (square centimeters), and L is the length (centimeters) of the porous medium, μ is the viscosity of the flowing fluid (centipoises), ΔP is the pressure differential across the sample (atmospheres), and K is the permeability (darcys). This equation satisfactorily describes viscous flow in a horizontal direction. (Where capillary pressure and gravitational terms exist, they must be included with the pressure term.) The unit of permeability in the above equation is the darcy. It is usually too large to be convenient, so the millidarcy, or one-thousandth of a darcy, is used instead. Depending on other conditions of the reservoir, porous sediments capable of commercial hydrocarbon production may exhibit permeabilities of a few millidarcys to several darcys.

In measuring permeability it is customary to use the same piece of core that was used for the porosity measurement. In some manner, either with sealing wax, epoxy resin, Lucite, or a rubber sleeve backed up with hydraulic pressure, the cylindrical surface is sealed so that no fluid can flow in or out of it. A fluid, usually air, can then be flowed into one end of the sample and out of the other. The dimensions of the sample are measured with a scale to get the cross-sectional area and length. The pressure, which may range between 1 and 80 cm of mercury, is measured with a manometer or a bourdon type pressure gage. Viscosity can be determined from the temperature of measurement, and the flow rate measured with a rotameter or an orifice. Permeability may then be computed.

If a gas is used for making the permeability measurement, it may be necessary to account for the effect of slip flow (or "Klinkenberg effect"). When a fluid is flowing through a capillary, the mean velocity of the fluid at the surface of the capillary tube is normally zero. When a gas flows through a capillary that is so small that its diameter is of the same order of magnitude as the mean free path of the molecules of the gas, this condition no longer holds; as a result, the flow rate is abnormally high for the given pressure gradient and the calculated permeability is also falsely high. This error becomes greater as the permeability becomes smaller, and may cause the reading to be as much as 70 percent too high. Klinkenberg (13) determined that the correction for this effect can be expressed by the equation

understand this

$$K_\infty = \frac{K_{air}}{1 + \dfrac{b}{P_m}} \tag{3-2}$$

where P_m is the mean pressure in the core during the measurement, and b is a constant which depends on the size and shape of the pores. In order to correct for slip flow, measurements must be made at more than one pressure and then extrapolated to infinite pressure as illustrated in Fig. 3-4. If several measurements have not been made, a rough estimate of b can be obtained from the relation

$$b = 0.777K_\infty^{-0.39} \tag{3-3}$$

K in this equation is in millidarcys.

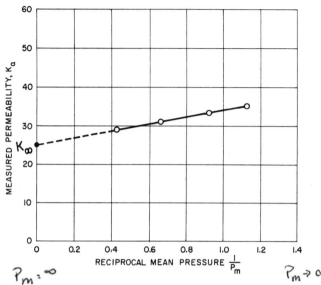

Fig. 3-4. Method of correcting air permeabilities for slip flow by extrapolating data to infinite pressure.

Should the sample contain any shaly material, the measurement of permeability will be very sensitive to the fluid used in the measurement. If air is used, it should be dried. Nonpolar hydrocarbons will usually give permeabilities comparable to those obtained with air. Fresh water, on the other hand, will result in swelling of the clay minerals with the consequent reduction of the permeability. If the sand is very shaly, the presence of fresh water may even cause the complete disintegration of the sample. The affinity of clay particles for water is very important in completion operations and in the interpretation of saturation data. Serious and permanent damage may be done to the productive capacity of a well if it is drilled with a fresh mud and there is shaly material present in the formation.

Saturation

In a routine core analysis the saturation of oil, water, and gas in the core is determined. While these saturations bear little resemblance to the corresponding saturations in the reservoir, they are useful in the qualitative determination of the locations of oil-water and gas-oil interfaces, or just as a check on the possible presence of hydrocarbons. Knowledge of the oil saturation of a well-flushed core can also be very useful in the interpretation of electric log data.

Saturation may be determined during the extraction operation in which the core is cleaned. An apparatus for the simultaneous determination of oil and water saturation is shown in Fig. 3-5. A weighed core sample is placed in a thimble in the long neck of the flask. Toluene is introduced into the flask until the lower bulb is half full. The apparatus is assembled, and the flask is then heated on a hot plate so that the toluene boils. The hot toluene vapor vaporizes the water in the core. The water vapor rises into the condenser where it is liquefied and then drains back into the trap. After a couple of hours of operation, all the water is usually removed and can be measured by means of the calibrations on the trap. The condensed toluene vapor runs back over the core and extracts the oil. Usually 24 hours' extraction is sufficient. The core is then dried and reweighed. The loss in weight represents the amount of oil and water removed, and if the volume of water is known, the volume of oil can be determined (provided that the density of the oil is also known). When the porosity has been determined, the fraction of the pore volume occupied by oil and water can be computed. These fractional values are the saturations. The saturation of gas is calculated by subtracting the sum of the oil and water saturations from unity.

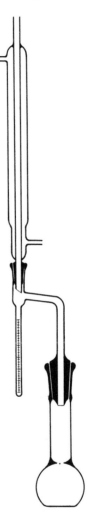

Fig. 3-5. Apparatus for the simultaneous extraction of oil and water from cores.

An alternate method of determining saturations is by retorting. This has the advantage of being much more rapid than the extraction method. In this method the sample is placed in a retort where it is heated to about 1200°F. The vapors that are driven off are condensed and collected, and the volumes of the oil and water phases are measured directly. Retorting results in cracking and coking of the crude oil so that the volume of oil collected will be low. Core analysis companies correct for this with empirical charts such as that shown in Fig. 3-6. (The gravity of the recovered oil is usually within 2°API of the true value.) In addition, the water of hydration of the clays is driven off. A correction for this effect may be made by plotting a curve of the rate of water production as illustrated in Fig. 3-7. At the end of 8 to 15 minutes the rate of water production drops sharply,

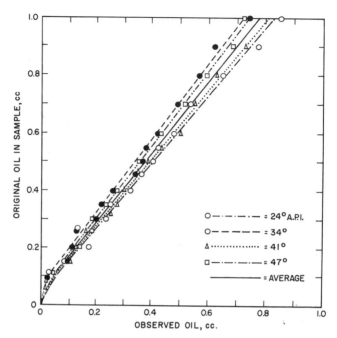

Fig. 3-6. Sample calibration curves for correcting saturations determined by the retort method. (Reproduced by permission from API RP 40: Core-analysis Procedure.)

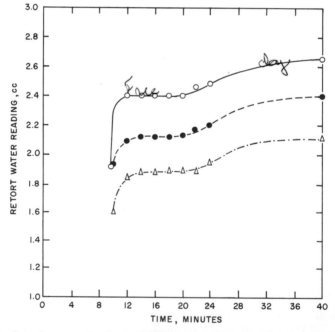

Fig. 3-7. Sample curves for determining the correct water saturation of a core from retort data. (Reproduced by permission from API RP 40: Core-analysis Procedure.)

marking the end of the "free-water" distillation. Water recovered thereafter is water of hydration of the clay.

Relative Permeability

Relative permeability is the measure of the ability of a porous medium to permit the passage of a fluid through it under a potential gradient when there are two or three phases present in the pore space. For a given rock sample, then, the relative permeability to a particular phase depends on the saturation or fraction of the pore space occupied by that phase. The effect of saturation is shown graphically in Fig. 3-8 and 3-9. The importance of relative permeability to an understanding of oil reservoir problems is obvious when it is realized that all hydrocarbon reservoirs contain at least two phases (water and oil/gas); therefore the amount of production and which fluid phase will be produced depends not only on the permeability of the rock but also on the saturation of each of the phases present. Relative permeability is also very important to understanding the relation between the saturations measured in core analysis and the saturations which exist in the reservoir.

Relative permeability is defined as the ratio of the permeability of the rock to a given phase as compared with the permeability of the rock when only one phase is present, e.g., the air permeability described in a preceding section. The relative permeability is always less than unity, and even the sum of all relative permeabilities is less than unity. The curves of Figs. 3-8 and 3-9 also indicate that the permeability to a given phase is zero until a certain minimum value of the saturation of

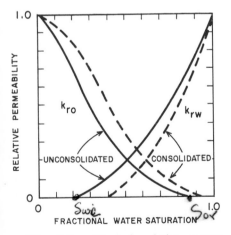

Fig. 3-8.   Typical relative permeability curves for a porous medium containing oil and water.

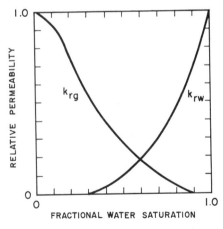

Fig. 3-9.   Typical relative permeability curves for a porous medium containing gas and water.

that phase is reached. Thus, in Fig. 3-8 the saturation of water must be at least 0.2 for the unconsolidated sand before any water can flow. In consolidated sands of the same nature, the minimum necessary water saturation is ordinarily even higher. The minimum saturation has a second significance in that it is not possible to reduce the saturation of a phase below its minimal value by any kind of a flooding operation.

The measurement of relative permeability in the laboratory requires a much higher degree of technical competence than an ordinary permeability measurement. The equipment and methods used are too complicated to be described here, and the reader is referred to several excellent papers which are available on this subject (3, 6, 9, 15, 17, 19). Because of the additional time and effort required in making the measurements, they are not made as a matter of course. Fortunately, the absence of specific relative permeability data is not usually of serious consequence in formation evaluation work.

Capillary Pressure

Another property of the rock that is a function of the saturation is the capillary pressure. Capillary pressure is the difference in pressure that exists between two phases because of the curvature of the interface that separates them. In small-diameter tubes, such as exist in reservoir rock, this pressure can be considerable. The lower pressure occurs on the convex side of the interface. This is the wetting phase side, and in most reservoirs water is the wetting fluid.

The most popular theory of the genesis of oil proposes that the porous rocks which make up an oil reservoir were filled with water at the time of deposition, and that the oil later migrated into them from other "source rocks." Since this migrating oil is lighter than water it moved into the highest structural position in the trap. The accumulated oil gradually displaced the water downward; this displacement continued until the water saturation was reduced to the point where the water became discontinuous and would no longer flow. This irreducible saturation is always found in oil reservoirs at those places that are a sufficient distance above the water table. Between this irreducible saturation condition and the fully water-saturated water table, there exists a transition zone where the saturation gradually changes from one condition to the other. This transition zone is the result of capillary action.

The capillary pressure in a pore is dependent on the pore size and the

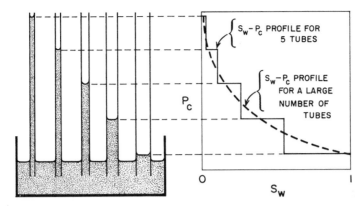

Fig. 3-10. Capillary tube analogy to the capillary pressure-saturation relationship found in reservoir rocks.

two fluids that are in contact. This relation can be expressed quantitatively by

$$P_c = \frac{2\sigma \cos \theta}{r} \qquad (3\text{-}4)$$

where r is the radius of curvature of the pore, θ is the angle that the wetting fluid makes with the wall of the pore, and σ is the interfacial tension. In the capillary tubes of Fig. 3-10, surface tension causes the water to rise in the tubes until the capillary pressure across the interface is just balanced by the pressure created by the column of water. At this point,

$$P_c = \Delta\rho\, gh \qquad (3\text{-}5)$$

where $\Delta\rho$ is the density difference between the two phases, g is the acceleration of gravity, and h is the height of the water in the tube above the free-water surface. As the height above the free-water level increases, only the smaller capillaries contain water.

Reservoir rock is composed of pores of a variety of different sizes. Suppose that at the bottom of a core the water saturation is 1.0. This fully saturated condition will continue until the height is reached where the capillary pressure is equal to that of the largest sized pore in the sample. This is the displacement pressure, P_D. Thereafter, the saturation of the core will decrease continuously as the height is increased until the irreducible saturation is reached. This relation between capillary pressure (or height) and saturation will generally give a curve like that shown at the right side of the Fig. 3-10.

As was said before, the permeability of a rock is strongly dependent on the grain size and pore size. Since the capillary pressure is also dependent on pore size, it is not surprising that low-permeability rocks have high capillary pressure and long transition zones. This relationship has been used as the basis of an electric logging method for determining permeability.

Some typical capillary pressure curves for a San Andres dolomite are shown in Fig. 3-11. These have been obtained from various samples of reservoir rock of different permeabilities. Five representative curves are shown for permeabilities ranging from 0.1 md to 10 md. If curves like these are available, along with relative permeability curves, it is possible to calculate the probable production of fluid from any interval once its permeability and height above the water table are known.

Formation Resistivity Factor

The significance of this measurement is covered in Chapter 5 on Electric Logging. The formation resistivity factor, F, is the ratio of the electrical resistivity, R_0, of a porous medium saturated with water to the resistivity, R_w, of the water in the pores. This is a very important

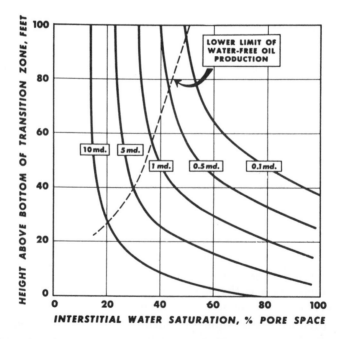

Fig. 3-11. Capillary pressure curves for a San Andres dolomite. (Aufricht and Koepf, courtesy of the AIME.)

factor in electric log interpretation. It has been found to be related to the porosity according to the general equation

$$F = \frac{1}{\phi^m} \tag{3-6}$$

where m is a constant, characteristic of a particular rock. In addition, measurements are sometimes made of the ratio of the resistivity, R_t, of a partially saturated rock to the resistivity, R_0, of the completely saturated rock. This ratio has been found to be related to the water saturation by

$$I = \frac{R_t}{R_0} = \frac{1}{S_w^n} \tag{3-7}$$

The exponent n is a constant, characteristic of the particular rock; m and n are frequently assumed to be 2 if they are unknown. If measured values of these parameters are available, however, electric log interpretation can be improved accordingly.

INTERPRETATION OF CORE DATA

When the drill bit penetrates an oil sand during a coring operation, the hydrostatic pressure differential and jetting action of the mud cause the sand to be flushed by the mud filtrate. If this action is continued for a sufficient period of time, the oil saturation in the core will be reduced to the point where the relative permeability to oil becomes zero. If only partial flushing takes place, the oil saturation will lie somewhere between this irreducible value and the original saturation. The degree of flushing depends on the drilling rate, the permeability of the rock, the rate of circulation of mud, the diameter of the core, the viscosity of the oil and the mud filtrate, the mud weight, and the water loss. The relative importance of these factors is usually in the order listed. The water loss character of the mud, which usually controls the filtration rate into the wall of the borehole, has little influence on the rate of filtration ahead of the bit because the mud cake is continuously removed by the drilling action. Most sands in the range of commercial permeability are flushed to such a degree that the minimum oil saturation is almost always reached.

The next important changes in the saturations within the core occur as the core is pulled to the surface. During this operation the pressure on the core is decreased. Gas dissolved in the residual oil in the core at reservoir conditions comes out of solution and expands as the pressure is reduced. Since 1 cc of oil may release as much as 30 cc of gas, a very sizable gas flushing operation may occur on withdrawal, with the result that the mud filtrate is pushed out of the core until the irreducible water saturation condition is approached. There will be no expulsion of oil if it was already reduced to the minimum saturation during the drilling process, but there will be a small reduction in the oil saturation because its volume will shrink when the gas comes out of solution.

TABLE 3-1.   TYPICAL SATURATIONS IN A CORING OPERATION

	S_o	S_w	S_g
Undisturbed in the reservoir	0.60	0.40	0
In the core barrel at bottom hole conditions	0.15	0.85	0
At the surface	0.12	0.42	0.46

Table 3-1 gives a typical example of what might be expected during the coring of an oil sand. The core in place contains oil, some water, and no gas. The core in the barrel contains very little oil and no gas. But by the time the core arrives at the surface and is sampled for analysis, the predominant fluid is gas. This table points up the fact that the saturations measured in the laboratory during core analysis bear little resemblance to the saturations that exist in the ground; and yet the measured saturations may be used successfully to determine the nature of the fluids in place and the probable production from the interval.

In the interpretation of core data, it is necessary to consider all the factors, porosity, permeability, and lithology, as well as the oil, water, and gas saturations. The presence of shaly material is of particular significance in the interpretation so that it is somewhat easier to approach the problem by considering first the shale-free or clean-sand condition.

Clean sands are generally characterized by conditions of uniform porosity and permeability. When this is true, all the rock properties are constant and interpretation becomes a matter of assigning the proper significance to the measured oil, water, and gas saturations. Here the factor of localized experience becomes important. Within a given area and for a given formation, it is possible to assign tentative limits to the core analysis saturations which will correspond to oil, gas, or water production. Table 3-2 gives general limits within which the saturation values for a clean sand might be expected to fall. These limits can be narrowed by experience and by a knowledge of other factors which control saturation.

Dry gas sands have practically zero oil saturation. The relative water and gas saturations depend on the permeability of the sand and the depth. Low-permeability sands normally have higher connate water saturations and consequently show higher water saturations after the expansion gas drive that occurs when the core is brought to the surface. The extent of the gas flushing process depends on the depth since the deeper formations are normally under higher pressure and there is a greater expansion of the residual gas which remains after flushing with drilling fluid.

TABLE 3-2. APPROXIMATE SATURATION LIMITS FOR
VARIOUS TYPES OF PRODUCTION

	S_o	S_w	S_g
Dry gas	0	0.30-0.55	0.45-0.70
Condensate	0.01-0.04	0.30-0.55	0.40-0.65
Oil	0.05-0.30	0.30-0.55	0.30-0.60
Water	0-0.08	0.55-0.90	0.10-0.35

Oil sands exhibit the same dependence on permeability and depth as gas sands and for the same reason. The situation here is more complicated, however, because the viscosity of the oil can vary over very wide limits. Low-gravity oils, which are usually found at shallow depths, have high viscosities and contain little solution gas; here the saturation to oil might be expected to be high because of incomplete flushing with mud filtrate, and the saturation of gas would be expected to be low because of the small amount of solution gas. Deeper sands containing high-gravity oil show the opposite effect, with low oil saturations and high gas saturations. Abnormally high oil saturations may be encountered in the footage directly beneath an impermeable streak if the coring rate is high. The impervious streak in this case prevents flushing ahead of the bit so that an unflushed condition prevails. On the other hand, the first foot or two of core taken in a permeable sand usually has an abnormally low oil saturation. This is the result of mud filtrate invasion during the time that it takes to put on a coring bit.

Water-productive clean sands are usually characterized by core analysis water saturations that are greater than 0.60. They may also contain small amounts of oil or gas, but the high water saturation will generally indicate that water production is to be expected. Water sands that contain some oil are easier to interpret if there is some oil productive sand above it. In this case, any reduction in oil saturation and increase in water saturation that cannot be assigned to some other cause can be interpreted as probable water production. In many cases, particularly in the less permeable sandstones, a transition zone between the oil-productive and water-productive intervals may be recognized.

If a core has been mishandled in the field, either by being pumped out of the barrel under high pressure, or by being exposed to the atmosphere for a long period of time, no definite interpretation can be assigned to the measured laboratory saturations.

The presence of shale in a sand section causes difficulties in the interpretation procedure. In the first place, the measured laboratory permeability will be greater than the permeability in place. This is because clay swells when it comes in contact with water, even salt water. A laboratory core which has been cleaned of all liquids and then dried will develop permeability where the clay shrinks and forms cracks. If the measured permeability is very low, the sample should be moistened with a few drops of water and its permeability remeasured. It is possible that such a core sample should actually be treated as impervious in the subsequent interpretation, and the second measurement should indicate this.

Because of its small grain size, shaly material in a sandstone core will cause three changes in the core analysis. There will be a small reduction in porosity, a large reduction in permeability, and an increase in the water saturation. Measured water saturations in clayey sands that are oil productive may be as high as 0.7. The change in porosity, and particularly the change in permeability, can help to identify the cause of the anomalous water saturation behavior so that a proper interpretation can still be assigned to the sample. The amount of clay in a shaly sandstone can vary over wide limits. It is therefore best to base the interpretation of a cored interval on the clean footage, and then, by using the clean interpretation as a guide, to fill in the probable production from the shaly sections. An example will serve to clarify this procedure.

Figure 3-12 is a core analysis from a Texas well. The report lists the sample depth, the horizontal permeability of the bed, the porosity, the saturations of oil and water, the vertical permeability, and the probable production of the interval. All this information, with the exception of the vertical permeability, is also plotted on the coregraph. The horizontal permeability, which gives a measure of the ability of the formation to transmit fluids to the wellbore, is the more important permeability value since it indicates the productivity of the sand. The vertical permeability, which is usually lower than the horizontal value, is important in considering special effects such as the possibility of water coning

COMPLETION COREGRAPH

TABULAR DATA and INTERPRETATION

PERMEABILITY o—o MD 1000 750 500 250 0
POROSITY x---x % 40 30 20 10 0
TOTAL WATER o—o % PORE SPACE 80 60 40 20 0
OIL SATURATION x---x % PORE SPACE 0 20 40 60 80

DEPTH FT	PERM. MD	Φ %	So %	Sw %	VERT. PERM.	PROD.
5523-24	0.0	19.0	0.0	66.0	0.0	
24-25	92	25.9	0.0	53.5	11	GAS
25-26	65	25.2	0.0	55.1	5	GAS
26-27	551	30.8	0.0	42.2	72	GAS
27-28	846	32.3	0.0	38.0	321	GAS
28-29	365	30.0	0.0	38.3	216	GAS
29-30	433	28.6	0.0	39.1	192	GAS
5530-31	238	29.7	1.0	40.4	146	GAS
31-32	58	25.6	4.2	50.2	2.5	GAS
32-33	240	30.1	22.2	48.2	118	OIL
33-34	0.0	22.6	13.3	54.0	0.0	
34-35	68	26.0	17.8	48.4	4.1	OIL
35-36	89	24.6	22.0	51.5	22	OIL
36-37	575	30.7	27.2	43.9	195	OIL
37-38	880	32.1	26.1	37.1	437	OIL
38-39	0.0	21.1	0.0	78.0	0.0	
39-40	4540	34.4	32.3	28.2	1850	OIL
5540-41	4970	33.3	29.1	29.8	3260	OIL
41-42	5780	38.4	33.8	24.0	2200	OIL
5543-44	1665	34.6	25.2	35.3	820	OIL
44-45	452	32.3	27.3	35.0	156	OIL
45-46	424	31.8	23.0	42.8	375	OIL
46-47	531	33.2	24.7	41.3	420	OIL
47-48	572	32.6	20.3	41.6	263	OIL
48-49	353	36.9	22.8	39.6	95	OIL
49-50	185	31.2	18.6	53.5	47	OIL
5550-51	429	35.1	22.5	41.6	185	OIL
51-52	715	35.3	22.7	42.2	627	OIL
52-53	2220	36.0	17.0	46.1	1920	OIL
53-54	1138	34.3	17.8	38.2	685	OIL
54-55	1732	33.1	20.9	45.3	1140	OIL
55-56	1740	35.9	22.6	39.5	1560	OIL
56-57	992	33.9	32.4	29.2	920	OIL
57-58	231	30.9	12.3	51.7	13	TRANS.
58-59	1131	35.0	14.0	49.4	245	TRANS.
59-60	270	34.8	10.6	61.7	310	TRANS.
5560-61	167	31.7	13.9	54.5	125	TRANS.
61-62	160	34.3	6.4	67.7	6.0	WATER
62-63	1130	37.2	11.8	59.5	251	WATER
63-64	67	26.4	0.0	78.9	3.6	WATER
64-65	917	34.3	3.8	64.2	624	WATER
65-66	88	33.6	5.0	66.1	19	WATER
66-67	123	29.5	6.1	62.2	24	WATER
67-68	420	32.1	0.0	68.0	28	WATER
68-69	12	24.0	0.0	79.2	0.8	WATER
69-70	0.0	23.5	0.0	82.0	0.0	WATER

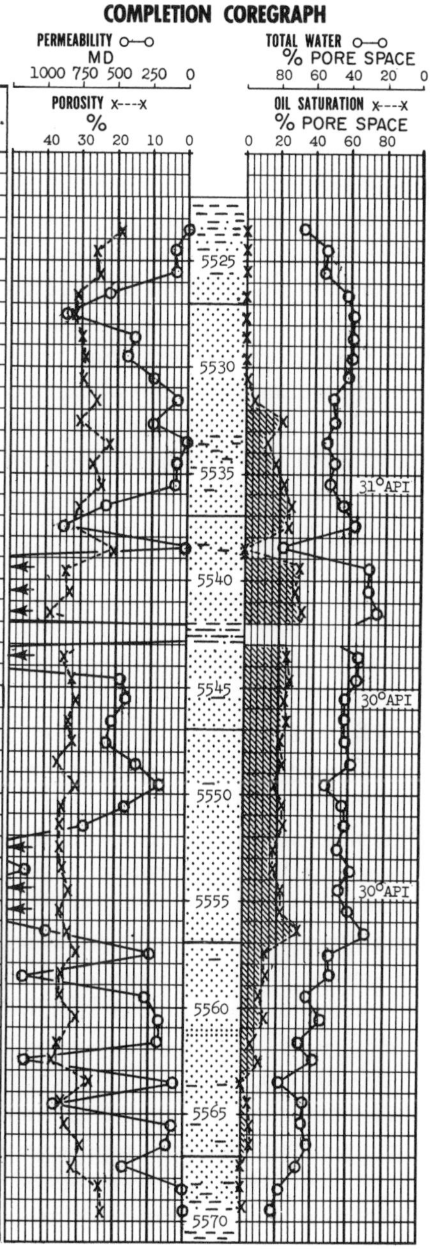

Coregraph depth marks: 5525, 5530, 5535, 5540, 5545, 5550, 5555, 5560, 5565, 5570

API markings: 31°API, 30°API, 30°API

Fig. 3-12. Core analysis report for the Sinton sand, Texas. (Courtesy of Core Laboratories.)

or negative separation on the microlog curves of the electric log. Both of these conditions are associated with high vertical permeability.

Consideration of the coregraph shows that the porosity and the permeability vary in the same manner with depth, although variations in permeability are greater; also, these variations can be seen to correspond to the lithology log which has been prepared from visual inspection of the samples. Intervals of low porosity and permeability correspond to shaly sections. By reference to Table 3-2, it can be seen that the clean footage down to 5530 ft corresponds to the conditions for dry gas production: 5530 to 5532 is in the limits for condensate production. At 5532-33 the oil saturation suddenly jumps to 22 percent, while the water saturation remains about the same as in the gas zone. From here down to 5557 ft the oil saturation falls within the limits of 13 to 34 percent, with the shalier intervals showing the higher water saturations and lower oil saturations. At 5557-58 the oil saturation drops below these limits and the water saturation starts to increase. The coregraph quite clearly shows the transition zone down to 5561 ft. At 5561-62, the first interval is encountered which has saturations indicating that it will probably produce principally water, and the footage below this point is listed as water productive even though there is still a small amount of oil present for the next several feet.

The interpretation of core data from carbonate rocks is considerably more complex and requires a great deal of experience. This is because the porosity in carbonates can be intercrystalline, oolitic, vuggy, or fracture, and usually is a combination of two or more of these types. Intercrystalline and oolitic limestones and dolomites resemble sandstones in porosity, permeability, and relative permeability properties and ranges. Carbonate rocks which contain fractures and vugs, on the other hand, seldom have a high porosity, but the permeabilities are frequently tremendous. A fracture consisting of a 0.01-in. gap across the face of a 1-in.-square core plug would give a permeability of 5,400,000 md, but would represent a porosity of only 1 percent. Vugs and fractures hold almost no capillary water when they contain oil; all the connate water is represented by a thin surface film which might be no more than 5 percent of the total pore space. Oil in this type of porosity is almost completely flushed during coring, and the oil saturation in the cores is no more than a trace. Frequently, the oil in a carbonate reservoir is contained primarily in the low-permeability, intercrystalline pores, with the fractures serving mainly as a means of communication of these pores with the wellbore.

Figure 3-13 is a core analysis report for the Ellenberger dolomite in

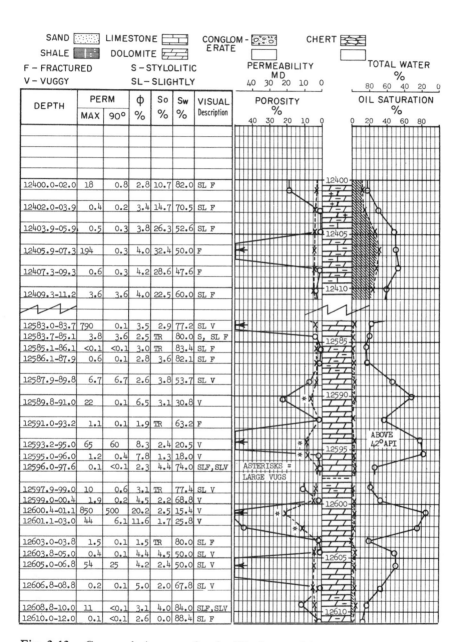

DEPTH	PERM MAX	PERM 90°	φ %	So %	Sw %	VISUAL Description
12400.0-02.0	18	0.8	2.8	10.7	82.0	SL F
12402.0-03.9	0.4	0.2	3.4	14.7	70.5	SL F
12403.9-05.9	0.5	0.3	3.8	26.3	52.6	SL F
12405.9-07.3	194	0.3	4.0	32.4	50.0	F
12407.3-09.3	0.6	0.3	4.2	28.6	47.6	F
12409.3-11.2	3.6	3.6	4.0	22.5	60.0	SL F
12583.0-83.7	790	0.1	3.5	2.9	77.2	SL V
12583.7-85.1	3.8	3.6	2.5	TR	80.0	S, SL F
12585.1-86.1	<0.1	<0.1	3.0	TR	83.4	SL F
12586.1-87.9	0.6	0.1	2.8	3.6	82.1	SL F
12587.9-89.8	6.7	6.7	2.6	3.8	53.7	SL V
12589.8-91.0	22	0.1	6.5	3.1	30.8	V
12591.0-93.2	1.1	0.1	1.9	TR	63.2	F
12593.2-95.0	65	60	8.3	2.4	20.5	V
12595.0-96.0	1.2	0.4	7.8	1.3	18.0	V
12596.0-97.6	0.1	<0.1	2.3	4.4	74.0	SLF, SLV
12597.9-99.0	10	0.6	3.1	TR	77.4	SL V
12599.0-00.4	1.9	0.2	4.5	2.2	68.8	V
12600.4-01.1	850	500	20.2	2.5	15.4	V
12601.1-03.0	44	6.1	11.6	1.7	25.8	V
12603.0-03.8	1.5	0.1	1.5	TR	80.0	SL F
12603.8-05.0	0.4	0.1	4.4	4.5	50.0	SL V
12605.0-06.8	54	25	4.2	2.4	50.0	SL V
12606.8-08.8	0.2	0.1	5.0	2.0	67.8	SL V
12608.8-10.0	11	<0.1	3.1	4.0	84.0	SLF, SLV
12610.0-12.0	0.1	<0.1	2.6	0.0	88.4	SL F

PERMEABILITY MD: 40 30 20 10 0
TOTAL WATER %: 80 60 40 20 0
POROSITY %: 40 30 20 10 0
OIL SATURATION %: 0 20 40 60 80

ABOVE 42°API

ASTERISKS = LARGE VUGS

Fig. 3-13. Core analysis report for the Ellenberger dolomite, Texas. (Courtesy of Core Laboratories.)

Texas where the porosity is primarily fractures with some vugs in the lower part of the section. The upper part of the report represents an obviously oil-bearing section. Below 12,583 ft the oil saturation is very low, and the water saturation is very erratic, varying from 15 to 80 percent. It is not possible to do a foot-by-foot analysis of this type of formation. It is necessary rather to look for saturation changes over a large section. Drill stem tests on this interval indicate that water would be produced from below 12,605 ft, probably as a result of coning through fractures.

Figure 3-14 is a special core report for a San Andres dolomite section

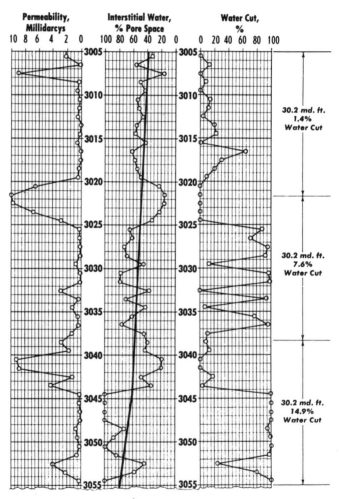

Fig. 3-14. Special core analysis report for the San Andres dolomite. (Aufricht and Koepf, courtesy of the AIME.)

which illustrates quite clearly the gradual change in saturations, as indicated by the solid line on the water saturation plot. The report also shows that as a result of the highly variable nature of the porosity and permeability in a carbonate rock, it is possible to have an interval producing water above an interval which produces oil (e.g., 3025 to 3037 has a very high water cut). Such intervals are characterized by low permeability, however, so that their contribution to the total production from a well is usually quite small. The water cuts shown in this report are calculated from capillary pressure and relative permeability data (2).

Sometimes an interval of either sandstone or carbonate contains oil, and then through a geological disturbance of some sort, e.g., fracturing of the cap rock, the oil is permitted to seep away and is replaced by connate water. The core analysis of such a section appears just the same as if the reservoir contained oil at the time of drilling and the oil were flushed away by the drilling fluid. This is one instance where the electric log can be helpful in the interpretation. If the sand is clean, the absence of significant amounts of oil in the uninvaded zone will be indicated by a low reading on the deep penetration resistivity curve.

The discussion of core analysis interpretation thus far has assumed that water-base muds have been used as the drilling fluid. Oil-emulsion muds in which water is the continuous phase act much like straight water-base muds with the possible exception that in very permeable gas sands some of the emulsified oil may get into the core. Generally, the emulsified oil droplets are retained in the filter cake, and only the watery mud filtrate penetrates the core in significant quantities. Conversely, oil-base drilling fluids provide a filtrate which is oil, and all permeable beds will show some oil saturation. Interpretation in this situation becomes more difficult, but is not impossible. Sometimes reservoir oil can be distinguished from drilling oil by the gravity of the oil retorted from the core. Also, in an oil or gas sand there will be a gas expansion drive as the core is brought to the surface so gas saturation in the analyzed core will still be of the same order of magnitude as indicated in Table 3-2. Oil from the mud contains no gas, and so there will be no gas flushing if only this oil is present. Figure 3-15 shows an analysis report for a core that was taken with an oil base mud.

If a core is taken with oil-base mud above the transition zone, where the water in the reservoir represents the irreducible minimum, then there will be no further change in water saturation during the coring process, and the analyzed water saturation will be the saturation of formation water in the reservoir. This is, in fact, the best method of determining formation water saturation. It should be emphasized here

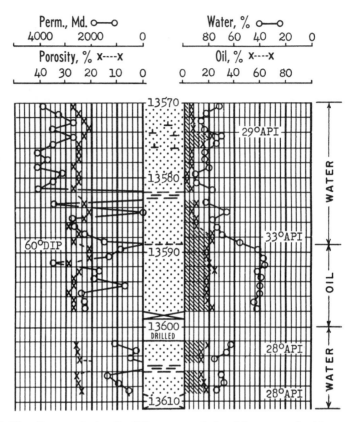

Fig. 3-15. Core analysis of a Miocene sand, Louisiana, cored with an oil-base mud. (Courtesy of Core Laboratories.)

that this method requires good mud control. If there is any free water present in the drilling fluid, it will be retained by the core and show up as a high water saturation. This is especially true if there are clay minerals present. Also, certain chemical additives in the mud cause a reduction in the amount of water in the core. In this classification are unslaked lime, which will dehydrate the core, and strong surfactants, which will cause the rock to become oil wet and thereby lose its capillary held water.

FULL DIAMETER CORE ANALYSIS

Because of the difficulties presented by the random porosity of carbonate rocks, it is common to analyze a section of the whole core, rather than just a plug taken from the core. Measurements of porosity and saturations are made in essentially the same manner as for core plugs, but with larger equipment. Whole core permeabilities are measured in a permeameter that is designed to flow air in through one 90° segment of the core face and out the opposite 90° segment. The other two 90° segments and the ends of the core section are sealed. The apparatus for doing this is shown schematically in Fig. 3-16. Measurements of the permeability are made on the core in different positions until a maximum value is obtained. The core is then rotated 90° and a second measurement is made. These two values are reported as K_{max} and $K_{90°}$. (See Figure 3-13.) In many cores the smaller, or 90° value, represents the matrix permeability.

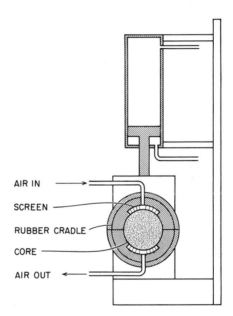

Fig. 3-16. Whole core compression permeameter. (Reproduced by permission from API RP 40: Core-analysis Procedure.)

AIR IN

SCREEN

RUBBER CRADLE

CORE

AIR OUT

A recent innovation by Core Laboratories is the surface gamma-ray log (12). In making this log the entire core is run under a gamma-ray counter and a plot is made of the natural gamma activity as a function of footage. A sample gamma log is shown in Fig. 3-17. When used with a downhole log, the surface gamma log can provide the necessary information for properly orienting the core in the geologic section. This can be helpful in locating lost core intervals, in providing accurate perforating in thin sections, and in reducing the amount of coring that is necessary.

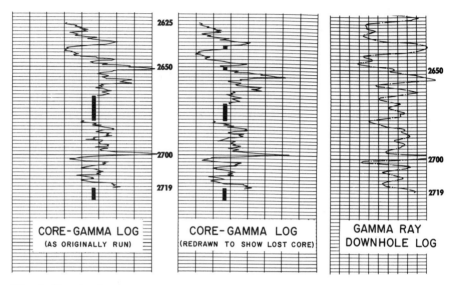

Fig. 3-17. Application of the core gamma-ray log for identifying lost core intervals. (Courtesy of Core Laboratories.)

REFERENCES

1. *API RP 40: Recommended Practice for Core-Analysis Procedure:* American Petroleum Institute, Division of Production, Dallas, Texas, 1960.
2. Aufricht, W. R., and Koepf, E. H., The interpretation of capillary pressure data from carbonate reservoirs: *Jour. Petroleum Technology*, October, 1957, Tech. Note 443, p. 53.
3. Brownscombe, E. R., Laboratory determination of relative permeability: *Oil and Gas Jour.*, February 9 and 16, 1950.
4. Elmdahl, B. A., Fundamental principles of core analysis and their application to Gulf Coast formations, *Symposium on Formation Evaluation:* AIME, Houston, Texas, 1955, p. 86.
5. *Fundamentals of Core Analysis*, Core Laboratories, Inc., Dallas, Texas.
6. Gates, J. I., and Tempelaar-Lietz, W., Relative permeabilities of California cores by the capillary pressure method: *API Drilling and Production Practice*, 1950, p. 285.
7. Gatlin, C., *Petroleum Engineering, Drilling and Well Completions:* Prentice-Hall, Inc., Englewood Cliffs, New Jersey, 1960, p. 168.
8. Gondouin, M., and Scala, C., Streaming potential and the SP log: *Trans. AIME*, v. 213, 1958, p. 170.
9. Hassler, G. L., Method and apparatus for permeability measurements: U.S. Patent 2,345,935.
10. Henderson, H., and Earl, J. F., New drilling technique recovers 100 percent continuous core: *World Oil*, January, 1960, p. 111.

11. Hurd, B. G., and Fitch, J. L., The effect of gypsum on core analysis results: *Trans. AIME*, v. 216, 1959, p. 221.
12. Jenkins, R. E., and Meurer, M. C., Surface gamma-ray logging of sub-surface cores: *The Petroleum Engineer*, February, 1958, p. B-64.
13. Klinkenberg, L. J., The permeability of porous media to liquids and gases: *API Drilling and Production Practices*, 1941, p. 200.
14. Koepf, E. H., and Granberry, R. J., The use of sidewall core analysis in formation evaluation: *Formation Evaluation Symposium*, AIME, Houston, Texas, 1960, p. I-7.
15. Leverett, M. C., Flow of oil-water mixtures through unconsolidated sands: *Trans. AIME*, v. 132, 1939, p. 149.
16. Leverett, M. C., Capillary behavior in porous solids: *Trans. AIME*, v. 142, 1941, p. 152.
17. Loomis, A. G., and Crowell, D. C., Relative permeability studies: II. Water-oil systems: *Producers Monthly*, August, 1959, p. 18.
18. Luffel, D. L., and Randall, R. V., Core handling and measurement techniques for obtaining reliable reservoir characteristics: *Formation Evaluation Symposium*, AIME, Houston, Texas, 1960, p. I-21.
19. Owens, W. W., Parrish, D. R., and Lamoreaux, W. E., An evaluation of a gas drive method for determining relative permeability relationships: *Trans. AIME*, v. 207, 1956, p. 275.
20. Purcell, W. R., Capillary pressures—their measurement using mercury and the calculation of permeability therefrom: *Trans. AIME*, v. 186, 1949, p. 39.
21. Rust, C. F., Electrical resistivity measurements on reservoir rock samples by the two-electrode and four-electrode methods: *Trans. AIME*, v. 195, 1952, p. 217.

4

Drilling Fluid and
Cuttings Analysis Logging

Since World War II the continuous analysis of drill returns has become a very important method of formation evaluation on exploratory wells. As yet it is not possible to use the measurements quantitatively for the determination of the amount of oil and gas in place in the undisturbed reservoir, and consequently, the method leans heavily on experience for proper interpretation. Several new devices are being introduced to improve the quality of the measurements, and it is quite likely that the effect of these improvements will be felt in the interpretation of the data. Until such time as a quantitative application is possible, however, mud logging must be considered primarily as a lead to coring and testing. It has an added usefulness as a safety measure for the early detection of hazardous mud conditions which could result in a blowout.

As the name implies, this logging method utilizes a continual inspection of the drilling mud and cuttings for traces of oil and gas. The techniques evolved from the early day drilling practices of looking for an oil rainbow in the mud pit and smelling the mud to see if any hydrocarbon gas was being evolved from it. The first real effort to improve these practices was made by J. T. Hayward, chief engineer of the Barnsdall Oil Company. In 1938 he applied for patent rights (3) on a method that he developed to determine the amount of oil in the mud by centrifuging, and to determine the amount of gas in the mud by a hot wire analyzer. Hayward also established the method for accurately determining the time necessary for the cuttings to arrive at the surface so that a surface sample could be correlated against the drilling depth.

The Hayward patents were licensed to Baroid in 1939 and were offered by that company as a mud logging service. The predictions of oil accumulations made with the Hayward method were at first very erratic, partly because of the lack of experience and partly because there was not sufficient information in these two pieces of data. In 1943 E. F. Peters and J. E. Bliss concurrently introduced a method of systematic examination of the cuttings for traces of oil and gas. The additional information obtained by this procedure made mud logging an effective and important evaluation method. Today there are over three hundred mud logging units operating in the western hemisphere; roughly one-half of the exploratory wells drilled in the United States use this service.

INSTRUMENTS FOR HYDROCARBON ANALYSIS

The instruments used for detecting and measuring the quantities of hydrocarbons in the samples are contained in a service company trailer which is set up at the drilling site adjacent to the drill rig. The location of the trailer should be such as to give the logging operator ready access to the mud returns area. The trailer remains at the site at all times while drilling is in progress and mud logging is in use.

Analysis for Oil

The basic instrument for the detection and measurement of oil in the mud and cuttings is the fluorescent light, and under the proper conditions it can detect as little as 10 ppm. Fluorescence occurs when a substance is exposed to ultraviolet radiation. The absorption of this high-energy electromagnetic radiation causes an electronic transition in some of the atoms, so that they are in an excited state. If this additional energy is not removed within a very short time (10^{-7} sec), the excited electron will return to a lower energy state with the simultaneous emission of radiation corresponding to the difference in the two energy levels. This radiation is seen as fluorescence. The wavelength of the fluorescence may be equal to or longer than the wavelength of the exciting radiation. Usually, the wavelength of the fluorescence is longer, because most absorbing molecules are in the ground energy state, while a fluorescing molecule will usually return to some slightly higher energy state.

Not all materials fluoresce. The fluorescence caused by ultraviolet excitation may be in the ultraviolet region, and hence will not be seen. Simple organic molecules rarely fluoresce in the liquid state, presumably because there are too many deactivating collisions which convert the excitation energy into kinetic energy, and hence into heat. Some organic substances may even undergo decomposition, and lose the energy that way. Fortunately, there are a sufficient number of organic molecules (aromatics and naphthenes) in most crude oils to provide a distinctive fluorescence in the visible region when viewed under a suitable ultraviolet light.

Figure 4-1 shows a portion of the spectrum of electromagnetic radiation. Wavelengths from 1000 to 4000 A constitute the ultraviolet portion of the spectrum. (A is the angstrom unit and is equal to a ten-millionth of a millimeter). Between 4000 and 7800 A is the visible portion of the spectrum, and above 7800 is the infrared portion. The standard Mineralite for the investigation of fluorescence in minerals has a wavelength of 2700 A. It has been found in petroleum work that the long ultraviolet (3600 A) source is much more effective in producing fluorescence in the visible region, since it is itself on the threshold of visibility and even a small change in the energy of the fluorescing radiation will bring it in to the visible region. Ultraviolet light of this wavelength causes fluorescence of almost all crude oils over the entire range of gravities. The color of fluorescence is, in general, characteristic of the gravity of the crude oil, as shown in Table 4-1 and Fig. 4-1.

TABLE 4-1.   FLUORESCENCE COLOR OF CRUDE OILS

Gravity, °API	Color of Fluorescence
Below 15	Brown
15-25	Orange
25-35	Yellow to cream
35-45	White
Over 45	Blue-white to violet

Very low gravity oils are difficult to see because they fluoresce very little, probably because of molecular decomposition. The high-gravity oils are difficult to see because some of their fluorescence occurs in the ultraviolet region, because they have high concentrations of the low molecular weight paraffin hydrocarbons which do not fluoresce at all, and because the human eye is insensitive to light in the blue-violet region. The presence of refined rig oils complicates detection of the light crudes because refined oils may fluoresce white or blue-white. Visible light from the source also causes difficulty in this region, although it is possible to filter out most of this with cobalt-nickel filters. Fortunately, where the greatest difficulty exists in locating oil by fluorescence,

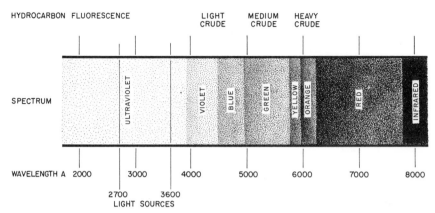

Fig. 4-1. Electromagnetic radiation spectrum in the visible light region.

the greatest amount of gas is present, and this may be detected readily with a gas analyzer.

The relation between the color of fluorescence and the gravity of the oil can be very useful in the interpretation of the mud logging data. It may also be helpful in analyzing data from other formation evaluation methods where it is sometimes important to know the type of crude oil that is present.

Some of the lighter components of the oil fraction of a show are now being removed from the mud by steam distillation and analyzed with a gas chromatograph. This device, which can detect quantities of the order of a few parts per million, will be described in a later section.

Analysis for Gas

Hot-Wire Analyzer. For many years the standard method of determining the amount of gas in the mud and cuttings was the hot-wire analyzer. The principle of this instrument is shown schematically in Fig. 4-2. The analyzer is essentially a Wheatstone bridge. Two of the usual bridge resistors are replaced by a pair of matched platinum filaments, one of which is in a cell that is open to the atmosphere, and the other is in a cell through which the sample gas is passed. The filaments are heated to a high temperature by passing current through the bridge; the filament temperature depends on a steady-state balance between the rate of heat generation at the filament and the rate of heat conduction through the gas to the cell walls. When air is in the sample cell, the conditions of heat generation and heat loss are identical in both cells, and the bridge is balanced; the recorder reads zero. When the sample filament is operating in an atmosphere that contains hydro-

Want to see this on mud Log of wildcat well.

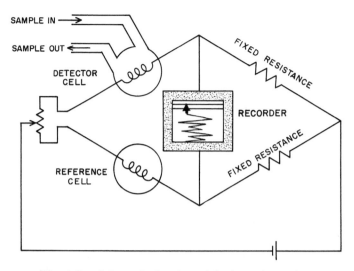

Fig. 4-2. Schematic drawing of the hot-wire analyzer.

carbons, there is catalytic oxidation of the hydrocarbon gases at the filament. This causes an increase in the temperature of the filament and an increase in its resistance. The increase in resistance causes an unbalance of the bridge and results in a reading on the recorder that is roughly proportional to the amount of hydrocarbon gas in the sample, provided that this does not exceed a critical amount.

The hot-wire analyzer can sample continuously the gases evolved from the mud and provide a continuous log of gas concentration on the electronic recorder. It is simple in construction and inexpensive. Sensitivity is about 200 ppm.

The minimum temperatures necessary for ignition of a gas-air mixture are given in Table 4-2. If the potential on the bridge is adjusted

TABLE 4-2. MINIMUM IGNITION TEMPERATURES FOR VARIOUS GASES

Gas	Temperature, °C	Ignition Voltage, volts
Methane	632	0.9
Ethane	520	0.6
Propane	481	0.45
Butane	441	0.3
Hydrogen	580[a]	0.2

[a] In the presence of a platinum catalyst, hydrogen will react vigorously with oxygen at much lower temperatures.

so that there is a 1.2-volt drop across the reference filament, the filament will reach a temperature of approximately 900°C when it is in an atmosphere of air. If the voltage is set so that there is a 0.65-volt drop across the reference filament, the temperature will be approximately 550°C. The higher voltage, therefore, will cause burning of all the hydrocarbon gases in a sample, while the lower voltage will cause burning of all gases except methane. In theory, at least, operation of a hot wire analyzer alternately at the two different voltages should make it possible to determine the amount of methane in the sample. The presence of methane is important because methane is almost always associated with productive oil sands. In practice this system does not work very well. As soon as the higher molecular weight gases start to burn at the lower temperature, they cause an increase in the temperature of the cell and consequently cause the ignition of all or part of the methane.

The presence of hydrogen in the gas stream is also a troublesome factor in analysis by means of a hot-wire analyzer. Hydrogen in the mud comes from the corrosive action of low pH muds on the drill pipe or from a reaction between aluminum parts and caustic muds, but to the analyzer it appears like another hydrocarbon gas. In order to get a good gas-in-mud curve it is necessary to remove the hydrogen by absorption before the gas is analyzed. This type of procedure can also be used to separate the heavier hydrocarbon gases from the sample stream so that only the methane is measured by the detector. This method is much more effective in getting a methane curve than is the use of two different voltages across the detecting cell.

The greatest difficulty in using the hot-wire type of analyzer arises from the fact that it actually burns the combustible gases in the sample. The maximum concentration at which the instrument will function properly is limited therefore by the minimum quantity of air that is necessary for complete combustion. This results in an instrument response curve like that shown in Fig. 4-3. The peaks of these curves correspond to the maximum theoretical concentration of hydrocarbon at which complete combustion is possible; the heights of the peaks correspond to the theoretical heat of combustion. An actual cell may vary considerably from these curves, depending on the cell design, but the same general trend will be noted. It can be seen that the methane curve reaches a peak at 9.5 percent, so that readings of the hot-wire analyzer are good only as long as this concentration is not exceeded. The maximum theoretical concentration for ethane is 5.65 per cent; for propane it is 4.02 percent; and for butane it is 3.12 percent. When

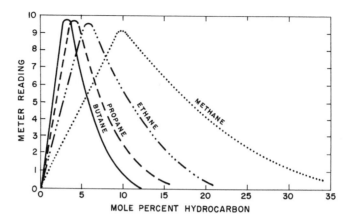

Fig. 4-3. Approximate response of a hot-wire analyzer to various concentrations of methane, ethane, propane, and butane.

these concentrations are exceeded, the temperature of the filament starts to decrease for several reasons: (a) incomplete combustion results in the formation of CO instead of CO_2, with a loss of 67 kcal of heat per mole of gas formed. (b) an increase in the amount of hydrocarbon results in a decrease in the amount of air present, and consequently there is even less hydrocarbon burned. (c) CO has 1.6 times the thermal conductivity of CO_2 so that the formation of CO results in a greater rate of heat loss from the filament. If the hot-wire analyzer is to be used for samples which contain more than the critical amount of gas, then the sample must first be diluted with a known amount of additional air. Alternately, thermal conductivity cells may be used for high gas concentrations.

The platinum filament of the hot-wire detector serves as a catalyst for the oxidation reaction. Like all catalysts its action can become inhibited if it is poisoned by certain substances. High concentrations of sulfur compounds or silicones in the mud gases can cause this fouling. Also, decomposition products from the hydrocarbons themselves can coat the filament and reduce its effectiveness.

Gas Chromatograph.   In order to obtain a more accurate and quantitative analysis of the individual components of the sample, the partition gas chromatograph (2) is used. This device is shown schematically in Fig. 4-4. A sweep gas flows continuously through a column that is packed with an inert solid coated with a nonvolatile organic liquid. The column is a long 1/4-in.-diameter tube made of copper, aluminum, or stainless steel. At the inlet end of the column a small measured volume of the unknown sample is injected into the sweep gas stream. The heavier components of the sample tend to be absorbed into the column material and are swept very slowly through it. The lighter components, such as methane, are relatively insoluble in the column material and move along rapidly. At the exit of the column, then, the various components of the sample appear separately, and the amount of each can be determined with a gas analyzer. The component is identified by the length of time that it takes for it to move through the column, since this transit time is fixed for a given compound at set conditions of temperature, pressure, and rate of flow of the elution gas. Transit times for pure gases are determined experimentally.

The signal from the gas analyzer is fed to a strip chart recorder to produce a time vs concentration record like that shown in Fig. 4-5. The position of the peak in the time sequence identifies the compound, and the area under the peak gives the amount of the compound that is present. Since all the peaks have approximately the shape of an isosceles triangle, and since they sometimes overlap, it is simpler to take the peak height a times the half-band width b to get the area, as illustrated for n-butane. If the half-band widths are all about the same, or if the instrument has been calibrated with known concentrations of the various compounds, then a measure of the peak heights alone will suffice to indicate the concentration.

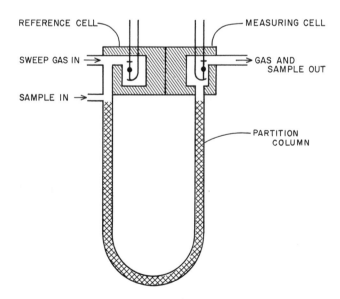

Fig. 4-4. Schematic illustration of a partition gas chromatograph.

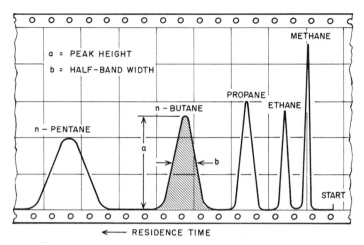

Fig. 4-5. Typical analysis chart (chromatogram) from a gas chromatograph.

The hydrocarbons heavier than C_6 are usually not of great interest in the analysis of mud gases because they exist in very small amounts, and because it becomes increasingly difficult to separate and identify them. If they were allowed to pass completely through the column, there would be an excessive delay before the next analysis could be started. It is customary therefore to "cut" the analysis at some convenient point and remove the heavy materials from the column by a reverse flush. If this procedure is followed, it is possible to run a chromatographic analysis through butane about once every 5 minutes. Chromatographs are also being developed which will sample and analyze automatically.

Adsorption columns in which the sample components are adsorbed on a solid material, such as silica gel, may also be used in elution chromatography. They are not generally suitable, however, because there is an adsorption hysterisis which causes the chart bands to exhibit very long tails; this causes overlapping of successive peaks, and also requires an accurate integration of the area under the curve because such a large fraction of the area is in the tail. Adsorption columns also have extremely long retention times for high-boiling materials, so that they are limited almost entirely to compounds that are normally gaseous (e.g., separation of methane and air).

Analysis for the amount of gas in the exit stream from the partition column may be made with a number of instruments. In laboratory work the thermal conductivity cell is most commonly used. This type of analyzer functions as part of a bridge circuit similar to the hot wire analyzer. The thermal conductivity cell, however, operates at a lower temperature so that there is no combustion in the cell; temperature fluctuations of the filament depend solely on the rate at which heat is conducted from the filament to the cell walls, and this depends on the thermal conductivity of the gas in the cell. Thermistors are commonly used as filaments because of their high sensitivity to temperature changes. The thermal conductivities of some common gases are given in Table 4-3.

TABLE 4-3. THERMAL CONDUCTIVITY OF GASES AT 212°F

Gas	Thermal Conductivity Btu/(hr) (sq ft) (°F/ft)
Helium	0.101
Hydrogen	0.129
Air	0.0183
Methane	0.0235
Ethane	0.0175
Propane	0.0151
Butane	0.0135
Carbon dioxide	0.0126
Water vapor	0.0160

Helium is generally used as the sweep gas with the thermal conductivity analyzer because its thermal conductivity is several times higher than that of most other gases (except hydrogen). Dilution of the helium by the hydrocarbon gases therefore gives a very pronounced change in the thermal conductivity of the mixture, and to a first approximation this change is proportional to the volume fraction of gas that is present.

The columns that are used to make a general separation of the hydro-carbons in mud logging unfortunately have about the same retention time for both air and methane. If helium is used as the sweep gas, these two will appear as part of the same peak. In this situation three alter-natives are possible. First, a second column with a different stationary phase may be used to separate the air and methane and analyze these separately. Second, air may be used for the sweep gas, in which case the methane peak will represent methane alone. This system has a great disadvantage over the helium system because the thermal conductivities of air and the hydrocarbons are about the same, and there is a great loss in sensitivity. This can be partly overcome by using a larger sample, but if the sample is too large, the column will be overloaded and the analysis bands on the chart will become distorted. Third, the hot-wire

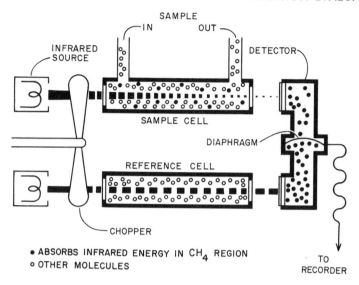

Fig. 4-6. Schematic drawing showing the principle of operation of a device for the continous analysis for methane by infrared absorption. (Courtesy of Beckman Instruments, Inc.)

analyzer can be used. This solution to the problem is frequently chosen by mud logging companies. Some correction to the analysis must be made if the hot-wire analyzer is used because it responds to the total weight of combustible material in the gas stream, rather than to the volume fraction. If the compound is identified, however, these corrections are easily made.

Infrared Analyzer.   A third device which may be used for gas analysis is the infrared analyzer (4). This device may analyze continuously, but for only one specific component, usually methane. Figure 4-6 is a schematic drawing of an instrument of this type that is manufactured by Beckman. In operation, two constant and similar energy sources situated adjacent to a rotating chopper provide pulsed infrared beams in the range of 2 to 10 cps. The infrared sources are Nichrome filaments heated by an electric current; they provide a continuous and uniform spectrum throughout the infrared range. The infrared beams pass through the reference cell (filled with air) and through the sample cell and then pass into the detector. The detector is filled with the gaseous component for which the analysis is to be made (e.g., methane).

Every polyatomic gaseous material absorbs infrared energy in the form of vibrational energy of the interatomic bonds. The energy level, or band, which is absorbed is characteristic of the molecule. (Part of the infrared spectrum of methane is shown in Fig. 4-7.) Thus, the air in the reference cell absorbs some of the radiation passing through it, but it does not absorb energy in the same band as that of the methane gas in the detector. Therefore, the radiation arriving at the detector, by way of the reference cell, undergoes further absorption and causes heating of the detector gas. Energy passing through the sample cell undergoes the same absorption when the sample cell contains air, or, in fact, any gas other than methane. If the gas volumes on both sides of the diaphragm in the detector are heated equally, there will be no movement of the diaphragm. If, on the other hand, some of the gas in the sample cell is methane, part of the critical energy band will be absorbed in the sample cell. This will result in greater heating of the reference side of the detector than the sample side, and the diaphragm will be displaced. The diaphragm is made of metal so that it can act as one plate of an electrical condenser. Movement of it changes the capacity of the condenser and thereby produces an electrical signal whose magnitude is proportional to the amount of the particular gaseous component in the sample stream.

Very good analysis of the gas in mud can be made if the infrared and gas chromatograph analyzers are used together. The mud gases can be monitored continuously for the presence of methane with the infrared analyzer, and when a good show is obtained, a sample can be run through the chromatograph for a complete analysis. In this way the advantages of a complete analysis are combined with a continuous survey.

Infrared analyzers are vibration sensitive so that they must be mechanically damped. In addition, they must have a power supply that

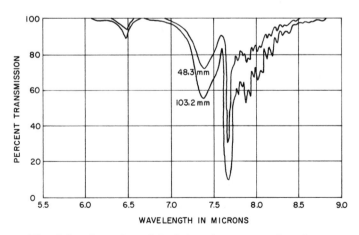

Fig. 4-7. A portion of the infrared spectrum of methane.

is of constant frequency and voltage. Some compensation must also be made for large changes in the amount of water vapor and carbon dioxide in the sample gas stream. On the other hand, they are very simple to operate and have a good sensitivity (about 100 ppm for methane under normal operating conditions).

Mass Spectrograph. Another instrument that has been tried for analysis of the gases from the mud stream is the mass spectrograph. This is a device for separating and determining the relative amounts of various ions on the basis of the mass to charge ratio. Its use in gas analysis is based on the fact that positive ions can be produced by bombardment of a gas with a stream of electrons. These ions will have masses equal to that of the parent molecule and to various fragments of the molecule. The distribution of these masses is characteristic of a particular molecule and is termed the mass spectrum. The masses are separated from one another by accelerating them under a high potential gradient and then forcing them into a curved path with a magnetic or electric field. By adjusting the accelerating voltage, or the magnetic field, any particular mass can be made to focus on a collector plate: the charge on the collector plate represents the concentration of the mass species.

The spectrometers that have been used in mud logging were capable of following six mass peaks simultaneously. The peaks of mass 15 and 43 were found to be particularly useful in indicating the presence of methane and the heavier hydrocarbons. In spite of its great versatility as an analytical instrument, however, the mass spectrograph has not been successful in mud logging. It is expensive, sensitive to mechanical shock, requires constant and continuous power sources, and needs the services of a trained technician to operate and maintain it.

LOGGING TECHNIQUES

Sampling

Sampling is of fundamental importance in any logging method, and the proper sampling of the cuttings and of the gas in the mud can do much to improve the significance of mud logging results. The trend in mud logging is toward sampling of the mud returns line at the bell nipple and pumping this sample into the trailer unit. Within the trailer the mud passes through an agitator to break out the gas which is then analyzed and plotted as the gas-in-mud curve. The mud stream continues through a rotating conical screen or miniature shaker arrangement so that the cuttings may be separated and sampled. Sometimes a simple settling box is used to get the cuttings sample. The mud is then returned to the drilling mud system. Sampling within the trailer allows the operator to spend more time on the many measurements that he must make.

Some companies still prefer to sample at some point in the normal circulation system of the drilling rig, and when difficult mud conditions warrant it (e.g., heavy mud, mud containing lost circulation material, extremely cold weather which might freeze the sampling line), this type of sampling must be used by all operators. Cuttings samples may be collected at the shale shakers, or in a settling box placed in the mud ditch. Gas samples may be obtained by using a closed agitator in the mud ditch to break the gas out of the mud. It is also possible to get a gas sample by using a simple hood over the mud ditch or over the shakers, but this gives a questionable sample.

Figure 4-8 is a schematic representation of the gas sampling system. The agitator continuously pumps part of the mud stream through itself, and aerates and agitates it in the process. The mixture of air and gas is then withdrawn from the top of the agitator tank at a constant and measured rate and fed to a gas analyzer in the trailer. The signal from the analyzer is recorded by an electronic recorder as the concentration of gas in the gas-air mixture.

The type of agitator illustrated here is excellent for breaking methane out of the mud but is neither efficient nor reproducible in releasing other gaseous components such as ethane and propane; the efficiency for these compounds varies with the mud viscosity, mud temperature, and air temperature and humidity. Baroid has recently introduced a steam still (7) for getting a complete separation of low-boiling hydro-

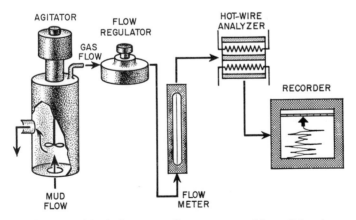

Fig. 4-8. Typical gas sampling system used in well logging.

carbons from the mud, but it is a batch operation. A 5-cc sample of mud is placed in the still and then swept with about 1000 cc of steam. The gases released from the mud are caught in a condenser and then analyzed with a gas chromatograph. The introduction of this method of extracting hydrocarbons promises to be an important step in making mud logging a quantitative evaluation tool.

Sampling for cuttings is continuous, but the samples are grouped in intervals of 2, 5, or 10 ft of drilled section. At the end of each sampling interval the sample box is emptied completely, and the samples analyzed as soon thereafter as possible.

Determination of Lag Time

In order that the measurements made at the surface may be correlated with the proper depth, it is necessary to make some accurate measurement of the lag time, or the time for the cuttings to come to the surface. As a rule of thumb it can be estimated at 1 minute per 90 ft of hole. On a deep hole the lag time may amount to as much as 3 hours, and this can mean an appreciable depth correction. Lag time can be determined by either of two methods:

1. The circulation rate is determined from the size of the mud pump cylinders, the number of strokes per minute, and the pump efficiency (usually about 90 percent). When a new joint of pipe is added to the drill string, a tracer can be put into the pipe. When circulation is resumed, the time for the tracer to make the round trip and reappear at the surface is measured. From the circulation rate, the time for the tracer to go to the bottom through the drill pipe can be calculated. The difference in time between the round trip and the down time is the lag time. The tracers that are used include cellophane strips, rolled oats, and stained cuttings. These can be seen quite easily when they reach the shakers. It is also possible to use an envelope containing about 100 grams of calcium carbide. When the envelope is destroyed by the bit, the calcium carbide reacts with the mud to produce acetylene. This can be detected at the surface with the gas analyzer. This type of tracer also serves to check the gas analyzer.

2. A direct measurement of log time can be made by tying a brick on the bit when a new bit is put on. The brick will be crushed as soon as drilling starts, and the time for the chips to arrive at the surface can be measured. Another direct method of determining lag time is by measuring the elapsed time between a drilling break (see page 76) and the change in the type of cuttings arriving at the surface.

Lag time should be checked at least once a tour. It is desirable to have the lag time in terms of pumping rate in case the rate is changed.

Testing the Samples

The systems of analysis for oil and gas in the drill returns are not the same for all logging companies, nor do all companies attach the same significance to the results of a particular test. We will therefore outline the tests that are usually run and indicate their significance where this is possible. In the final analysis much depends on the skill of the individual operator, both in getting the information and in evaluating its importance.

Analysis for Oil. 1. An unwashed sample of cuttings is placed in an evaporating dish and covered with water. The dish is placed in a light-tight box which contains an ultraviolet light source. While under the UV light, the cuttings are broken up with a probe, and the surface of the water watched for traces of oil. If there is fresh, producible oil in the sample, it will come to the surface with an effervescent appearance and spread out quickly. This is called "live" oil. If the oil in the sample is "dead" oil it will rise slowly to the surface and tend to remain in small drops; this oil is assumed to come from contamination or from residual oil within the sample which has lost all its gas and therefore cannot be produced easily. One operator considers this the most diagnostic of all his tests; some other operators do not run this test at all.

2. A sample of cuttings is washed to remove adhering mud and then examined directly under fluorescent light. Cutting chips which have oil adhering to them will fluoresce, but so will a number of rocks such as bentonite, chert, calcite, limestone, and anhydrite, and some mud additives. The distinction is made by taking some of the particles and putting them into a small evaporating dish with chlorethene. If oil is present, it will dissolve in the chlorethene and the surface of the liquid will show some fluorescence. The strength of fluorescence remaining on the dish after the liquid has evaporated is considered by some as a significant measure of the oil potential of the rock. In reporting this factor, the operator usually depends to some extent on his skill to distinguish the tars, residual oil, and oil stains from the producible oil by the manner in which the fluorescence develops in the solvent. A straight report of the strength of the fluorescence of the solvent cut has little significance.

3. The examination of the mud for traces of oil under the fluorescent

light is much less important than the examination of the cuttings. The possibility of recirculation, dilution with mud, and contamination with rig oils and oil emulsion additives always raises some question about this piece of data. In regions where the sands are very friable, however, it may not be possible to get good cuttings samples, and then the burden of evidence falls on the oil-in-mud determination. An effort is being made at the present time to improve the data through an accurate chromatographic analysis of the hydrocarbons recovered from the mud.

Analysis for Gas. 1. A continuous analysis is made for gas in the mud with either the hot wire or infrared analyzer. This record can be used to correlate with other analyses or to serve as a guide for using the more precise chromatographic analysis. Gas appearing in the mud may come from several sources:

a. *Shale contamination.* Many shales will bleed small quantities of gas into the hole. Alone, these may be too small to be detected, but cumulatively they provide an unwelcome background for the analysis of gas in the mud. This type of gas contamination may be the result of a poor mud condition, and probably indicates a need for an increase in mud weight. If the mud pumps are shut down for a period of time for making connections, this source of gas may show an appreciable reading when circulation is resumed (trip gas or connection gas). A gas-bearing formation which has been penetrated previously and left uncased will also provide contamination of the mud, particularly when the drill pipe is moved in the hole so as to create a swabbling action.

b. *Recirculated gas.* High mud viscosity will prevent the mud from releasing all its gas when it arrives at the surface so that the same show of gas will be logged when it comes around for the second and third time. If there is a cyclic nature of the gas show, it is possible to recognize the source. One logging company analyzes the gas from the mud entering the pump suction and subtracts this reading, properly lagged, from the reading obtained from the returns flow line. A degasser may also be used on the mud in the pits if the recirculated gas problem becomes serious.

c. *Gas from the drilled portion of the hole.* This is the gas sample that is desired. In a good oil or gas sand it may be of a relatively small magnitude, and if there is much gas contamination in the mud, it can be very difficult to recognize a valid show. Occasionally, gas in the mud stream will not show up until the bit has penetrated several feet into the sand. The reason for this phenomenon is not understood.

In addition to normal gas shows from hydrocarbon-bearing formations very large gas concentrations may be obtained from high-pressure gas pockets. Such gas pockets are found in bituminous shales and small sand lenses. These will produce very high gas readings for a very short duration, and may even create a blowout condition in the well. The examination of the lithology log and drilling rate curve will often serve to discount these shows because of the absence of significant porosity.

2. A sample of cuttings taken from an appropriate sampling point is placed in a Waring Blendor, covered with water, and pulverized for a period of time from 30 seconds to 2 minutes, depending on the logging company. The blender is sealed during this operation with a cap having connections to the gas analyzer. At the completion of the pulverizing operation, the gas-air mixture in the blender is analyzed for hydrocarbons. This is referred to as the gas-in-cuttings or microgas. Microgas need not be contained in the cuttings in the free form, but may be evolved from oil in the cuttings during the destruction process.

If the microgas is negligible when there are other indications of oil, one logging company examines the cuttings further by covering a sample of the washed cuttings with water, placing them in a windowed vacuum chamber, and examining them with a microscope for evidence of gas evolution. They refer to this as vacuum gas.

Additional Data

In addition to the direct analyses for hydrocarbons that are indicated above, the operator will usually record several other items which are useful in an overall study of the well and also in the immediate problem of locating possible productive intervals. One of these is the lithology log which is handled as a normal part of the examination of the cuttings. This information is useful in the immediate problem because commercial hydrocarbon accumulations are associated with certain types of sedimentary rocks. It is of importance to the oil company in its more general studies of the geologic column in an area. Whether or not oil is located, the company will be faced with the prospect of drilling another well, possibly in this area. The more information available to the company geologists, the better will be their choice of subsequent drilling sites.

A record that is kept automatically for the operator is the rate of penetration of the drill bit. There are two types of instruments in general use. One uses a wireline connected to the swivel, and vertical movement of the swivel is translated into a penetration rate curve. The second type uses a liquid reservoir on the top of the Kelly or the swivel with a hose connection to a recorder; the movement of the Kelly causes a change in the fluid pressure at the recorder and gives a rate of penetration curve. The rate of penetration taken from one of these charts can be presented on the log in either feet per hour or minutes per foot, as desired by the customer. The rate of penetration is usually plotted so that the higher rates are to the left and the lower rates to the right. If the higher rates are experienced in the porous intervals, then a rate curve plotted this way will correspond with the SP curve of the electric log (see Chapter 5, Part II) where porous intervals are usually indicated by excursions to the left. In many places the drilling rate makes an excellent lithology curve. If there is no mud logging unit on a well, the wellsite geologist should make his own drilling rate log.

Obviously, a number of factors govern the rate of penetration in addition to the lithology. The weight on the drill, the rotary table speed, the condition of the bit, and the various techniques of the different drillers are some of the contributing factors. The rate curve is therefore more important in a relative rather than an absolute sense. Of particular importance is a rapid change in the rate, or a drilling break. Such a sudden increase in penetration rate may signal a porous interval, so that it is a common practice on a drilling break to stop after 2 or 3 ft of penetration and circulate out the cuttings. If evidence of oil is obtained, it is then possible to core ahead, and in reduced hole if this is desired. Not only is a core of the interval obtained in this way, but also more favorable conditions have been created for a subsequent drill stem test if the core evidence warrants it. If a core is taken, most mud logging operators are equipped to run a core analysis for water and hydrocarbon saturation, porosity, and permeability.

The properties of the drilling fluid are of great interest to the logging companies in the interpretation of the data. Consequently, it is customary for the operator to keep a record of the mud treatment, the filtration rate, and, if requested, the resistivity of the mud and mud filtrate. This information on resistivity can be useful also in the interpretation of electric log data.

The standard log form recommended by the API is shown in Fig. 4-9. This log contains all the information mentioned heretofore such as drilling rate, lithology, gas and oil analysis, and mud analysis; in addition, provision is made for a record of the bit changes, cored intervals, and description and remarks about the rock and the shows. If drill stem tests are run, the results of the tests will be indicated in the remarks column.

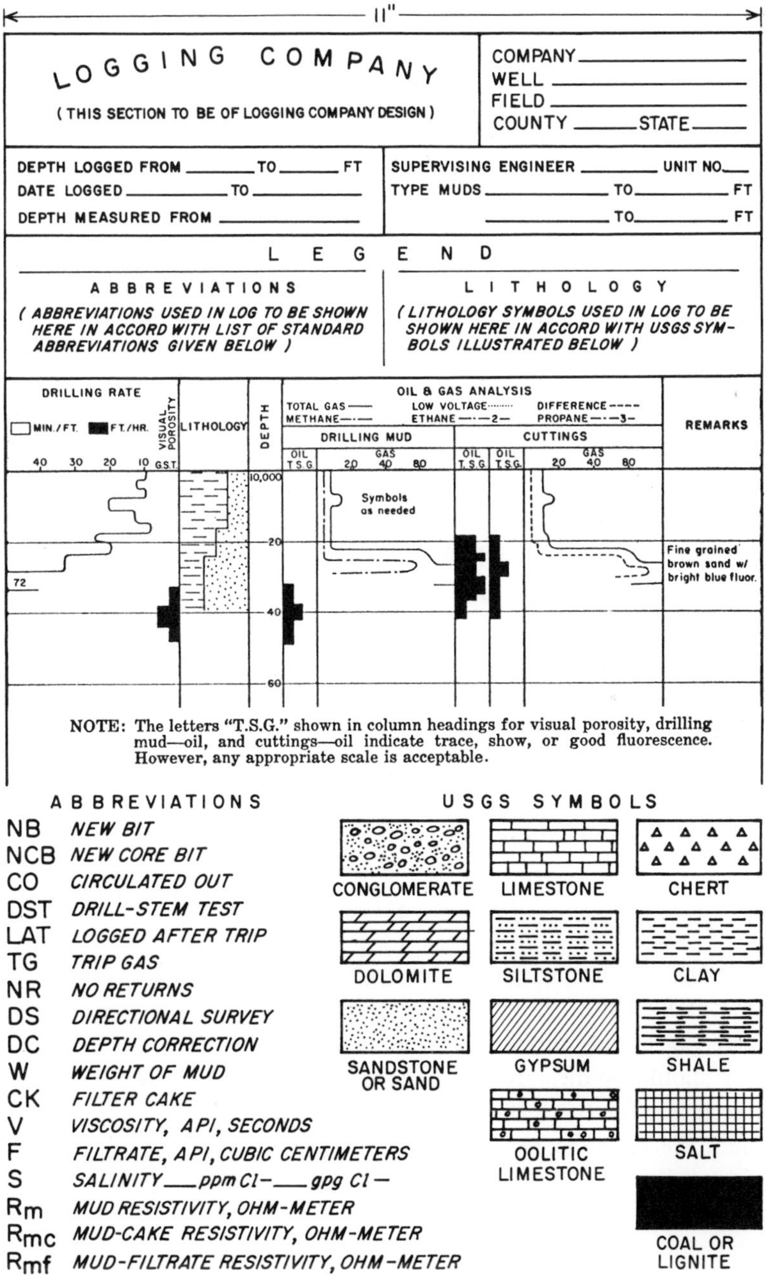

⊢————— 11" —————⊣

COMPANY_____
WELL _____
FIELD _____
COUNTY _____STATE_____

DEPTH LOGGED FROM _____TO _____ FT
DATE LOGGED _____TO _____
DEPTH MEASURED FROM _____

SUPERVISING ENGINEER _____ UNIT NO.___
TYPE MUDS _____ TO_____ FT
_____ TO_____ FT

L E G E N D

ABBREVIATIONS

(ABBREVIATIONS USED IN LOG TO BE SHOWN HERE IN ACCORD WITH LIST OF STANDARD ABBREVIATIONS GIVEN BELOW)

LITHOLOGY

(LITHOLOGY SYMBOLS USED IN LOG TO BE SHOWN HERE IN ACCORD WITH USGS SYMBOLS ILLUSTRATED BELOW)

DRILLING RATE — VISUAL POROSITY — LITHOLOGY — DEPTH — OIL & GAS ANALYSIS — REMARKS

☐ MIN./FT. ■ FT./HR.

TOTAL GAS —— LOW VOLTAGE········ DIFFERENCE----
METHANE—·— ETHANE—·—2— PROPANE—·—3—

DRILLING MUD — CUTTINGS

OIL T.S.G.   GAS 20 40 80   OIL T.S.G.   OIL T.S.G.   GAS 20 40 80

40 30 20 10 G.S.T.

10,000
20
40
60

72

Symbols as needed

Fine grained brown sand w/ bright blue fluor.

NOTE: The letters "T.S.G." shown in column headings for visual porosity, drilling mud—oil, and cuttings—oil indicate trace, show, or good fluorescence. However, any appropriate scale is acceptable.

ABBREVIATIONS

NB NEW BIT
NCB NEW CORE BIT
CO CIRCULATED OUT
DST DRILL-STEM TEST
LAT LOGGED AFTER TRIP
TG TRIP GAS
NR NO RETURNS
DS DIRECTIONAL SURVEY
DC DEPTH CORRECTION
W WEIGHT OF MUD
CK FILTER CAKE
V VISCOSITY, API, SECONDS
F FILTRATE, API, CUBIC CENTIMETERS
S SALINITY___ppm Cl-___ gpg Cl-
R_m MUD RESISTIVITY, OHM-METER
R_{mc} MUD-CAKE RESISTIVITY, OHM-METER
R_{mf} MUD-FILTRATE RESISTIVITY, OHM-METER

USGS SYMBOLS

CONGLOMERATE LIMESTONE CHERT
DOLOMITE SILTSTONE CLAY
SANDSTONE OR SAND GYPSUM SHALE
OOLITIC LIMESTONE SALT
COAL OR LIGNITE

Fig. 4-9. Standard hydrocarbon mud log form. (Reproduced by permission from API RP 34: Standard Hydrocarbon Mud Log Form.)

INTERPRETATION OF THE DATA

The interpretation of the data in terms of possible oil and gas production will depend to a large extent on the conditions under which the
hole was drilled. Logging can be done most effectively if the drilling
contractor is using modern efficient drilling equipment and mud pumps,
if there is an adequate drilling mud program, good shale shakers and
settling pits to remove the cuttings, if mud degassers are available
should they be required, and if there is automatic control of weight
on the drilling bit. Even with the proper control over these operations,
there are several factors which must be considered in the interpretation
of the data.

When an oil sand is penetrated by the drill bit, the first process that
occurs is the flushing of the formation fluids by the mud filtrate and
a resulting increase in the fractional water saturation from the original
S_w to a new value, S_F. S_F will probably approach the saturation of a
completely flushed sand, which is designated in electric logging as S_{xo}.
After this, the rock is crushed by the bit, and the residual hydrocarbon
is brought to the surface in the mud and the cuttings. The number
of cubic feet of rock pulverized per foot of penetration is $\pi d^2/576$,
where d is the bit diameter in inches. This volume of rock contains
$(\pi d^2/576)\,\phi(1 - S_F)$ cubic feet of residual hydrocarbon. If the drilling
rate is R_D feet per hour, and the rate of mud circulation is C cubic
feet per hour, then the amount of hydrocarbon which is brought to
the surface per unit volume of mud is

$$V_H = \frac{\pi d^2}{576}\phi(1 - S_F)\frac{R_D}{C} \qquad (4\text{-}1)$$

If G is the amount of gas (measured at surface conditions) per unit
volume of formation fluid, then V_H multiplied by G is the amount of
gas arriving at the surface per unit volume of mud. The gas-in-mud
reading should be directly proportional to this product. If the formation
volume factor for the oil is B barrels of formation oil per barrel of tank
oil, then the above expression (4-1) divided by B is the amount of oil
arriving at the surface per unit volume of mud. This oil may be either
in the mud or in the cuttings.

Values of G and B can be estimated from correlation charts (see
Appendix C) if the gravity of the oil, the gravity of the gas, and the
reservoir temperature and pressure are known. Oil gravity can be
estimated from fluorescence; gas gravity can be calculated if a chromatographic analysis is made. It would appear, then, that if accurate

measurements could be made of the amounts of oil and gas coming to the surface, it would be possible to calculate S_F. From S_F and a knowledge of lithologic and drilling factors, a very good estimate could be made of the potential of the zone. Unfortunately, at the present time accurate concentration measurements are not being made, and the evaluation of the shows is still qualitative.

Factors That Influence a Show

Some of the factors to be considered in the interpretation of the magnitude of a show are:

Physical Characteristics of the Rock. Under this heading are the porosity and permeability. The chemical nature of the rock matrix has very little effect, but the type of porosity and the magnitude of the porosity and permeability greatly influence the analysis for gas and oil in the cuttings and the mud. As can be seen from equation 4-1, the magnitude of the porosity enters directly into the size of the show. High permeability, on the other hand, will tend to decrease the size of the show because it permits a rapid flushing of the rock by mud filtrate and thereby reduces the magnitude of the residual oil saturation, $(1 - S_F)$. In general, high-permeability sandstones will give larger shows in the mud than in the cuttings, whereas impermeable rocks tend to hold their contained fluids throughout the drilling process so that there will be a small show in the mud stream, but the gas-in-cuttings and oil-in-cuttings readings will be high. It must be remembered that the porosity and permeability will affect the drilling rate and thereby influence the magnitude of the show in another way. This point will be discussed later on.

Porosity that is of a vuggy or fractured nature has a very high permeability and a very simple pore geometry. This type of rock will be flushed almost entirely of its contained fluids the instant it is penetrated so that the shows will be quite small, even for good producing intervals.

Type of Hydrocarbon. The physical properties of the hydrocarbon will affect the magnitude of the shows in several ways. In the first place, the viscosity of the hydrocarbon is related to the permeability effect mentioned above since it is the mobility, or the ratio of permeability to viscosity (K/μ), which determines the ease with which the fluid will flow when the rock is flushed with mud. Other factors being equal, heavy-oil sands will be flushed less than sands containing light oils or gas. Second, the amount of gas evolved from the oil as the pressure is reduced during the rise to the surface will govern the magnitude of the gas-in-mud and to some extent the oil-in-mud concentration. Evolution of large amounts of gas from the oil will also increase the shrinkage factor of the oil. Third, the nature of the in-place hydrocarbon will have a great effect on the diagnostic ability of mud logging. A dry gas is the most difficult to evaluate because it produces a show only as gas in the mud. There will be no evidence of oil in either the mud or cuttings, and very little gas in the cuttings. Dry gas shows are characterized by a high methane concentration with very little wet gas. A chromatographic analysis would be very useful in this instance. A distillate reservoir will give a similar reaction when drilled, but the gas analysis will show the presence of the propane and butane gases, and there may be some minor oil staining on the cuttings. Oil reservoirs give a gas-in-mud analysis similar to the distillate reservoir, but in addition there may be significant amounts of gas and oil in the cuttings. The oil reservoir is the easiest of the three types to detect because it does give the strong substantiating evidence in the cuttings.

Drilling Rate.   The amount of flushing of the rock ahead of the bit depends not only on the mobility, but also on the time that the formation is subjected to the differential pressure which exists between the mud and formation fluids. A fast drilling rate, therefore, will tend to give less flushing of the cuttings and will increase the magnitude of the shows through an increase in the term $(1 - S_F)$. Reference to equation 4-1 indicates also that the magnitude of the show in the mud will be directly proportional to the drilling rate because this is the rate at which hydrocarbon is being added to the mud stream. A high drilling rate will consequently make the job of logging easier. If the drilling rate is too high, however, the operator may not be able to keep up with his analyses. A drilling rate of 20 ft per hour is about the optimum for mud logging.

Density of the Drilling fluid.   The greater the density of the drilling fluid, the greater will be the pressure differential existing between the mud and the formation. This will result in greater flushing action. Jet action of the drilling bits also will increase this effect. On the other hand, if the mud is too light, there will be a tendency for the formations up the hole to bleed small amounts of gas into the mud and provide an undesirable background for logging.

Viscosity of the Mud.   High mud viscosity inhibits the release of the gas and cuttings from the mud. Not only does this reduce the magnitude of the gas show and increase the difficulty in getting representative cuttings samples, but if the mud is not degassed, there will be a gradual build-up of circulation gas over a period of time which will make logging of the gas in mud almost hopeless.

Depth of the Hole.   A deep hole is usually associated with high-pressure differentials between the mud and the formation fluids and slow drilling rates, both of which will reduce the magnitude of the shows by reducing the residual oil saturation. In addition, deep holes are usually drilled with smaller size bits so that there is less rock pulverized per foot of penetration and less hydrocarbon released into the mud. There is also more time for the shows to come from the bottom so that there is a greater chance for mixing and dilution. On the other hand, deep reservoirs exist at high pressures so that there will be greater amounts of gas released from the oil and greater expansion of the gas as it comes to the surface; this factor will tend to improve the gas-in-mud shows. In general, deeper holes make the problems of mud logging more difficult.

Circulation Rate.   High circulation rates cause greater dilution of the mud shows but do not affect the cuttings. It must be remembered, however, that the ability of the mud to lift the cuttings depends on the annulus velocity so that the circulation rate will influence the spread of the cuttings arriving at the surface from a particular drilled interval.

With experience in the weighing of the data in the light of the contributions of these drilling factors, mud logging can be very effective in locating hydrocarbon bearing formations. On an exploratory well it is often unwise to operate without this service.

REFERENCES

1. *API RP 34: Standard Hydrocarbon Mud Log Form*, American Petroleum Institute, Division of Production, Dallas, Texas.
2. Hausdorff, H. H., and Brenner, N., Gas chromatography-powerful new tool for chemical analysis: *Oil and Gas Jour.*, v. 56, No. 26, June 30, 1958, p. 73.
3. Hayward, J. T., U.S. Patent Nos: 2,213,138; 2,214,674; 2,280,075; 2,280,086; 2,489,180.
4. Jenkins, R. E., An evaluation of three electronic methods to analyze drilling fluid gases: *The Petroleum Engineer*, October, 1959, p. B-75.
5. Patterson, R. O., Logging from drill returns: *The Mines Mag.*, October, 1953, p. 127.
6. Peters, E. F., Well logging from drill returns: *The Petroleum Engineer*, v. 27, April, 1955, p. B-112.

7. Pixler, B. O., Mud analysis logging: *Formation Evaluation Symposium*, AIME, Houston, Texas, 1960, p. III-1.
8. *Technical Guide, Hydrocarbon Well Logging Service*, Rotary Engineering Co., Midland, Texas.
9. Wilson, R. W., Mud analysis logging: *Symposium on Formation Evaluation*, AIME, Houston, Texas, 1955, p. 79.

5

Read to 224.

Electric Logging

In 1927, the Schlumberger brothers introduced a new logging method in the Pechelbronn field in France that they called "electric coring," thereby implying that this method would be a possible alternate for coring as a means of examining subsurface rocks. Logging was accomplished by making a series of three-electrode resistivity measurements at a number of closely spaced points in the well. In the four years that followed, similar continuous logs were run in wells in Venezuela, Oklahoma, Russia, and Rumania. During logging operations in Rumania, Schlumberger engineers confirmed the existence of a natural electrical potential in the well whose magnitude was related to the lithologic character of the rocks. This potential came to be known as the spontaneous potential or SP. It greatly increased the value of electric logging because of the lithologic information which it provided. The use of electric logging soon mushroomed throughout the world. It was introduced in California in 1932 and in the Gulf Coast in 1933.

The procedure for electric logging is shown schematically in Fig. 5-1. The sonde containing the instruments and electrodes for making the measurements is lowered into the well on an armored steel cable that may contain as many as six separate conductors within its core. The sonde is usually $3\frac{5}{8}$ in. in diameter and several feet long. It may be a simple insulated mandrel with plain cylindrical lead electrodes mounted on it, or it may be a highly specialized electronic cartridge. As the sonde is withdrawn from the hole, the measurements are transmitted continuously up the conductor wires to the logging truck where they are recorded by galvanometers on a moving strip of film. A gear shift in the cable-to-film drive allows recording of the log with depth scales ranging from 1 in. of film for 100 ft of hole to 60 in. of film for 100 ft.

83

Until recently, the basic electrical survey was composed of the SP curve, and three resistivity curves, the 16-in. normal (two-electrode) curve, the 64-in. normal curve, and the 18-ft 8-in. lateral (three-electrode) curve. An example of this type of log is shown in Fig. 5-2. Within the last few years this survey has been largely replaced by the induction-electric log which consists of the SP curve and two resistivity curves, the 16-in. normal and the induction log. Figure 5-3 is an example of this type of log. Four-, ten-, fifteen-, and twenty-millivolt subdivisions are commonly used on the SP log. Resistivity scales all start at zero and may go as high as several thousand ohm-meters.

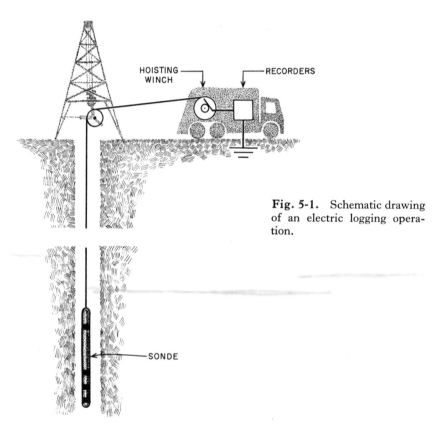

HOISTING WINCH

RECORDERS

SONDE

Fig. 5-1. Schematic drawing of an electric logging operation.

In addition to these basic logs we shall also consider in this chapter the focused-current logs (laterolog, guard log), the wall resistivity logs (microlog, contact log, minilog, microsurvey), and the focused microdevices (microlaterolog, proximity log, FoRxo log).

There are three major uses of electric logs. Probably the widest use is for the correlation of structure on the basis of the log differentiation

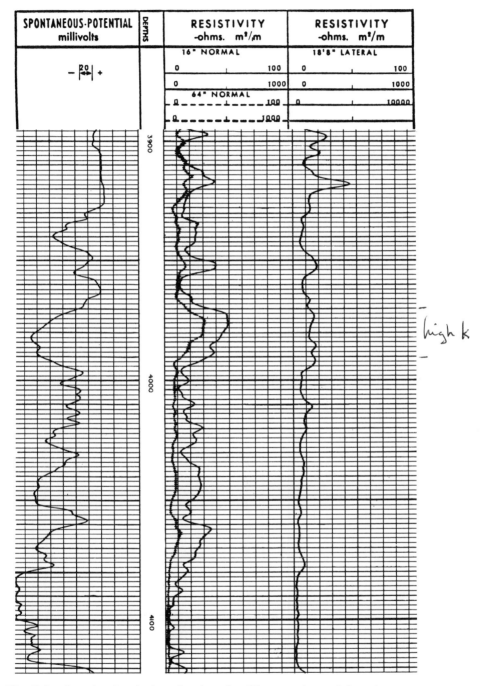

SPONTANEOUS-POTENTIAL millivolts	DEPTHS	RESISTIVITY -ohms. m²/m	RESISTIVITY -ohms. m²/m
		16" NORMAL	18'8" LATERAL
		0 ... 100	0 ... 100
- 20 +		0 ... 1000	0 ... 1000
		64" NORMAL	
		0 ... 100	0 ... 10000
		0 ... 1000	

high k

Fig. 5-2. Sample electric log showing the SP, normals, and lateral curves. (Courtesy of California Standard Co.)

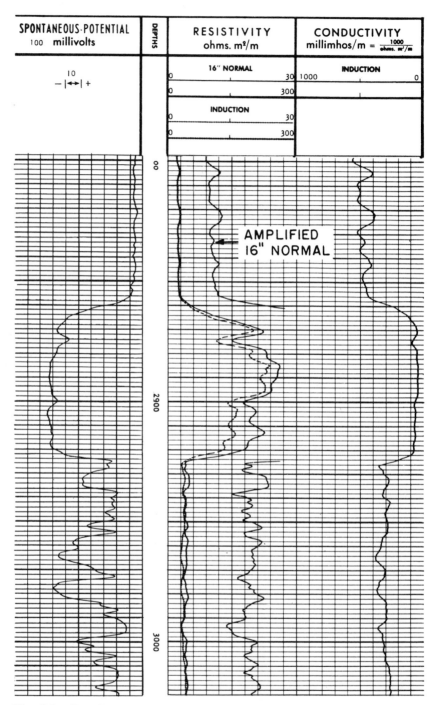

Fig. 5-3. Sample electric log showing the SP, 16-in. normal, and induction log curves. (Courtesy of Schlumberger Well Surveying Corporation.)

between shales, dense carbonates and evaporites, and permeable beds. An example of this is shown in Fig. 5-4. It amounts, in essence, to a comparison of the wiggles on the logs from adjacent wells. Such correlation is useful in the construction of structural maps, isopachous maps, the location of faults, and in guiding development and exploratory drilling. The second use of the electric log, and the one which will receive primary attention in this chapter, is for the determination of water saturation and porosity. This use is of critical importance in exploratory drilling for evaluating the commercial significance of the formations penetrated by the bit; but the same information is used by reservoir engineers in the determination of reserves. The accuracy of the electric log when used for this purpose depends on a large number of factors which will be considered in detail in a later part of the chapter. Electric logs have a third use, which is the coordination of other formation evaluating techniques. The electric log serves as the basis for selecting zones of promise for side wall coring and drill stem testing. When tests are run in open hole, the electric log may be useful in helping to select a suitable packer seat and in insuring that water-bearing formations are not included in the test interval. When casing has been set, the electric log is useful as a guide for gun perforating operations.

The frequency with which the electric log is run during the drilling of an oil well depends on the conditions of the drilling operation. In a development well a log will usually be run once at total depth. In an exploratory well logging will be done more often. The frequency of logging is controlled by the drilling rate, the type of formations being penetrated, the mud properties, and the number and distribution of possible horizons. In general, the log is run more often as the depth of the hole increases. There are two reasons for this. First, the increased pressures and temperatures encountered at greater depth cause an increase in the invasion of mud filtrate into the formations, and deep invasion makes log interpretation extremely difficult. Second, a deep hole represents a large investment and increased dangers in drilling. In case the hole is lost it is desirable to have at least an electrical record of what has been drilled.

Part I. FUNDAMENTALS

This section of the chapter on electric logging will be devoted to a discussion of the fundamentals of physics and physical chemistry that must be considered in the understanding and interpretation of electric logs.

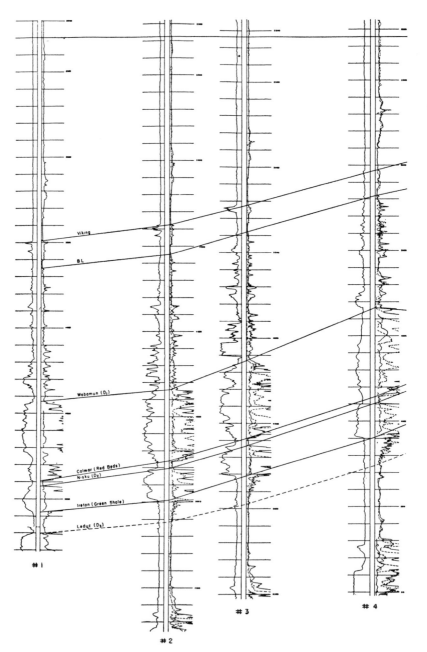

Fig. 5-4. Example of the use of electric logs for correlation. (Courtesy of Schlumberger Well Surveying Corporation.)

RESISTANCE AND RESISTIVITY

The basic postulate of electric theory is Ohm's law which states that the rate of flow of electric current, i, in a conductor is proportional to the electric potential difference, ΔE, causing that flow. The constant or proportionality is called the resistance, r. Expressed as an equation,

$$\Delta E = ir \qquad (5\text{-}1)$$

The difference in potential between two points is defined as the work necessary to carry a charge from one point to the other. The current is defined by the electromagnetic field strength around a conductor. Equation 5-1, therefore, completely defines the resistance. The unit of resistance is the ohm, and it is equal to a volt/ampere.

Consideration of the above concept of resistance leads to the conclusion that the resistance is an extrinsic property; that is, it depends not only on the material which is conducting the current, but also on its physical dimensions. Thus, doubling the length of the conductor will double its resistance; doubling the cross-sectional area perpendicular to the flow of current will halve the resistance. By incorporating the length and area terms with the resistance, a property is obtained which is a function only of the material of which the resistor is composed. This property is called the resistivity, R, and is defined as

$$R = r\frac{A}{L} \qquad (5\text{-}2)$$

where A is the cross-sectional area of the conductor and L is its length. The units of resistivity are resistance times length. In electric logging practice the units of ohm-meters are used. With these units resistivity can be defined also as the resistance between opposite faces of a cubical block of material, the edges of which are 1 meter in length. Occasionally it will be more convenient to speak of the reciprocal of the resistivity which is called the conductivity, C, or of the reciprocal of the resistance which is the conductance, c.

The three general classes of conductors are electronic, electrolytic, and insulators. Electronic conductors are characterized by movement of loosely bound electrons within the material during the transfer of electricity. The common metals, iron, copper, aluminum, etc., fall into this classification. This is the most efficient type of conduction for the transfer of electric current, so it is widely used in everyday electric apparatus. The resistivities of conductors in this classification are of the order of 10^{-8} ohm-meter. Electronic conductors encountered

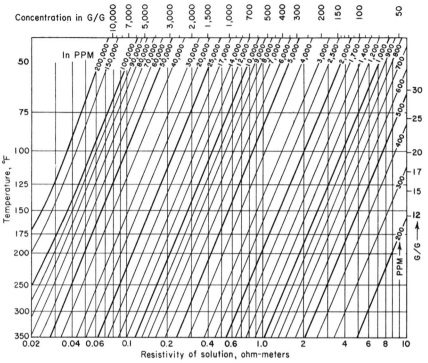

Fig. 5-5. Resistivity chart relating the salinity and temperature of NaCl solutions. (Courtesy of Schlumberger Well Surveying Corporation.)

in logging practice are found only in the circuits of the logging equipment, and so are of limited concern in formation evaluation.

The second classification, electrolytic conductors, is limited to solutions of salts which are ionized into electrically positive and negative parts. Both the anions (negatively charged ions) and the cations (positively charged ions) contribute to the conductivity of the solution. Since current is carried in electrolytic solutions by movement of the ions to the electrodes, the composition of the solution will change with time if direct current is passed through it. To avoid this difficulty, alternating current is always used in measuring the resistivity of electrolytes. The resistivity of electrolytic solutions formed by adding inorganic salts to water is in the range of 0.02 ohm-meter to several hundred ohm-meters, depending on the concentration. The resistivity of pure water is 200,000 ohm-meters.

Electrolytic conductors are important in electric logging because all porous sedimentary rocks contain some salt water. The predominant salt in these formation waters is sodium chloride. Figure 5-5 shows the resistivities of sodium chloride solutions over the range of concentration and temperature usually encountered in electric logging. Dunlap and Hawthorne (25) have developed a method of estimating the resistivity of solutions containing other ions commonly found in formation waters or drilling muds. If the concentration of the ion in parts per million is known, it can be multiplied by the proper factor, as determined from Table 5-1, to get the electrically equivalent amount of sodium chloride. The resistivity of the equivalent solution can then be obtained from Fig. 5-5. For example, a solution containing 2000 ppm of Ca^{++} and 4800 ppm of SO_4^{--} would be equivalent to a solution of $2000 \times 0.95 + 4800 \times 0.50 = 4300$ ppm of NaCl; the resistivity of such a solution at 75°F would be 1.29 ohm-meters. In a review of the work of Dunlap and Hawthorne, Martin (39) determined that the coefficients given in Table 5-1 were relatively independent of temperature but varied considerably with changes in concentration, as might be expected from the Debye-Hückel theory.

TABLE 5-1.   FACTORS FOR CHANGING THE
CONCENTRATION (PPM) OF VARIOUS IONS TO THE
EQUIVALENT CONCENTRATION OF SODIUM CHLORIDE

Ion	Multiplying Factor
Na^+	1.00
Ca^{++}	0.95
Mg^{++}	2.00
Cl^-	1.00
SO_4^{--}	0.50
HCO_3^-	0.27
CO_3^{--}	1.26
OH^-	5.10 (theoretical)

The last class of conductors, the insulators, conduct current poorly or not at all. Substances in this group have fixed chemical structure in which the electrons and atoms have definite and relatively immobile positions. Materials in this class include petroleum hydrocarbons and the solid matrix of all sedimentary rocks. Even dry shale is an insulator. The resistivity of these substances is of the order of ten thousand or more times that of the average connate water, and by comparison they can be considered to be completely nonconducting. It is interesting to note that very fresh water is almost in this resistivity class, although it is classified as an electrolyte.

Two extensions of Ohm's law were made by Kirchhoff. Kirchhoff's first law states that at any point in a circuit there is as much current flowing away from the point as there is flowing toward it. In the electric circuit of Fig. 5-6, therefore, the sum of the currents, i_1, i_2, and i_3,

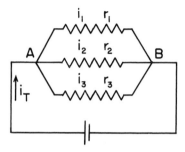

Fig. 5-6. Illustration of Kirchhoff's first law.

flowing in the parallel conductors away from point A is equal to the current i_T flowing toward point A. If the effective resistance of the three resistors in parallel is r_T, then by Ohm's law

$$\frac{E_A - E_B}{r_T} = (E_A - E_B)\left(\frac{1}{r_1} + \frac{1}{r_2} + \frac{1}{r_3}\right) = i_T = i_1 + i_2 + i_3$$

and

$$\frac{1}{r_T} = \frac{1}{r_1} + \frac{1}{r_2} + \frac{1}{r_3} \tag{5-3}$$

or

$$c_T = c_1 + c_2 + c_3 \tag{5-4}$$

Equation 5-3 is the basic expression for determining the resistance of parallel circuits.

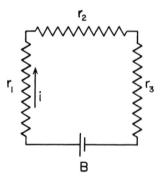

Fig. 5-7. Illustration of Kirchhoff's second law.

Kirchhoff's second law states that the sum of the products of the current by the resistance taken around any closed path of a network of conductors is equal to the sum of the electromotive forces which exist in the circuit. In the circuit of Fig. 5-7, the sum of the *ir* potential drops must be equal to the electromotive force of battery B. If the total resistance of the circuit is r_T, then it may be shown that

$$r_T = r_1 + r_2 + r_3 \tag{5-5}$$

This is the basic expression for the resistance of a series circuit.

The simple examples of Fig. 5-6 and 5-7, which were used to demonstrate the basic laws of electricity, are one-dimensional models, but these laws are by no means limited to one dimension. Consider the situation illustrated in Fig. 5-8. A is a small spherical electrode that is embedded in a uniform homogeneous conducting material of infinite extent. The electrode B is very large and is placed at an infinite distance from A. With this arrangement the current flow A will be radial and the surfaces of constant potential around A will be concentric spheres. Two such spheres are M and N, which have radii of l_M and l_N, and are at potentials E_M and E_N. If we take a spherical element of volume within the region M to N with an inner radius of l and a thickness of dl, the potentials on either side of this element will be E and $(E - dE)$. Ohm's law may then be written for this volume element as

$$E - (E - dE) = iR\frac{L}{A} = \frac{iR[l - (l + dl)]}{4\pi l^2} \tag{5-6}$$

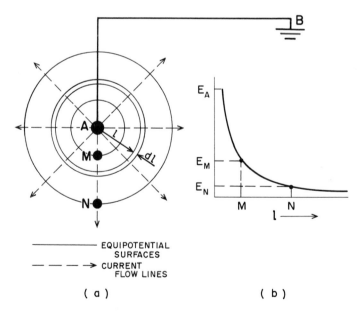

EQUIPOTENTIAL SURFACES

CURRENT FLOW LINES

(a)   (b)

Fig. 5-8. Schematic illustration of the potential distribution in the radial flow of electricity.

The current, i, is the same through all successive volume elements. Integration of equation 5-6 from M to N gives

$$E_M - E_N = \frac{iR}{4\pi}\left(\frac{1}{l_M} - \frac{1}{l_N}\right) \qquad (5\text{-}7)$$

Equation 5-7 may be solved for R to give the basic equation for determining the resistivity of a uniform medium by means of a four-electrode method (two current and two potential electrodes).

$$R = \frac{4\pi(E_M - E_N)}{i\left(\dfrac{1}{l_M} - \dfrac{1}{l_N}\right)} \qquad (5\text{-}8)$$

In logging practice, the distances l_M and l_N are sometimes referred to as AM and AN. The midpoint of the distance between M and N is given the designation of O.

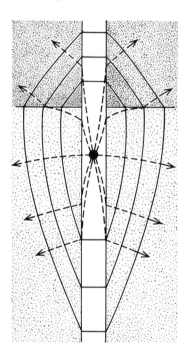

Fig. 5-9. Current distribution around a logging power electrode in the vicinity of a bed boundary. (Courtesy of Schlumberger Well Surveying Corporation.)

Equation 5-8 is the fundamental equation which is used in electric logging practice for determination of resistivity with any nonfocused electrode type of logging device. The potentials E_M and E_N are necessarily measured by electrodes in the borehole, but because of the theoretically spherical distribution of current, these potentials correspond to similar potentials in the rock formation. The greater the distance of these two electrodes from the current electrode A, the deeper in the formation will be these corresponding potentials. In electric logging, therefore, the long spacing curves are referred to as the deep penetration curves.

The development of equation 5-8 required the assumption of a uniform medium of infinite extent. This condition is rarely encountered in practice. Figure 5-9 shows the distortion of the current pattern that occurs during an actual logging operation. In order to allow for borehole effects, invasion, and adjacent bed resistivities, departure curves have been developed. These curves provide corrections which are applied to the apparent resistivity, R_a, determined from equation 5-8 to get the true resistivity, R_t, of the formation. More will be said about this in a later section.

INDUCED ELECTRIC CURRENT

Any discussion of modern electric logging devices must include a consideration of the fundamentals of electromagnetic phenomena because of the increased use of devices which depend on inductive coupling to the formation.

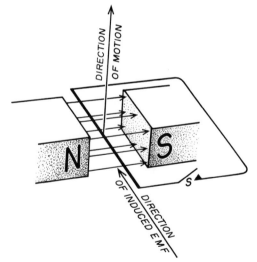

Fig. 5-10. Schematic diagram of the induction of an electric current.

If an electrical conductor is moved through a magnetic field, as illustrated in Fig. 5-10, an electromotive force (emf) will be set up in the conductor which, in turn, can cause the flow of electric current. The direction of the current flow will depend on the direction of relative motion of the conductor and the field. The magnitude of the emf per unit length of conductor will depend directly on the strength of the field, and the velocity of movement of the conductor.

The magnetic flux density, B, in a material depends on the magnetizing force, H, and the magnetic permeability, μ.

$$\mu = \frac{B}{H} \tag{5-9}$$

The permeability is unity by definition for a vacuum and is practically unity for air and all nonmagnetic materials. In the example of Fig. 5-10, then, if the magnetizing force is H, the flux density in the gap is B lines per square centimeter or $H \times 1$. If the wire is moving through the field at a velocity v centimeters per second, and the length of the wire is L centimeters, then the potential developed in the wire is

$$E = \frac{BvL}{10^8} = \frac{HvL}{10^8} \text{ volts} \tag{5-10}$$

If the resistance of a unit length of this wire is r, then the current that could be made to flow in the wire by closing switch S is

$$i = \frac{Hv}{10^8 r} \tag{5-11}$$

The method of induction illustrated by Fig. 5-10, where the conductor moved through a stationary magnetic field, is commonly used for the production of electric power. This is not the only possible arrangement for generating an emf, however. The only necessary condition is that the conductor must cut magnetic lines of force. This can be accomplished by having a moving magnetic field, or a magnetic field of varying strength such that the magnetic lines move past the conductor as the field alternates. An electric transformer or an induction coil is an example of this type of application. The induction log that is used for logging is another example.

An alternating magnetic field can be produced by passing an alternating electric current through a conductor. It was demonstrated by Oersted in 1809 that the flow of current is always accompanied by the formation of a magnetic field, the strength of which is directly proportional to the current. The magnetic field forms a circular path around the current in a plane perpendicular to the current path. This is illustrated in Fig. 5-11. (The cross on the circle represents the tail of the arrow that indicates the conventional direction of flow of the current. A single dot marked on the conductor would represent the arrow head.) According to Lenz's law, the direction of this magnetic field is such that it opposes the conditions which gave rise to the electric current causing the field.

Fig. 5-11.   Magnetic field around a conductor.

In the example of Fig. 5-10, for instance, closing switch S causes current to flow in the conductor and creates a magnetic field around it. This secondary magnetic field is in a direction such that it opposes the movement of the conductor. In the case where the conductor is stationary and the magnetic field is varying, the secondary field is such that it opposes or weakens the net primary field.

Figure 5-12 illustrates the interaction between magnetic fields in parallel conductors. In Fig. 12a the currents are in opposite directions and the fields oppose each other. This creates a force which tends to push the conductors apart. In Fig. 12b the currents are in the same direction and the magnetic fields reinforce each other. It is possible to make a very strong magnetic field by winding wires in a coil so that the field from each turn reinforces the field of the other turns.

If an alternating current from an oscillator is transmitted through a coil to produce an alternating magnetic field, this field propagates, or moves away from the transmitting coil, as a wave train. If the current producing the field is sinusoidal, then the wave train appears as illustrated in Fig. 5-13. The distance between any two corresponding points on this wave train is the wavelength λ. The frequency f is the number of waves per second that pass a given point. The velocity v with which the wave propagates is the multiple of the frequency and the wavelength.

$$v = \lambda f \qquad\qquad\qquad (5\text{-}12)$$

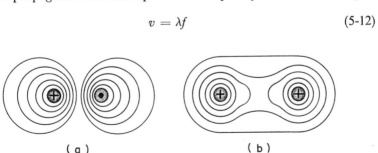

(a)   (b)

Fig. 5-12.   Interaction of the magnetic fields around two parallel conductors.

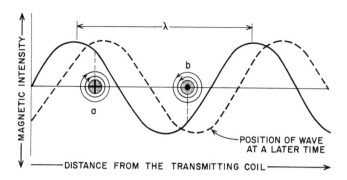

Fig. 5-13. Propagation of a sinusoidal electromagnetic wave and the induction of current in two parallel conductors.

In a vacuum, electromagnetic radiation moves at the speed of light. If the oscillator is operating at 20,000 cps, then the wavelength in a vacuum is

$$\lambda = \frac{186,000 \times 5280}{20,000} = 49,100 \text{ ft}$$

In a conductive material, the wave travels more slowly. The velocity in a conductor is given by (34)

$$v = \left(\frac{1.08 \times 10^8 fR}{\mu}\right)^{1/2} \tag{5-13}$$

Thus, in a medium with a resistivity of 1 ohm-meter, the velocity of a 20,000-cps wave is 1.47×10^6 ft/sec, and the wavelength is 73.5 ft. Since the wave causes eddy currents to be set up in the material, it loses energy. For the conditions given here, the strength of the wave is reduced to about one-half for each 8 ft of travel.

In Fig. 5-13, the point a is 180° out of phase with point b. Current generated in a conductor located at a is therefore 180° out of phase with the current generated in a conductor located at b, i.e., it is of equal magnitude and flowing in the opposite direction. The magnetic fields around the two conductors are also equal in magnitude and opposite in direction. In a vacuum the points a and b would be miles apart, but in a conductive medium, they would be sufficiently close together so that the effect of the phase shift would have to be considered in any calculation concerned with the induction of eddy currents by an alternating magnetic field.

SOURCES OF POTENTIAL IN ELECTROLYTIC SOLUTIONS

Electrochemical Potentials

A proper understanding of the theory of electrochemical potentials requires a thorough grounding in chemical thermodynamics. This is beyond the scope of this text. However, we shall attempt to outline some of the more important thermodynamic concepts underlying the equations which are in common use for the analysis of the SP curve, and to develop them in their more fundamental and more generally useful form.

A logical starting point in this abbreviated discussion is the Gibbs potential function which is known as the "free energy," and which will be given the symbol G. It is defined thermodynamically as the difference between the enthalpy and the product of the absolute temperature and the entropy.

$$G = H - TS \tag{5-14}$$

It therefore combines within it the power of both the first and second laws of thermodynamics. From the definition it can be demonstrated that the change in the free energy of a system is the maximum amount of useful work that can be obtained from the system during that change. For example, when an electric battery produces current, there are chemical reactions within the battery that change its chemical constitution. The chemical substances change from one free energy, G_1, to another, G_2. The amount of work that can be done by the electricity under ideal thermodynamic conditions is numerically equal to the total change in the free energy within the cell, $\Delta G = G_2 - G_1$.

In any spontaneous change, the free energy of the final state is less than the free energy of the initial state; or the change in free energy, ΔG, is negative. The free energy is therefore a measure of the tendency of a substance or system to go from one condition to another. In this sense, G. N. Lewis (36) refers to it as "the escaping tendency." It can also be considered as the potential that is responsible for chemical or physical changes. Whenever a condition of equilibrium exists, the free energy is the same in all possible states.

Consider again the chemical battery. If one equivalent weight of chemical reacts within the battery, this will produce a current flow of 96,500 coulombs, or one faraday, F, of electricity. The amount of useful work that is done by this electricity is the product of the current by the voltage by the time.

$$\text{Work} = Ei\theta = EF \tag{5-15}$$

Since the work is also equal numerically to the change in free energy, then

$$\Delta G = -E\mathbf{F}$$

and

$$E = -\frac{\Delta G}{\mathbf{F}} \qquad (5\text{-}16)$$

This is the voltage produced by a battery where there is a change of free energy of ΔG for each equivalent of chemical going from one state to another. The negative sign allows for the fact that ΔG has a negative value when the work is positive.

This equation for the electrochemical potential is not convenient to use in this form because of the difficulty of evaluating G from the entropy and enthalpy. For that reason we shall define two additional functions, the fugacity and the activity.

If one mole of a perfect gas undergoes a reversible expansion at constant temperature, the change in the free energy can be shown by thermodynamics to be

$$\Delta G = RT \ln \frac{P_2}{P_1} \qquad (5\text{-}17)$$

where R is the universal gas constant, and P_1 and P_2 are the pressures before and after the expansion. So for a perfect gas, it is possible to express the free energy in terms of the pressure. This equation is, of course, of very limited usefulness because of the rarity of perfect gases; however, it does provide a *form* of equation which is very useful. In order to retain this form for nonideal substances, liquid, solid, and gaseous, we introduce a property called the fugacity, f. The fugacity is defined in terms of the free energy so that the form of equation 5-17 is retained.

$$G = RT \ln f + G_0 \qquad (5\text{-}18)$$

where G_0 is an arbitrary constant at a given temperature. The change in the fugacity of a substance when it goes from one state to another, therefore, is

$$\Delta G = RT \ln \frac{f_2}{f_1} \qquad (5\text{-}19)$$

The absolute fugacity of a substance is also very difficult to determine. Relative fugacity, i.e., the fugacity f relative to some arbitrarily chosen, convenient, reference fugacity f_0, is frequently available, however. This relative value of fugacity is designated the activity, a.

$$a = \frac{f}{f_0} \qquad (5\text{-}20)$$

Equation 5-19 can now be written

$$\Delta G = RT \ln \frac{a_2}{a_1} \qquad (5\text{-}21)$$

and the electrochemical potential is defined as

$$E = \frac{RT}{\mathbf{F}} \ln \frac{a_1}{a_2} \qquad (5\text{-}22)$$

This is the electrical potential developed in a cell where one equivalent weight of the substance producing the potential changes from activity a_1 to activity a_2. Since activities are usually known on a mole basis, it is easier to use equation 5-22 in the form

$$E = \frac{RT}{n\mathbf{F}} \ln \frac{a_1}{a_2} \qquad (5\text{-}23)$$

where n is the number of equivalents per mole.

A solution formed by dissolving a salt in water will approach the ideal solution laws when the concentration of the solute is very small. For this reason, the reference fugacity f_0 of the solute is chosen so that the activity of the solute is equal to the concentration of the solute for the infinitely dilute case. With this reference condition the activity and the concentration will usually be numerically equal over a fair range of concentration and will differ appreciably from one another only for concentrated solutions (30). Correction factors that must be used in obtaining the activity when the concentration is known are usually nearly unity, and for rough work it is often possible to use the concentrations as a direct substitute for the activities in equation 5-23. With this type of approach, it is not necessary to know the value of either the fugacity, or the reference fugacity, and yet be able to solve quickly and easily for the free energy and the electrochemical potential.

If two solutions containing the same salt in different concentrations are brought into contact in some manner, the salt will tend to go from the more concentrated into the more dilute solution. Expressed in another way, the free energy of the concentrated solution is greater than that of the dilute solution. Properly applied, this difference in free energy can be used to generate an electrochemical potential in what is known as a concentration cell. It is this type of cell which is operative in the earth when the very saline formation water comes into contact with the fresh-water drilling mud.

Consider the situation represented by Fig. 5-14 where two electrodes are placed in a solution of sodium chloride. When a potential is applied to the electrodes by the battery, current is carried through the solution by the sodium and chloride ions. The amount of current that each type

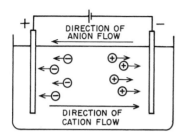

Fig. 5-14. Schematic representation of electrical conduction through a NaCl solution.

of ion carries depends on its concentration in the solution and on its mobility, i.e., the speed at which it moves under a fixed potential gradient. (The mobilities for some common ions are given in Table 5-2.) The

TABLE 5-2. IONIC MOBILITIES AT 25°C AND INFINITE DILUTION

Cation	Mobility, cm/sec	Anion	Mobility, cm/sec
Potassium	7.61×10^{-4}	Hydroxyl	20.5×10^{-4}
Sodium	5.19	Sulfate	8.27
Barium	6.60	Chloride	7.91
Calcium	6.10	Bicarbonate	4.70
Magnesium	5.30		

fraction of the current that the sodium carries is

$$t^+ = \frac{5.19m}{5.19m + 7.91m} = 0.397 \tag{5-24}$$

where m is the concentration in moles per liter of sodium chloride. The fraction of current carried by the positive ion is called the positive ion transference number, t^+. Similarly, the negative ion transference number is

$$t^- = \frac{7.91m}{5.19m + 7.91m} = 0.603 \tag{5-25}$$

By definition,

$$t^+ + t^- = 1. \tag{5-26}$$

The transference numbers of the ions in a sodium chloride solution are relatively independent of concentration, changing less than 5 percent over the range of concentration from infinite dilution to $0.2N$. Increasing temperature causes all transference numbers to approach 0.5, but over the range of temperature experienced in petroleum drilling, the transference number of the chloride ion decreases only about 6 percent. So for free solutions, at least, the values of the transference numbers given here will be sufficiently accurate for logging work at all temperatures and concentrations of sodium chloride.

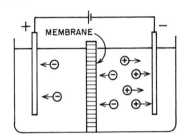

Fig. 5-15. Schematic representation of conduction through a charged membrane.

If a charged membrane were placed in the solution of Fig. 5-14 so that the ions would have to move through it (see Fig. 5-15), the conclusions reached about the transference numbers would no longer hold. If the charge on the membrane were negative (the usual case in well logging), the movement of the negatively charged ions through it would be restricted, while the positively charged ions would be unaffected. As a result, the positively charged ions would carry an increased fraction of the current. The effect of such a cation selective membrane is to decrease the negative transference number. If the membrane were "perfect," the negative transference number would be zero, i.e., no negatively charged ions could pass through it.

A charged membrane can be prepared by compaction of charged particles into a porous, slightly permeable solid. The common ion exchange resins would be suitable particles for such a membrane. A bentonic clay would be another suitable material, somewhat closer to the present problem. These substances have a common structural characteristic. They are all composed of a very heavy base molecule or crystal lattice which is not soluble in water. This solid particle has attached to it one or more easily ionized cations. Thus, when sodium bentonite is placed in water, the individual clay platelets do not dissolve, but remain in a colloidal suspension. The sodium, however, becomes ionized and goes into solution in the water. The result is that the clay particles assume a negative charge. This negative charge is responsible for many of the unusual properties of bentonitic clays which are not seen in other types of clays. If this clay suspension is compacted so as to form a solid, the resulting solid material will retain a negative charge, with the sodium ions dispersed throughout so as to provide electrical neutrality.

Consider now the cylindrical cell represented by Fig. 5-16 which contains two solutions of sodium chloride of activities a_1 and a_2. The direct contact between the solutions is such that there is free movement across the boundary by diffusion, but convective mixing is prevented.

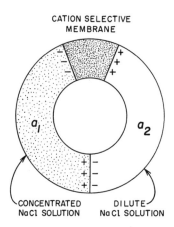

Fig. 5-16. Generation of a potential at the junction between two solutions of different concentration.

The other contact between the solutions is through a negatively charged membrane. The sodium and chloride ions move preferentially from the concentrated solution to the dilute one. At the free boundary, the chloride ions move more rapidly than the sodium and cause a potential to be created, with the dilute solution being negative. At the junction through the membrane, the sodium ions move more rapidly, so that the potential generated across the membrane has its positive side in the dilute solution.

It can be shown by thermodynamics that for any liquid junction, the potential developed by ionic movement can be expressed by (46)

$$E = -\frac{RT}{F} \int_1^2 \sum_i \frac{t_i}{z_i} d\ln a_i \qquad (5\text{-}27)$$

where t_i is the transference number of the ith ion, a_i is its activity, and z_i is its valence (both sign and number). This equation is derived from the differential form of equation 5-23.

Applying equation 5-27 to the problem of the two sodium chloride solutions:

$$E = -\frac{RT}{F} \int_1^2 \left(\frac{t^+}{+1} d\ln a^+ + \frac{t^-}{-1} d\ln a^- \right) \qquad (5\text{-}28)$$

For sodium chloride, the activity of the positive ions is approximately equal to the activity of the negative ions and is also approximately equal to the mean activity, a. Since $t^+ + t^- = 1$, equation 5-28 can be simplified to

$$E = \frac{RT}{F}(2t^- - 1)\ln\frac{a_1}{a_2} \tag{5-29}$$

Equation 5-29 is generally applicable for the potential developed at the liquid junction between any two monovalent solutions provided that there is only one common solute in both. It is equally applicable for a free junction between the solutions, or one where the junction is through a charged membrane. The proper value of t^- must be used, however. A more general form of this equation for any salt is (26)

$$E = \frac{RT}{z^+F}\left(t^- \frac{v}{v^+} - 1\right)\ln\frac{a_1}{a_2} \tag{5-30}$$

v is the total number of ions formed when the salt is dissolved and v^+ is the number of positive ions formed.

When the solute in the two solutions is different, or when there are mixtures of solutes in the solutions, the problem of calculating the junction potential becomes very complex. Gondouin and his co-workers (28) have treated the case of solutions of mixtures of calcium, magnesium, and sodium chlorides separated by a *perfect membrane* in a semi-empirical approach that appears to be quite satisfactory. Their expression for the potential developed across the membrane is

$$E = -\frac{RT}{F}\ln\frac{(a_{Na} + \sqrt{a_{Ca}} + a_{Mg})_1}{(a_{Na} + \sqrt{a_{Ca}} + a_{Mg})_2} \tag{5-31}$$

The activities given in equation 5-31 are the activities of the positive ions only. The relation between activity and concentration for these ions is shown in Figs. 5-17 and 5-18. Since the transference number for the negative ions is zero for a perfect membrane, the anion activity has very little influence on the membrane potential.

The junction potential for a free liquid boundary between mixed electrolytes has been treated extensively by Henderson (31). His equation is

$$E = \frac{RT}{F}\frac{(U_{II} - V_{II}) - (U_I - V_I)}{(\bar{U}_{II} - \bar{V}_{II}) - (\bar{U}_I - \bar{V}_I)}\ln\frac{(\bar{U}_I - \bar{V}_I)}{(\bar{U}_{II} - \bar{V}_{II})} \tag{5-32}$$

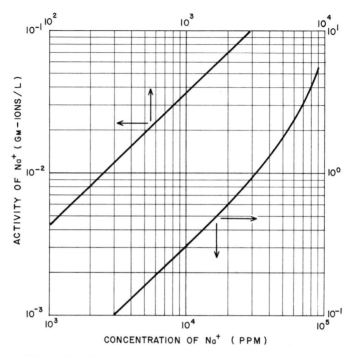

Fig. 5-17.   Activity of the sodium ion in a NaCl solution.

where

$$\bar{U}_{II} = \sum_{+} u_i'' z_i m_i'' \qquad \bar{V}_{II} = \sum_{-} v_i'' z_i m_i''$$

$$\bar{U}_{I} = \sum_{+} u_i' z_i m_i' \qquad \bar{V}_{I} = \sum_{-} v_i' z_i m_i'$$

$$U_{II} = \sum_{+} u_i'' m_i'' \qquad V_{II} = \sum_{-} v_i'' m_i''$$

$$U_{I} = \sum_{+} u_i' m_i' \qquad V_{I} = \sum_{-} v_i' m_i'$$

and m_i' is the ionic concentration in solution 1 and m_i'' is the concentration in solution 2 of the ith ion; u_i is the mobility of the ith positive ion and v_i is the mobility of the ith negative ion; z_i is again the valence, having both sign and magnitude. In deriving this equation, it is necessary to assume that the various ionic mobilities are constant for all concentrations, that the activity and the concentration are equal, and that the solution at any point in the boundary is a simple mixture of the two end solutions, 1 and 2.

Electrokinetic Potential (Streaming Potential)

When a solid and a solution are in contact, a potential is set up at the phase boundary. This potential may be the result of the adsorption by the solid of ions from the solution, or it may be the result of ionization of the solid. For example, soaps, glass, and silica are all negatively charged because of the tendency of the light cation to pass into solution. As mentioned before, this is also true of bentonic clay.

A schematic representation of the potential at a glass surface is shown in Fig. 5-19. Because of the ionization of its light cation, the surface has a negative charge, and the solution in contact with it, containing positive and negative ions, has a net positive charge. The net positive charge of the solution is not uniformly distributed throughout it, however. The charge on the particle attracts counter ions to its surface. The first few molecular layers of cations exist in a relatively immobile position near the surface; farther away, the mobilities of the ions approach the free solution condition, but the positive ions still predominate through this diffuse layer. Finally the bulk solution is reached where the numbers of positive and negative ions are equal. This variation in the positive potential is represented in the figure by the curve ABC.

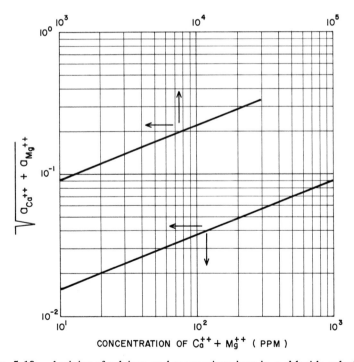

Fig. 5-18. Activity of calcium and magnesium ions in a chloride solution.

The potential difference between the bulk of the liquid (which is neutral) and the boundary between the fixed and diffuse layers (which has a net positive charge) is symbolized by ζ and is consequently known as the zeta potential.

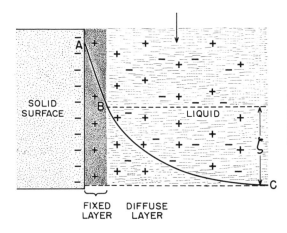

Fig. 5-19. Schematic representation of the potential generated at a solid-liquid interface.

Suppose pressure is applied to the solution in the direction indicated by the arrow. The movable part of the solution will flow past the solid surface carrying with it a charge which has a potential ζ. This movement of charge by liquid flow creates a potential between the upper and lower ends of the particle. This flowing potential is known as the electrokinetic or streaming potential.

In order to simplify the mathematical analysis of the streaming potential, the double-charged layer is treated as a simple condenser with plates x cm apart, carrying a charge of e electrostatic units per square centimeter. One plate is made up of the glass surface plus the fixed layer and carries a net negative charge. The other plate is the diffuse layer and carries a net positive charge. The potential difference between two such plates is ζ. From electrostatics, these factors may be related by

$$\zeta = \frac{4\pi ex}{D} \tag{5-33}$$

where D is the dielectric constant of the water.

Consider now the situation illustrated by Fig. 5-20 where the solid is in the form of a capillary tube and the solution is contained within it. The length of the capillary tube is L and the diameter is d. A pressure P applied at one end of the tube causes viscous flow of the liquid through it. The velocity at any point in the liquid under such conditions can be expressed as a function of the distance from the center of the tube, the pressure gradient, and the viscosity μ.

$$v = \frac{P(d^2/4 - y^2)}{4L\mu} \qquad (5\text{-}34)$$

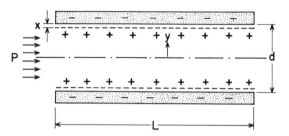

Fig. 5-20. Schematic representation of the generation of a streaming potential in a capillary tube.

If the hypothetical condenser is at a distance of $(d/2 - x)$ from the center of the tube, then the velocity at this point is

$$v_x \cong \frac{Pdx}{4L\mu} \qquad (5\text{-}35)$$

The rate at which positive charge is being carried to the right, then, is

$$i' = \pi dev_x = \frac{\pi d^2 exP}{4\mu L} \qquad (5\text{-}36)$$

The streaming potential E_k which is created by this flow of charge causes electrical flow of current in the opposite direction. If the resistivity of the solution in the capillary is R_w, then the electrical flow of current is

$$i = \frac{E_k}{r} = \frac{E_k \pi d^2}{4R_w L} \qquad (5\text{-}37)$$

At steady state, $i = i'$ and the streaming potential is

$$E_k = \frac{exPR_w}{\mu} = \frac{\zeta DPR_w}{4\pi\mu} \qquad (5\text{-}38)$$

This equation cannot be used for calculating the streaming potential because the zeta potential is generally unknown, but it does demonstrate some important facts. The first is that the streaming potential should be directly proportional to the resistivity of the solution in the capillary. Second, it is independent of the diameter, and hence the permeability of the capillary. Third, it is independent of the length of the capillary.

Part II.   ELECTRIC LOGGING PRACTICE

Figure 5-21 illustrates the situation encountered during electric logging in wellbores. The well has penetrated a series of rock strata of varying physical and chemical composition. Sequences of sandstones and shales, as pictured here, are quite common. The mud in the well, having a resistivity of R_m, is made heavy enough to prevent formation fluids from entering the borehole. The pressure differential which exists between the mud and formation fluid causes a continuous infiltration of mud liquid into the porous and permeable zones. A mud cake quickly forms on the face of the formation and limits the rate at which the filtrate enters. The resistivity of this mud cake is R_{mc} and its thickness at any time is t_{mc}. The resistivity of the watery filtrate is R_{mf}.

The filtrate enters the formation in a process known as invasion and pushes the formation fluids away from the wellbore. In the region directly behind the mud cake, flushing with mud filtrate is fairly extensive; almost all the formation water and most, say 70 percent, of the hydrocarbons will be displaced by the filtrate. It is never possible to

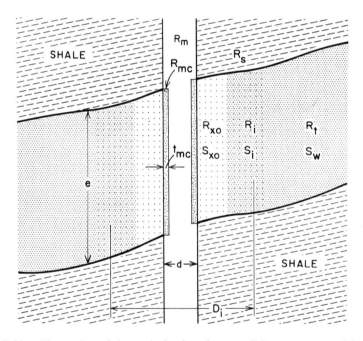

Fig. 5-21.   Illustration of the typical subsurface conditions encountered in wireline logging.

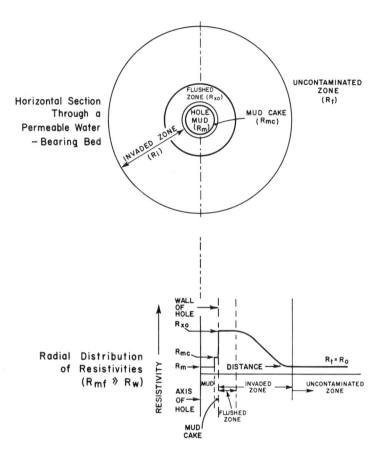

Horizontal Section
Through a
Permeable Water
– Bearing Bed

Radial Distribution
of Resistivities
$(R_{mf} \gg R_w)$

Fig. 5-22. Distribution of resistivities around the borehole in a water-saturated interval. (Courtesy of Schlumberger Well Surveying Corporation.)

remove all the hydrocarbon by flushing because the relative permeability to oil becomes zero when there is still some oil saturation (see Fig. 3-8). The resistivity of this completely flushed zone is R_{xo}, and if there is hydrocarbon present, the water saturation (primarily mud filtrate) is S_{xo}. Beyond this completely flushed zone is a region where flushing is less extensive as the distance from the borehole increases. The average resistivity of this invaded zone is R_i, and the average water saturation (both formation water and mud filtrate) is S_i. The average diameter of the invaded zone is D_i. Beyond the invaded zone is a section of formation where the fluids have been undisturbed by the drilling operation. This section has a true formation resistivity of R_t and a water saturation (formation water) of S_w. The resistivity of the formation water is R_w.

One of the major goals in quantitative electric log interpretation is the determination of S_w; the other is the determination of porosity.

The actual thickness of this permeable bed is h, and the apparent thickness measured parallel to the wellbore is e. Above and below the permeable bed are pictured beds of shale. The resistivity of these adjacent beds is R_s. Since the permeability of the average shale is of the order of 10^{-5} md, very little invasion of mud filtrate takes place and no mud cake forms at the surface.

Figure 5-22 illustrates the usual relative resistivities that may be expected for a water-saturated permeable sandstone that is invaded by fresh mud filtrate. The resistivity of the mud and mud cake are of about the same order of magnitude. The resistivity of the flushed zone, R_{xo}, is at least three or four times R_m and may be considerably more, depending on the porosity. If the water in the formation is relatively saline, then the resistivity $R_t = R_0$ will be correspondingly lower than R_{xo}. Between these two conditions there a gradual resistivity transition through the invaded zone where varying amounts of flushing have taken place.

Figure 5-23 represents the conditions which exist when the sandstone has an appreciable oil saturation before invasion starts. Again there is the completely flushed zone formed, but this zone now contains some residual oil. Because of the presence of the nonconductive oil in some of the pore space, the resistivity R_{xo} is higher than it was in the previous case. The resistivity R_t is also quite high for the same reason and in many cases it is even higher than R_{xo}. Between these two values of resistivity there is no longer a smooth transition zone. The tendency during invasion is for the mud filtrate to push the formation water ahead of it along with the oil. If the oil saturation is high, it will have a higher relative permeability than the water and will move away more rapidly. This results in an increase in the formation water saturation directly in front of the mud filtrate and causes the development of a bank of formation water. The mobility of the formation water in the bank is of the same order as the mobility of the oil. The bank comprises the "annulus," which contains formation water and oil, but which has a higher water saturation and lower resistivity than the uninvaded formation. This gives a resistivity profile which goes through a minimum between R_{xo} and R_t.

The existence of the annulus has been determined in the field and in the laboratory. While a knowledge of the factors involved in its development is still incomplete, some things may be concluded at this time. The minimum in the resistivity curve which occurs at the annulus

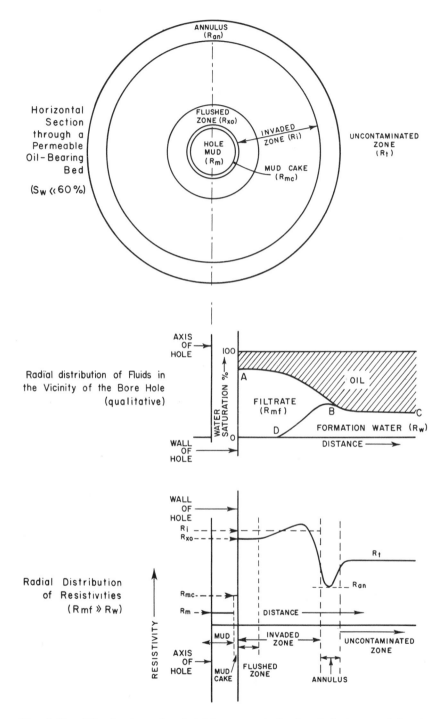

Horizontal
Section
through a
Permeable
Oil–Bearing
Bed

$(S_W \ll 60\%)$

ANNULUS
(R_{an})

FLUSHED
ZONE (R_{xo})

INVADED
ZONE (R_i)

HOLE
MUD
(R_m)

MUD CAKE
(R_{mc})

UNCONTAMINATED
ZONE
(R_t)

Radial distribution of Fluids in
the Vicinity of the Bore Hole
(qualitative)

AXIS
OF
HOLE

WALL
OF
HOLE

WATER SATURATION %

100

0

A

OIL

FILTRATE
(R_{mf})

B

C

D

FORMATION WATER (R_w)

DISTANCE

Radial Distribution
of Resistivities
$(R_{mf} \gg R_w)$

RESISTIVITY

WALL
OF
HOLE

R_i
R_{xo}

R_t

R_{an}

R_{mc}

R_m

DISTANCE

AXIS
OF
HOLE

MUD

MUD
CAKE

FLUSHED
ZONE

INVADED
ZONE

ANNULUS

UNCONTAMINATED
ZONE

Fig. 5-23. Distribution of resistivities around the borehole in an oil-bearing
formation. (Courtesy of Schlumberger Well Surveying Corporation.)

becomes less pronounced as the saturation, S_w, of the connate water in the uninvaded zone increases, and disappears almost entirely above a water saturation of 60 percent. The length of the bank of water comprising the annulus is between 15 and 25 percent of the diameter of the invaded zone, D_i. This means that the annulus gradually spreads as invasion increases. The presence of an annulus is very important in the interpretation of induction logs, but it has little effect on the response of logging devices that use electrodes.

Whether the problem of the annulus is serious or not, the depth of invasion will depend primarily on four factors: time, pressure differential between the mud and the formation fluids, filtration loss character of the mud, and the porosity of the formation. Time is important because the longer the time that the formation is exposed, the deeper the invasion is going to be. This factor points up the necessity for frequent logging on exploratory wells. The filtration loss character of the mud is important because the mud cake is the controlling factor in the movement of mud filtrate into the formation. Any formation that is capable of producing commercial amounts of hydrocarbon will have a permeability which is greater than 1 md and may range as high as several darcys. The permeability of the mud cake formed from a low water loss mud will be less than 0.01 md. This means that the permeability of the mud cake may be between one hundred and several hundred thousand times smaller than the formation permeability, and it will consequently constitute the major barrier to the movement of filtrate into the formation.

If the mud cake is the controlling factor in the volumetric rate of invasion of the formation, then the depth of invasion will depend on the amount of pore space available to contain the invaded fluid. For example, suppose a formation has been exposed for five days to mud with a pressure differential between the mud and formation of 485 psi. Suppose also that the average thickness of mud cake during this time is 1/4 in., that the viscosity of the filtrate is 0.5 cp, that the permeability of the mud cake is 0.001 md, and that the hole diameter is 8 in. With these conditions there would be about 3 cu ft of filtrate forced through the cake and into the formation in a period of five days for each foot of formation thickness. If the porosity of the formation were 30 percent, this amount of filtrate would occupy 10 cu ft of rock, or D_i would be 3.6 ft. If the porosity were 20 percent, 15 cu ft of rock would be necessary, and D_i would be 4.4 ft. If the porosity were 10 percent, 30 cu ft of rock would be required, and D_i would be 6.2 ft. These figures assume a sharp change between invaded and uninvaded portions of the formation.

Actually, an exact definition of the diameter of the invaded zone is not possible. D_i is the "electrically equivalent diameter of invasion." It corresponds to the diameter of a cylinder whose surface is located about midway between the completely flushed zone and the annulus (or the unflushed zone in a water saturated sand). This cylinder is such that it has the same effect on the measurements as the actual invaded zone. Since it is not generally used in quantitative calculations, only an approximate value of D_i is ever needed. For log interpretation purposes, D_i can be expected to be between $2d$ for high-porosity formations and $10d$ for low-porosity formations. Of course there are many exceptions to this rule; cases are known in carbonates where mud filtrate has been produced in wells a quarter of a mile away from the drilling well.

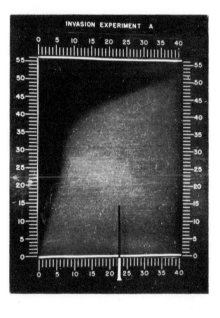

Fig. 5-24. Laboratory investigation of invasion in a homogeneous formation of high permeability. Pointer indicates depth of uniform invasion. (Doll, courtesy of *The Petroleum Engineer.*)

Some cases have been observed in the Gulf Coast area where the depth of invasion has been extremely small, sometimes less than 3 in. This phenomenon occurs in rocks having very high vertical permeability and containing very saline formation water. Invasion of mud filtrate takes place in the usual manner, but the density difference between the fresh mud filtrate and the formation water is sufficient to cause a vertical migration of the filtrate to the top of the interval. The result is that almost no invaded zone exists, except at the very top boundary, where invasion is quite extensive. Figure 5-24 shows this phenomenon in a laboratory test (21).

RESISTIVITY MEASURING METHODS

The Four-Electrode Method

In part one of this chapter the three-dimensional flow of electricity was discussed. In the example presented there, four electrodes were used; two of them, A and B, were current electrodes for introducing current into the material; the other two electrodes, M and N, were potential electrodes. All four of these electrodes were located in a uniform, isotropic substance. The resistivity of the substance was given by equation 5-8.

$$R = \frac{4\pi(E_M - E_N)}{i\left(\dfrac{1}{AM} - \dfrac{1}{AN}\right)} \tag{5-8}$$

Since the AM and AN spacings are constant for a particular logging tool, this equation can be simplified by introducing an instrument constant, K_i.

$$R = \frac{K_i(E_M - E_N)}{i} \tag{5-39}$$

Until recently, almost all resistivity measurements were made with some adaptation of this four-electrode method, and while they are not generally used now, a knowledge of the methods is still important. These systems will be described on the following pages.

Single-Electrode System.   The simplest theoretical arrangement for resistivity logging is shown in Fig. 5-25. In this method a single electrode is lowered into the hole on the logging cable, and the second electrode needed to complete the circuit is grounded at the surface. While there are only two electrodes in use here, each one is actually serving a double purpose. Thus, the surface of electrode A corresponds to the potential measuring point M. The surface of electrode B corresponds to electrode N. The potential drop through the metallic conductors is practically negligible compared with the potential drop through the earth, and the potential difference between A and B is equal to the generated voltage. Since the distance from A to B is very large, $1/AN$ is zero, and the equation for the resistivity is

$$R = \frac{4\pi(E_A - E_B)AM}{i} \tag{5-40}$$

With the distance AM equal to the effective radius of the electrode, the depth of investigation of this device is very small. In fact, it measures little more than the mud resistivity; the formation resistivity is merely a modulating factor. The device, therefore, has little use beyond that of a correlation tool in wells drilled with fresh mud. A variation of the single-electrode system, which is known as the monoelectrode scratcher, has been used occasionally in wells drilled with nonconducting fluids.

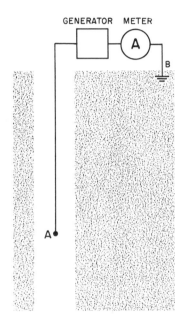

Fig. 5-25. Schematic arrangement for monoelectrode logging.

In this application, scratchers or knives are used to make contact with the formation. Where the oil-base mud cake is present, no contact is made and the resistivity is very high; where no mud cake exists, e.g., shales, the scratcher makes contact and gives a low-resistivity reading. It is thus able to delineate the sands and shales and provide a variety of lithology log.

Two-Electrode (Normal) System.   The two-electrode system is closely allied to the single-electrode system in principle, but in order to improve the depth of investigation, the potential measuring point M is moved from the surface of electrode A to some distance away. This requires two electrodes on the sonde. The theoretical circuit is shown in Fig. 5-26. Because the electrode N is a very large distance away from A, equation 5-40 still applies. The spacing AM is usually either about 1 ft or 5 ft, to give either the short normal or long normal curve. The reason for these spacings will be discussed in a later section.

Figure 5-27 shows the geometric factors for the various logging electrode arrangements in common use. These curves are drawn on the assumption that the electrodes are embedded in a homogeneous isotropic conductor of infinite extent. The geometric factor indicates the relative contribution of the various parts of the formation to the recorded signal, and the integrated geometric factor is the sum of all the geometric factors starting from the power electrode. For example,

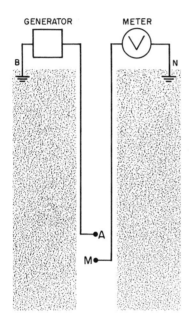

Fig. 5-26. Theoretical electrode arrangement for the normal logging system.

none of the signal of the 16-in. normal comes from the formation between the power electrode and the M electrode; 50 percent of the signal is from that part of the formation between the M electrode and a point 32 in. from the power electrode; 90 percent of the signal is caused by that part of the formation within about 13 ft of the power electrode. The geometric factor therefore gives some idea of the depth of investigation of the device. These curves indicate that for the short normal curve, the formation that is about 2 to 6 ft from the power electrode will dominate the reading of the device; for the long normal the formation from 6 to 16 ft from the power electrode contributes most strongly to the signal; for the long lateral curve (to be discussed in a later section), the formation between 17 and 20 ft contributes the entire signal. These curves are based on a radial current distribution. *When the bore hole is present, of course, these conclusions will no longer be exactly true.*

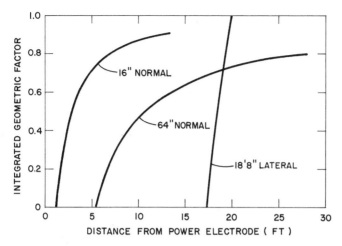

Fig. 5-27. Theoretical geometric factors for normal and lateral measuring systems in an infinite homogeneous medium.

For all logging systems utilizing multiple electrodes, some depth reference point must be selected for plotting the resistivity data. In the case of the normal curve this reference point has been selected as the midpoint of the AM spacing. The reason for choosing this location will become obvious as the discussion of the response of the instrument proceeds.

Figure 5-28a shows the theoretical response of the normal device when passing a bed whose thickness is $6AM$ and whose resistivity is 6 times that of the surrounding beds. The surrounding beds are assumed to be of infinite thickness. As the sonde approaches the bed from the bottom, there is a gradual increase in the resistivity until the A electrode enters the bed. This value of resistivity is then recorded until the M electrode also enters the bed. The result is a plateau of constant resistivity, and one AM spacing in length. As the sonde continues into the bed, there is a gradual increase in resistivity until the center of the bed is reached, and thereafter there is a symmetrical drop-off and plateau as the device passes out of the top of the bed. It can be seen that the recorded resistivity approaches, but does not equal, the true resistivity at its maximum value. Also, the bed appears on the resistivity curve to be one AM spacing thinner than it actually is, the main resistivity hump being one-half an AM spacing above the bottom boundary and one-half an AM spacing below the top. The actual curve, which includes the effect of the bore hole, follows the general trend of the theoretical curve, but all the details are rounded.

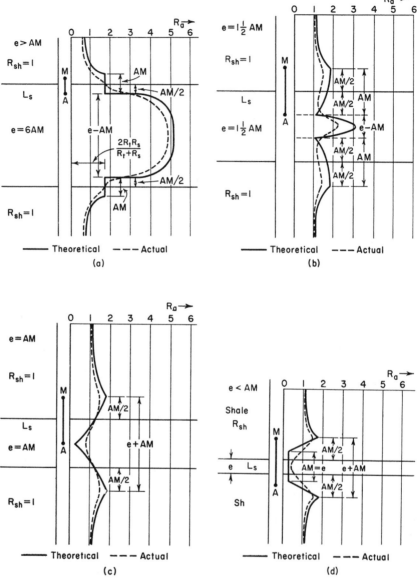

Fig. 5-28. Response of a normal device opposite beds of various thickness. (Courtesy of Schlumberger Well Surveying Corporation.)

As the bed thickness decreases relative to the spacing (Fig. 5-28b), the resistivity peak at the center of the bed gradually shrinks in size. When the bed thickness is equal to the spacing (Fig. 5-28c), or less than the spacing (Fig. 5-28d), the center resistivity hump disappears altogether;

the curve actually reverses and shows the resistive bed as if it were even more conductive than the surrounding beds. On either side of the thin resistive streak there are two reflection peaks. These peaks are $e + AM$ apart.

The characteristic reversal of the normal curve opposite a thin resistive bed is a serious limitation on the use of two-electrode devices. The depth of penetration of any device improves as the electrode spacing increases. The use of very long normal devices, however, is not feasible because many resistive beds that might be of interest would not only fail to be recorded at their proper resistivity, but they would also actually appear to be conductive on the log. For that reason, the longest normal curve has an AM spacing which is usually about 5 ft.

Figure 5-29 shows the fraction of the true resistivity that is recorded by a normal device as a function of the bed thickness (4). It can be seen that when the bed thickness becomes less than three to four AM spacings, the corrections that must be made to the recorded resistivity

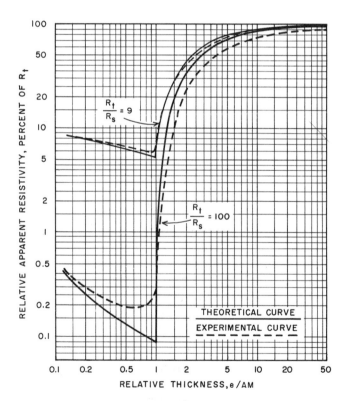

Fig. 5-29. Apparent resistivity indicated by a normal device for various bed thicknesses. (After Guyod, courtesy of Welex.)

to obtain the true resistivity become too large to make the normal device practical for obtaining quantitative values of formation resistivity. As the resistivity contrast with the adjacent beds becomes less, of course, slightly thinner beds may be logged successfully.

The preceding figures have given some hint of the difficulties that may be involved in the use of an electrode type resistivity device for the determination of the true resistivity of the uninvaded part of a formation. There are eight factors which must be considered in determining R_t from a resistivity log:

1. The true resistivity of the formation, R_t.
2. The resistivity of the invaded zone, R_i.
3. The diameter of the invaded zone, D_i, or the depth of invasion, L_i.
4. The resistivity of the mud, R_m.
5. The AM spacing.
6. The diameter of the hole, d.
7. The thickness of the bed, e.
8. The resistivity of the adjacent beds.

Fortunately, all these factors do not play a significant part in all cases where resistivity is to be determined. It is possible, in fact, to set up rather broad limits wherein the reading on the log may be used directly for R_t, or may be used with only a simple correction. In the more difficult cases, it is necessary to resort to departure curves or analog studies in order to make the proper interpretation.

Figure 5-30 is a set of departure curves which have been computed for normal devices when logging beds that are homogeneous, uninvaded, isotropic, infinite in extent, and penetrated by a cylindrical borehole. (Documents 3 and 7 (9, 12), published by the Schlumberger Well Surveying Corporation, contain departure curves for a wide variety of conditions. For a more complete discussion of the use of departure curves, Document 4 (10) should be consulted.) The axes are the ratio of the AM spacing to the hole diameter, and the ratio of the apparent resistivity (or the resistivity from the log) to the resistivity of the mud. The ratio of the true resistivity to the mud resistivity serves as the parameter. It can be seen from these curves that the measured resistivity may be greater than, less than, or equal to the true resistivity of the bed, depending on the magnitude of the various factors listed above. As the ratio of the spacing to the hole diameter becomes very small, all the curves approach a value of R_a/R_m of 1; or the measured resistivities all approach the resistivity of the mud. This bears out the previous conclusions about the monoelectrode, where the AM/d ratio is of the order of 0.25. As the *AM/d* ratio increases, the apparent resistivity approaches the true resistivity, then exceeds it for a while (or is less than the resistivity for low-resistivity beds), and then for very large

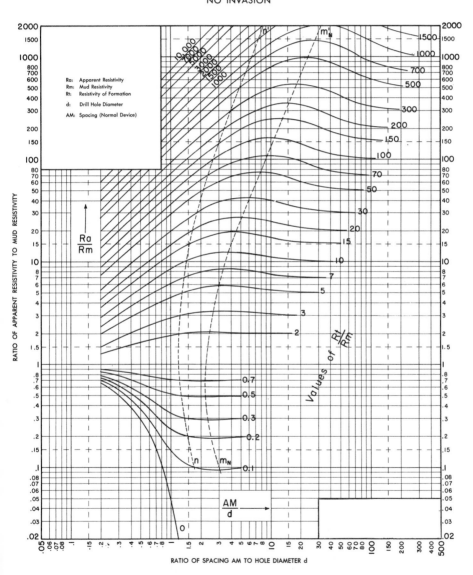

RESISTIVITY DEPARTURE·CURVES
Beds of Infinite Thickness

NORMAL DEVICE
NO INVASION

Fig. 5-30. Departure curves for the normal device—infinitely thick bed, no invasion. (Courtesy of Schlumberger Well Surveying Corporation.)

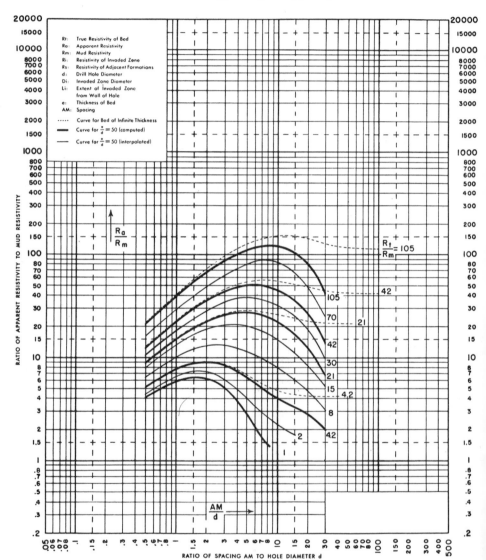

$\dfrac{e}{d} = 50$

RESISTIVITY DEPARTURE CURVES
Beds of Finite Thickness

NORMAL DEVICE

INVASION — $\dfrac{Ri}{Rm} = 21 \quad \dfrac{Di}{d} = 2 \left(\dfrac{Li}{d} = \frac{1}{2} \right)$

Rt:	True Resistivity of Bed
Ra:	Apparent Resistivity
Rm:	Mud Resistivity
Ri:	Resistivity of Invaded Zone
Rs:	Resistivity of Adjacent Formations
d:	Drill Hole Diameter
Di:	Invaded Zone Diameter
Li:	Extent of Invaded Zone from Wall of Hole
e:	Thickness of Bed
AM:	Spacing

----- Curve for Bed of Infinite Thickness
——— Curve for $\frac{e}{d} = 50$ (computed)
——— Curve for $\frac{e}{d} = 50$ (interpolated)

RATIO OF APPARENT RESISTIVITY TO MUD RESISTIVITY

$\dfrac{Ra}{Rm}$

$\dfrac{Rt}{Rm} = 105$

RATIO OF SPACING AM TO HOLE DIAMETER d

$\dfrac{AM}{d}$

CAUTION This chart should be used only when Rm is approximately equal to Rs **or** when Rt is equal to at least 2 times Rs (with conventional spacings)

Fig. 5-31. Departure curves for the normal device—finite, invaded bed. (Courtesy of Schlumberger Well Surveying Corporation.)

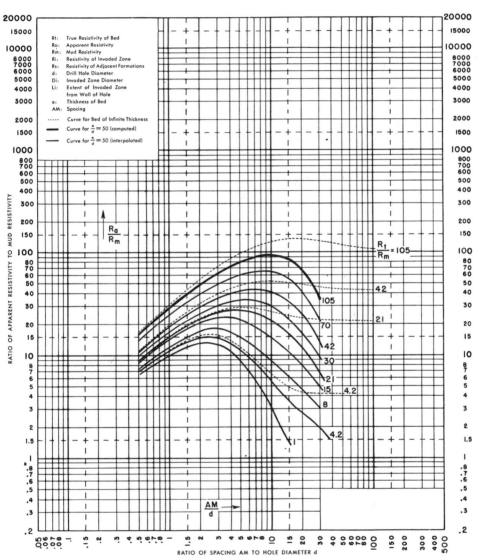

$\boxed{\dfrac{e}{d}=50}$

NORMAL DEVICE

$INVASION-\dfrac{Ri}{Rm}=21 \ \dfrac{Di}{d}=5 \left(\dfrac{Li}{d}=2\right)$

Rt: True Resistivity of Bed
Ra: Apparent Resistivity
Rm: Mud Resistivity
Ri: Resistivity of Invaded Zone
Rs: Resistivity of Adjacent Formations
d: Drill Hole Diameter
Di: Invaded Zone Diameter
Li: Extent of Invaded Zone
     from Wall of Hole
e: Thickness of Bed
AM: Spacing

----- Curve for Bed of Infinite Thickness
——— Curve for $\frac{e}{d}=50$ (computed)
——— Curve for $\frac{e}{d}=50$ (interpolated)

RATIO OF APPARENT RESISTIVITY TO MUD RESISTIVITY

$\dfrac{Ra}{Rm}$

$\dfrac{Rt}{Rm}=105$

105
42
70
21
42
30
21
15 ....4.2
8
4.2

AM / d

RATIO OF SPACING AM TO HOLE DIAMETER d

CAUTION This chart should be used only when Rm is approximately equal to Rs
or when Rt is equal to at least 2 times Rs (with conventional spacings)

Fig. 5-32. Departure curves for the normal device—finite, invaded bed. (Courtesy of Schlumberger Well Surveying Corporation.)

ratios approaches the true value asymptotically. The curve n-n represents the locus of points where the apparent and true resistivity are equal. For bed resistivities between $0.1R_m$ and $50R_m$, this curve lies between $1.2AM/d$ and $2AM/d$. This means that for an 8-in. hole a short normal device should have a spacing between 10 in. and 16 in. in order to give the most nearly correct resistivity value. Because the deviations become more severe at the higher resistivity values, the larger of these two spacings should be preferred.

Over this same range of resistivity, the apparent resistivity values approach the true values asymptotically when the ratio of AM/d is between 6 and 40. Because of the thin bed effect, however, it is not practical to use the longer spacing ratio. The long normal spacing in common use is 64 in. This gives good resistivity values on the log when the resistivity ratio R_a/R_m is less than 10, with the discrepancies becoming increasingly great as the resistivity increases beyond this value. However, for the more resistive beds the lateral device is used in preference to the normal device for determining R_t, so this limitation is not too important.

Figure 5-30 represents the response of the normal device for a fairly simplified and rather unusual set of conditions. Beds which may be of interest as hydrocarbon reservoirs are invariably invaded to some unknown degree and are rarely of a thickness that can be considered infinite. There are, however, a large number of charts of departure curves available for a wide variety of other conditions. Figures 5-31 and 5-32 are two such charts for the normal device which are taken from Document 3. These particular charts are for an e/d ratio of 50 and an R_i/R_m ratio of 21. Figure 5-31 is for an invasion diameter equal to twice the hole diameter, and Fig. 5-32 is for an invasion diameter of $5d$. The most striking difference between these charts and Fig. 5-30 is the sharp downward trend of all the curves at values of AM/d greater than 10. This is because the critical AM/d ratio for this particular case is 50, and the effect noted in Fig. 5-29 is becoming important. It will be noted also that there are slight differences between the curves of Fig. 5-31 and Fig. 5-32. If values of R_a/R_m are known for more than one electrode spacing, it is possible to use these curves to estimate the diameter of invasion. This point will be discussed in more detail later on.

Figures 5-33 and 5-34 are simplified versions of the departure curves which have been developed from the more elaborate charts for average conditions. These are only for the 16-in. AM spacing, with a hole size of 8 in., and an invasion diameter between $2d$ and $10d$. These particular charts were developed to aid in the interpretation of the resistivity survey that combines the 16-in. normal curve with the induction log. The 16-in. normal gives a reading that is strongly influenced by the invaded zone, and this can be used in correcting the deeper penetration induction log for invasion effects.

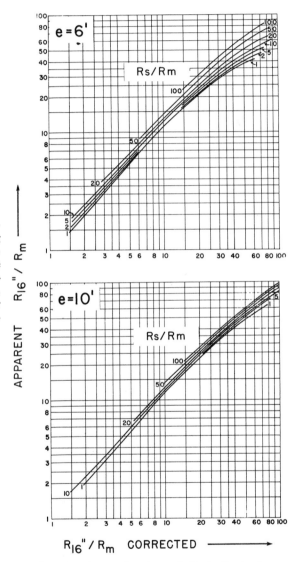

Fig. 5-33. Simplified departure curves for correcting for the effects of bed thickness and borehole on the 16-in. normal device—invasion with $R_{xo}/R_t > 5$. (Courtesy of Schlumberger Well Surveying Corporation.)

The use of normal curves for the determination of R_t is limited to high-porosity formations because of the short spacings used. In low-porosity formations the depth of invasion becomes so great that even the long normal curve gives a reading which is seriously affected by the invaded zone. The rules for estimation of R_t for various conditions will be given in a later section.

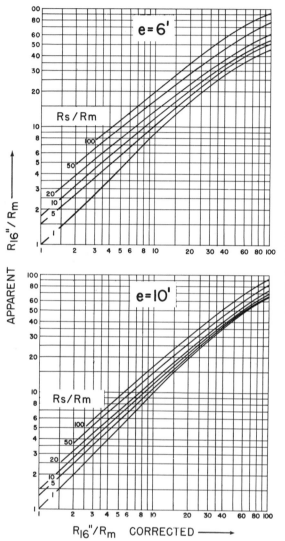

Fig. 5-34. Simplified departure curves for correcting for the effects of bed thickness and borehole on the 16-in. normal device— no invasion. (Courtesy of Schlumberger Well Surveying Corporation.)

Three-Electrode (lateral) System.   In the three-electrode systems, both potential electrodes, M and N, are located on the sonde. The current electrode A is also on the sonde and the electrode B is at the surface as before. This theoretical circuit is shown in Fig. 5-35. M and N are spaced quite close together compared to the average distance, AO, of these electrodes from the current electrode. Consequently, no simplification can be made to equation 5-8 for this type of device. The *AO* spacings in common use are approximately 9 ft and 18 ft for the short and long laterals respectively.

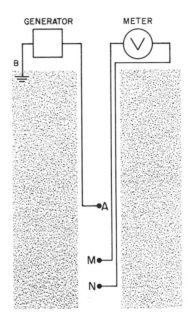

Fig. 5-35. Theoretical arrangement for the lateral logging system.

The three-electrode device is an unsymmetrical arrangement and it therefore gives unsymmetrical curves when logging beds of finite thickness. The reference point for this system is not taken as the midpoint of the spacing, but is taken rather at the midpoint of *MN* (or the point *O*). The reason for this selection is that the bottom portion of the curve recorded opposite a resistant bed will correspond very closely to the actual bed boundary. This condition can be seen clearly in Figs. 5-36a through 5-36d.

Fig. 5-36a shows the theoretical response of the lateral device when passing a bed thicker than four times the spacing. As the electrodes approach the bottom of the bed there is a small rise in resistivity because increasing amounts of current are deflected downward. A plateau occurs from the time that the *A* electrode enters the bed until the *M* and *N* electrodes reach the bed. When point *O* is at the bed boundary, a very high reading is obtained, even greater than the true resistivity. This peak occurs because of the unusual current distribution that exists right at the boundary between the conductive and resistive beds. A similar anomaly, but in the opposite direction, may be observed at the upper bed boundary. When all the electrodes are within the bed, the

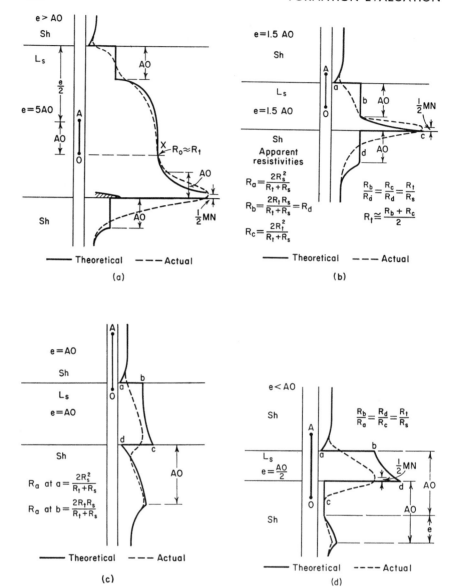

Fig. 5-36. Response of a lateral device opposite beds of various thickness. (Courtesy of Schlumberger Well Surveying Corporation.)

resistivity drops back and the true resistivity R_t is recorded over most of the bed length. As a general rule for beds thicker than three times the spacing, the resistivity is selected at a point which is half the bed thickness plus AO from the top of the bed. At this point the current electrode is at the center of the bed, and the current distribution will most nearly correspond to the radial distribution assumed in the derivation of equation 5-8. If the bed in question is as thick as the one shown in this figure, there is little doubt about what value of R_a should be chosen for R_t.

As the current electrode approaches the top of the bed, the current pattern is distorted increasingly upward and the apparent resistivity drops. From the time the A electrode leaves the bed until the M and N electrodes reach the boundary, the resistivity plateau is again observed. This is followed by the anomaly at the bed boundary with the gradual return of the resistivity reading to the resistivity of the adjacent bed.

As the beds become thinner relative to the spacing, the long plateau of true resistivity gradually disappears, although all the other features of the curve remain as long as the bed thickness is greater than the spacing. When the bed is equal to $1.3AO$ in thickness, the peak value observed at the lower bed boundary is exactly equal to R_t. For beds thinner than this, the apparent resistivity will be so far from the true value that the lateral curve should not be used for quantitative work. In the case of the long lateral curve this limiting thickness is about 25 ft. This is one of the reasons for the rapid decline in the use of the unfocused electrode type of logging devices.

Regardless of the bed thickness, the lateral device, unlike the normal, will always show a positive deflection when passing a resistive bed. When the bed thickness is less than the spacing, however, a complicated resistivity pattern arises as illustrated in Fig. 5-36d. As the sonde approaches the bottom of a thin bed, the rise in resistivity occurs as before, but after the A electrode enters the bed, the recorded resistivity drops to an extremely low value, even less than the resistivity of the adjacent conductive bed. This low value persists until the M and N electrodes move into the bed, when a small peak occurs which is much less than the true value. The usual anomaly is observed at the upper boundary. Logging a thin bed, then, results in a "reflection peak" located one AO spacing below the bed, and a "blind zone" or "shadow zone" directly below the bed. The lateral device will not record the resistivity of any beds which are in the blind zone. A series of thin resistant beds, each with a blind zone and a reflection peak, gives a log which is very difficult to interpret (see Fig. 5-37).

The dotted lines of Fig. 5-36 show the appearance of the lateral curve if the borehole effect is introduced. As with the normal, the theoretical details are clearly visible, but all the features of the curves are rounded. It can be seen that in picking the bottom bed boundary from a lateral curve, a point $\frac{1}{2}MN$ below the apex of the peak should

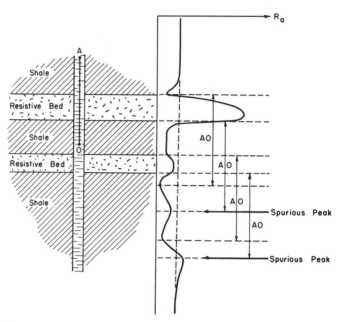

Fig. 5-37. Response of a lateral device opposite two thin resistive beds. (Courtesy of Schlumberger Well Surveying Corporation.)

be used. The upper boundary is usually too indistinct to be located from the lateral at all. An approximation can be made by adding on one AO spacing to the apparent upper boundary, but this is not too satisfactory.

Figure 5-38 shows the fraction of the true resistivity that is recorded by a lateral device as a function of the bed thickness. (The values of resistivity plotted here are the maximum or peak values that occur at the bottom bed boundary.) The curves clearly show that below $2AO$ thickness the recorded resistivity drops off sharply and the corrections that must be applied to get R_t become very large.

The determination of the true resistivity of a formation with a lateral device is a function of the same eight factors that were involved with the normal device. Again, not all these factors are always pertinent, and in many cases the reading from the log may be used directly. As with the normal, departure curves have been developed which are useful in the difficult cases.

Figure 5-39 is a set of departure curves which have been computed for the lateral device when logging beds that are homogeneous, uninvaded, isotropic, infinite in extent, and penetrated by a cylindrical borehole. These curves show very large deviations of R_a from R_t for small ratios of AO/d and pretty well preclude the use of laterals with short spacings. The long lateral device (18 ft 8 in.) corresponds to an AO/d spacing of the order of 30 for an 8-in. borehole. With this spacing, beds may be logged with no more than 10 percent error for R_a/R_m up to 10 and with no more than a 30 percent error for R_a/R_m of 50. As the resistivity of the formation increases, the long lateral device will show an increasing discrepancy of the apparent resistivity from the true value, and the apparent value will always be higher.

Departure curves for lateral devices logging invaded beds are available for various conditions of invasion, but only for beds of infinite thickness. Simplified versions of these departure curves are available for average invasion conditions as illustrated in Fig. 5-40. The fact that the apparent resistivity will be higher than the true resistivity (particularly at the higher resistivity values) is quite evident here, and emphasizes the conclusion that the long lateral resistivity reading will usually have to be corrected in formations of moderate and high resistivity.

Since the three-electrode system of logging is unsymmetrical, it is possible to have two arrangements of the electrodes. The one which has been described is the standard arrangement. It is generally used because it is possible to get a resistivity reading right to the bottom of the hole. The lateral curve, unfortunately, does not give a good resistivity

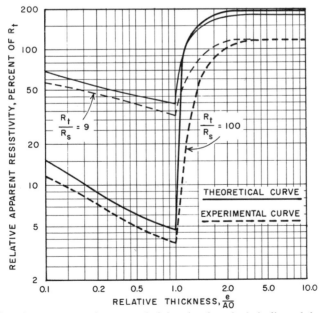

Fig. 5-38. Apparent maximum resistivity (peak value) indicated by a lateral device for various bed thicknesses. (After Guyod, courtesy of Welex.)

reading within one AO spacing of the top of the bed. In order to obtain a better value of the resistivity in this part of resistive beds, and to investigate directly under a casing shoe, an inverted lateral is sometimes

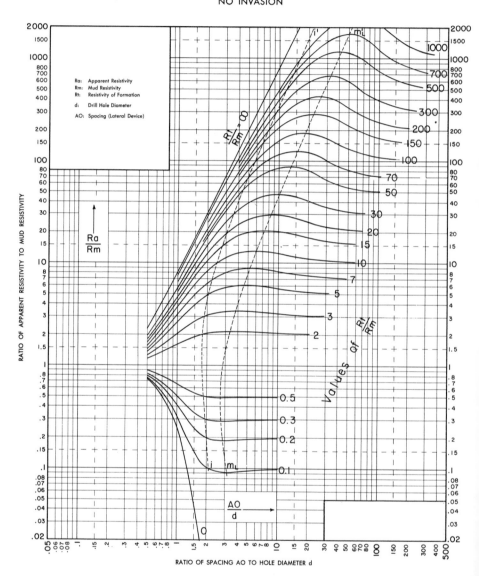

LATERAL DEVICE

NO INVASION

RESISTIVITY DEPARTURE CURVES
Beds of Infinite Thickness

Ra: Apparent Resistivity
Rm: Mud Resistivity
Rt: Resistivity of Formation
d: Drill Hole Diameter
AO: Spacing (Lateral Device)

$\frac{Ra}{Rm}$

RATIO OF APPARENT RESISTIVITY TO MUD RESISTIVITY

$\frac{AO}{d}$

RATIO OF SPACING AO TO HOLE DIAMETER d

Fig. 5-39. Departure curves for the lateral device—infinitely thick bed, no invasion. (Courtesy of Schlumberger Well Surveying Corporation.)

used. In this arrangement, the M and N electrodes are at the top of the sonde and the A electrode is at the bottom. The recorded curves appear as inverted forms of those shown in Fig. 5-36.

The logs presented in Figs. 5-41 and 5-42 illustrate some of the anomalies of the normal and lateral resistivity curves that have been discussed in the preceding pages. Both of these logs are from the same well. The upper part of this well contains a sandstone-shale sequence of beds. At 4384 ft the well penetrated an extensive limestone section, and the resistivities are seen to increase several fold at this point. The low resistivity streaks within the limestone are indicative of zones that contain some pore space.

These sample logs clearly show the reversal of the normal curves opposite thin beds, the lateral curve blind zone, reflection peaks on the lateral curve, lag zones, etc. In the limestone section the backup curves appear on the logs. These curves appear on the resistivity log with a $10 \times$ scale when the standard curve goes beyond the upper resistivity limit of the standard scale. The backup curve can be identified by the heavier trace.

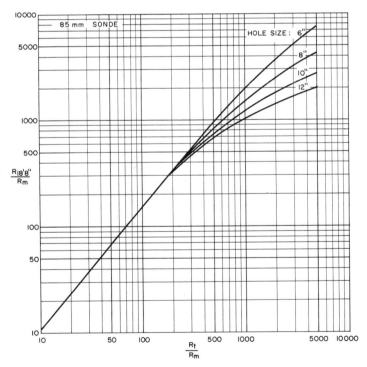

Fig. 5-40. Simplified departure curves for the long lateral device. (Courtesy of Schlumberger Well Surveying Corporation.)

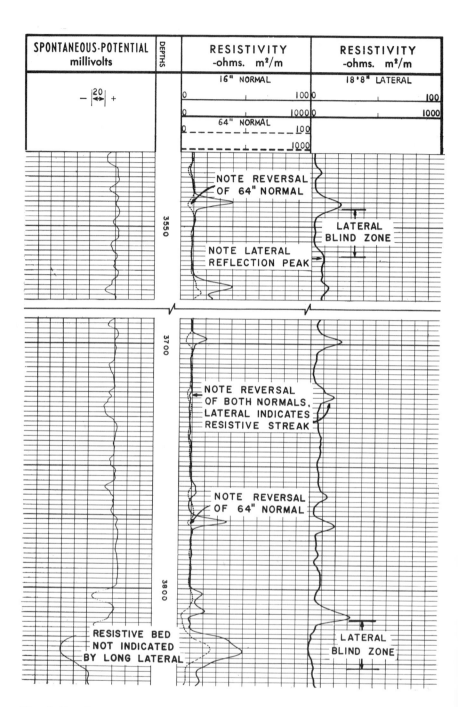

Fig. 5-41. Example of the response of the normal and lateral devices to various resistivity conditions. (Courtesy of California Standard Co.)

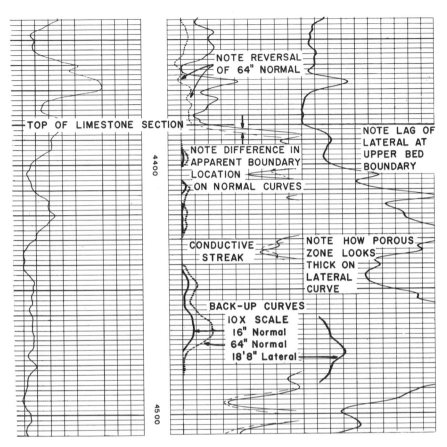

Fig. 5-42. Example of the response of the normal and lateral devices to various resistivity conditions. (Courtesy of California Standard Corporation.)

The Limestone Lateral.   When logging formations of very high resistivity, the current distribution around the power electrode is very far from the idealized situation of Fig. 5-8 which served as a basis for the resistivity equation. The current, in fact, travels almost entirely within the borehole to adjacent conductive formations. The resistivity indicated by the logging device then becomes primarily a function of the mud resistivity and the ratio of the spacing to the hole diameter. This situation is clearly reflected by the nearly straight line on Fig. 5-39 for R_t/R_m of ∞. In the case of the lateral device, a very high resistivity formation will give a curve which varies continuously and linearly from a very low resistivity value starting at one AO spacing below the top of the bed to a very high resistivity value at the bottom boundary. This effect is illustrated by Fig. 5-43.

In order to get around this distorted picture of the formation resistivity, the standard and the inverted arrangements of the lateral are combined and run together on one sonde. This arrangement, known as the limestone lateral, is shown in Fig. 5-44. Since M and M', and N and N' are connected together, the device records an average of the two potential drops. This produces a log like that shown in Fig. 5-45. As might be expected, the symmetrical arrangement produces a symmetrical curve. Depths are therefore measured from the center of the device.

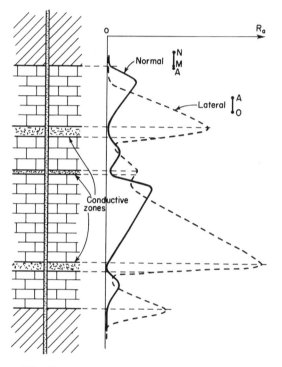

Fig. 5-43. Qualitative response of normal and lateral devices to a highly resistive formation containing conductive beds. (Courtesy of Schlumberger Well Surveying Corporation.)

The limestone device produces a flat top resistivity log when opposite a thick resistive bed. The indicated resistivity is independent of the bed thickness and the position of the device within the bed, but does depend on the hole size, the mud resistivity, and the spacing of the electrodes. The length of the resistive plateau is equal to the bed thickness minus the length of the NN' spacing. This NN' spacing is usually kept small in order to give better bed boundaries and to minimize the effect of small conductive streaks that may be contained within the bed. The length AO is about 32 in. and MN is about 4 in.

High-resistivity beds are frequently drilled with salty muds so that the resistivity recorded by the limestone lateral may be only a small

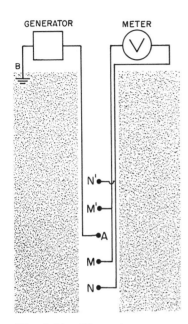

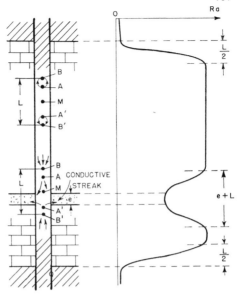

Fig. 5-44. Electrode arrangement for the limestone lateral device.

Fig. 5-45. Qualitative response of the limestone lateral device to a highly resistive formation containing a conductive streak. (Courtesy of Schlumberger Well Surveying Corporation.)

fraction of the true resistivity. In this case the scale of resistivity on the log is usually ignored, and a new scale is constructed through the use of the resistivity departure curves. Since the log is reading the average of two lateral curves, Fig. 5-39 is suitable for this purpose. For an average hole diameter of about 8 in., AO/d is 4.

Determination of the Depth of Invasion from Departure Curves. If the resistivity of the invaded zone is greatly different from the true resistivity of the formation, the depth of invasion can become a factor of prime importance in the interpretation of resistivity log data, regardless of the type of logging tool that has been run. An estimate of this factor can be obtained from the readings of the normal and lateral devices through the use of the departure curves.

Suppose, for example, that a very thick bed is logged with a 16-in. normal, a 64-in. normal, and an 18-ft 8-in. lateral. The resistivity readings on the logs are: $R_{16''} = 32$, $R_{64''} = 62$, and $R_{18'8''} = 74$. $R_m = 1.0$. If the hole size is 8 in., these spacings correspond to ratios of AM/d of 2 and 8, and AO/d of 28. A comparison of the 16-in. and 18-ft 8-in. readings indicates that the resistivity of the invaded zone is probably less than the 16-in. reading. A check of the departure curve

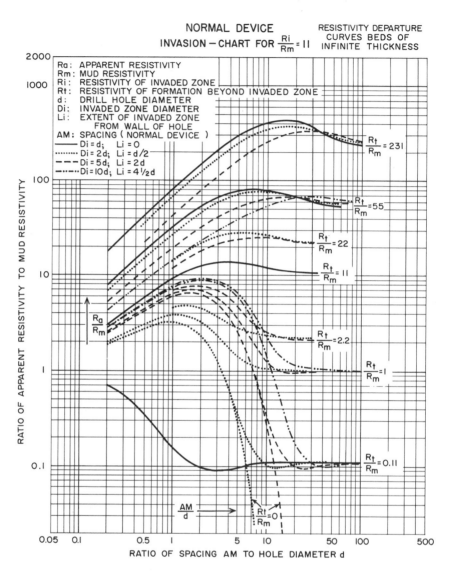

Fig. 5-46. Departure curves for the normal device—infinitely thick, invaded bed. (Courtesy of Schlumberger Well Surveying Corporation.)

charts (Document 7) for the lateral device indicates that with this resistivity pattern, the lateral is reading beyond the invaded zone if invasion is less than 10d. From Fig. 5-39, then, it would appear that R_t is about 55. Finally, reference to the charts of departure curves for the normal device shows that the two normal readings will fit the departure curves only for the case where $R_i/R_m = 11$ and $D_i = 5d$ (the dashed curve of Fig. 5-46 and 5-47).

This illustrative example is not meant to imply that all problems of interpretation are this simple. The resistivity of the invaded zone and the diameter of invasion are interrelated factors, and in some cases it is necessary to know one of them before the other can be determined. (If the porosity is known from some other source, the proper value of

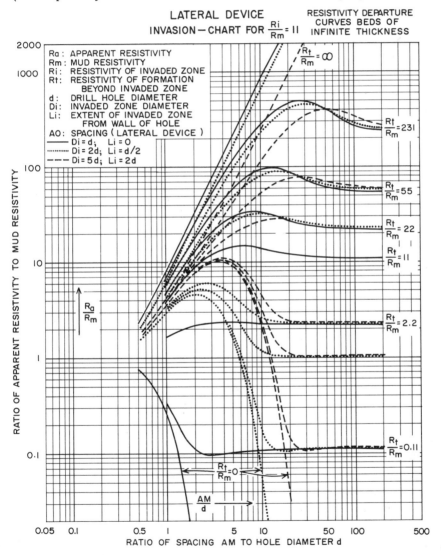

Fig. 5-47. Departure curves for the lateral device—infinitely thick, invaded bed. (Courtesy of Schlumberger Well Surveying Corporation.)

R_i/R_m may be estimated by means of equations 5-53 and 5-54.) Beds of finite thickness also complicate the problem. For a discussion of these more complex situations, the reader is referred to Document 4 (10).

The Principle of Reciprocity and the Arrangement of Electrodes. In order to reduce time and expense in logging and to provide an exact depth correlation between the different curves, it is desirable to run as many curves as possible on one trip into the hole. When logging with the standard electrode devices, it is customary to run the short normal, the long normal or short lateral, the long lateral, and the SP curve on one trip. This system of multicurve logging makes it impractical to retain the theoretical electrode arrangements which were illustrated in Figs. 5-26 and 5-35. A large measure of flexibility can be introduced in the design of the actual circuit by the application of the principle of reciprocity. This principle, which has been proved both mathematically and experimentally, states that in any system of four electrodes arranged in any way, the voltage difference between electrodes 1 and 2 resulting from the passage of current between electrodes 3 and 4 is exactly equal to the voltage difference between 3 and 4 resulting from the passage of an identical current between 1 and 2. This principle applies regardless of the medium in which the electrodes are embedded or of the electrode configuration. In the circuit of Fig. 5-35, for example, the power electrodes A and B could be placed on the sonde in the position occupied by M and N, and the potential electrodes M and N could be placed in the locations occupied by A and B on the sonde and surface respectively; if the flow of current through the power electrodes were the same, the reading on the voltmeter would be the same.

In actual practice this rearrangement is made. Figure 5-48 shows the arrangements of electrodes that are used for the three resistivity curves and how they are put together to form a single sonde capable of logging all three curves simultaneously. The reference point against which the log depth measurements are made corresponds to the location of the M_1 electrode. Since the reference point for the short normal is 8 in. below this point, and the reference point for the long normal is 16 in. above, small adjustments must be made in the location of the galvanometer spot in the recording equipment so that all the curves appear in the right relation to one another. The reference point for the long lateral and the SP is the M_1 electrode, and no correction need be made for these.

In addition to the changes made on the basis of the principle of reciprocity, all potential measuring electrodes for the normal and

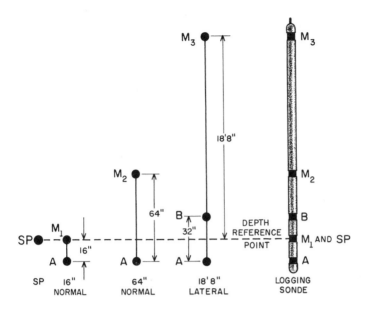

Fig. 5-48. The Schlumberger arrangement of electrodes for multicurve logging.

lateral curves are placed in the hole. The location of the N electrode is such that the distance to it from the M electrode is at least twelve times the AM spacing. This condition approximates having the N at infinity except for very thick resistive beds where distortion of the symmetrical character of the curve will occur (see Fig. 5-43). Making this change gets the potential electrodes away from stray surface currents and also eliminates inductive effects which result from having the power circuit and only half of the potential measuring circuit in the same cable.

The Schlumberger Method of Resistivity Logging. The composite arrangement of electrodes on the sonde as shown in Fig. 5-48 does not provide the whole answer to the problem of logging three resistivity curves and the SP simultaneously. The electrode M_1, for example, must do double duty as a resistivity and an SP electrode, and the power electrode B must be on the sonde for recording the lateral curve, but it must be an infinite distance away for recording the two normal curves. The Schlumberger method for solving this added problem makes use of a pulsed current and an ingenious switching arrangement.

The spontaneous potential curve is a measure of the potential developed by a concentration cell situated in the earth, and as such it is a direct current measurement. If this curve is to be measured at the same time that resistivity measurements are being made, it is essential that the power supplied to the power electrode, A, is a form of alternating current. Instead of using the usual sinusoidal type of alternating current,

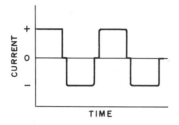

Fig. 5-49. Pulsed current form used by Schlumberger.

however, a pulsated square wave of very low frequency is used, thereby eliminating the usual inductive and capacitive effects associated with alternating current. This type of current is illustrated in Fig. 5-49. It is generated by the simple switching arrangement shown in Fig. 5-50.

Figure 5-50 illustrates not only the method of generating the pulsed current, but also the method of separating the alternating and direct signals received by the M_1 electrode. The switch on the power circuit

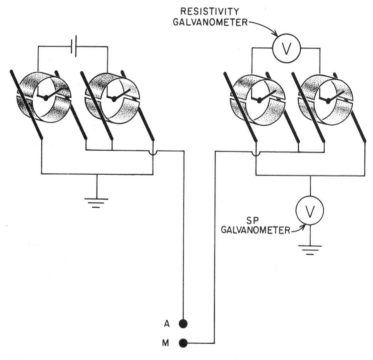

Fig. 5-50. Switching arrangement used to produce pulsed current and to separate SP and resistivity signals.

alternates the polarity of the *A* electrode at approximately 15 cps. This produces the signal shown in Fig. 5-49, which has a constant voltage but an alternating polarity. This switch on the power circuit is ganged to the switch on the recording circuit which contains two direct-current galvanometers as shown. The resistivity galvanometer, having the connections of its terminals alternated at a frequency of 15 cps sees the input power signal as a direct current, and the continuous direct-current potential of the SP as a 15-cycle alternating potential. The SP galvanometer, on the other hand, sees the SP as a direct current

and the power signal as an alternating 15-cycle current. Since both are direct-current galvanometers, each will record only that signal that it sees as a direct current.

A similar switching procedure is used to record the lateral and normal curves simultaneously. The galvanometers in this case are gang switched so that only the lateral curve galvanometer will read when the *B* electrode connection is on the sonde, and only the normal curve galvanometers will read when the *B* electrode connection is at the surface.

The Halliburton Method of Resistivity Logging. The Halliburton Company has developed a frequency-modulated system (54) of logging which requires only a single conductor cable (now used by Welex, Halliburton's logging subsidiary). This system is shown schematically in Fig. 5-51. The generator power source supplies a 400-cycle current to the conductor cable, with the return being through the ground. This 400-cycle current provides all the power needed for the *A* electrode

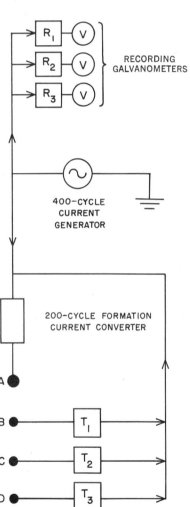

RECORDING GALVANOMETERS

400-CYCLE CURRENT GENERATOR

200-CYCLE FORMATION CURRENT CONVERTER

Fig. 5-51. The Halliburton method of frequency-modulated logging.

and for operation of the electronic gear on the sonde. Some of the 400-cycle current passes through a formation current converter which supplies 200-cycle current to the A electrode. The potentials are measured by the M electrodes as before, but the signals are now fed into the transmitters, T_1, T_2, and T_3, instead of being transmitted directly to the surface. These transmitters are frequency-modulated current transmitters centered at 8000, 10,500 and 14,000 cycles. The potentials of the M electrodes modulate these carrier frequencies, and the modulated signals are sent up to the surface receivers over the same cable used for the power supply. Each receiver is tuned to receive only one carrier frequency. The intelligence signal is then taken off the carrier, converted into direct current, and recorded by galvanometers. The standard logs run by Welex using this system are the 2Z18-in. normal and the 3iZ9-ft and 3iZ16-ft laterals.

Focused-Current Log

One of the major problems with the simple electrode methods of resistivity logging is the distorted current distribution that occurs when R_t/R_m is high, e.g., low-porosity rocks or very salty mud. The long lateral in this case gives resistivity readings which are far from the true values and which require tremendous corrections from the departure curves. In addition, the invasion is often so deep that the shorter spacing curves will not suffice to measure R_t, and good readings may be obtained from the long lateral curve only when the bed thickness is at least twice the AO spacing. This means that the problem of measuring R_t with simple normals and laterals is practically insurmountable for high-resistivity formations that are less than 40 ft thick.

The difficulty in logging when R_t/R_m is high arises from the fact that the current from the power electrode tends to flow almost entirely within the borehole. The limestone device represented an attempt to overcome this difficulty by placing potential measuring electrodes above and below the power electrode so that the current would be measured regardless of the direction it took. The focused-current system goes one long step beyond this by placing auxiliary power electrodes above and below the main power electrode. These auxiliary electrodes provide potential barriers within the mud column which prevent the main current from taking this path. It is therefore forced to penetrate the formation opposite the main electrode. Not only does this potential barrier control the current flow in the well, but it also maintains the current in the form of a thin cylindrical sheet for a considerable distance into the formation. The improvement in logging that is accomplished with this focusing action is clearly illustrated by Fig. 5-52 where the laterolog is compared with other nonfocused logs.

The operation of the auxiliary electrodes in creating a potential barrier can be illustrated by the two electrode arrangements of Fig. 5-53. Figure 5-53a shows the paths of current flow from a long cylindrical electrode that is embedded in a uniform medium. Since the entire electrode is at the same potential, all of the current lines leave in a direction perpendicular to the electrode face and do not assume a spherical distribution until they are a great distance away. Notice particularly that the current near the center of the electrode flows in a nearly horizontal direction for a considerable distance.

In Fig. 5-53b the same electrode has been divided into three parts so as to separate a small center section from the two end pieces. All three pieces are connected to the power supply and all are at the same potential. The current distribution remains unchanged. The sole difference here is that now only the current going to the center ring is measured. Since this current is directed into the formation in a horizontal beam, measuring this current and the potential of the electrode will give the resistivity of the formation directly opposite to the center section. The function of the two end sections is to control the current flow from the center measuring electrode into a horizontal sheet.

If this divided electrode arrangement is placed in a medium such that the resistivity opposite the center section is much higher than the resistivity opposite the two guard sections, the relative amounts of

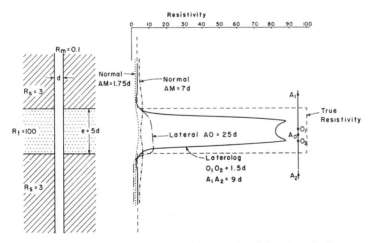

Fig. 5-52. Response of the laterolog and conventional logging devices opposite a thin resistive bed, noninvaded, $R_t = 100$, $R_s = 3$, $R_m = 0.1$. (Doll, courtesy of the AIME.)

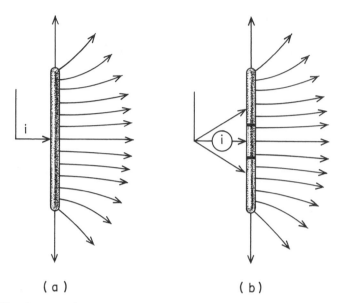

(a)   (b)

Fig. 5-53. Pattern of current flow from a long cylindrical electrode located in a homogeneous medium. (From *Subsurface Formation Evaluation Methods* by John Walstrom. Copyright 1955 by Standard Oil Company of California. All rights reserved under the Pan-American Copyright Convention. Reproduced by courtesy of the Copyright Owner.)

current going into the guards will increase proportionately, but the direction of current flow will remain essentially unchanged. Therefore, as long as the thickness of the resistive streak is greater than the length of the center section, the measurement of the resistivity will be very nearly correct. The presence of a mud column around the electrode makes an insignificant difference in its response, except in cases of extremely large holes such as result from caving.

The logging system illustrated by Fig. 5-53b is basically that used in the Welex guard log (42). The guard log has a central electrode that is only 3 in. long, with 5-ft guards above and below it. The current flowing to the central electrode and the potential of the electrode are measured, and from these the resistivity of the formation is estimated. Because of the very short center section, the guard log gets fine resistivity detail.

The action of the guard electrodes can be assured by the addition of a device to control the potential of the guard sections. Figure 5-54 shows the arrangement of the electrodes that is used in the Schlumberger laterolog 3 (19). The generator supplies a constant current to the electrode A_0, and the controller supplies an auxiliary current to the two outer electrodes, A_1 and A_2. A_1 and A_2 are connected together and so are at an equal potential. The potentials of A_1 and A_0 are fed continuously into the controller where they are compared; the auxiliary current is then adjusted automatically so that the difference of these two potentials is always nil. Since the two potentials are equal, no current can flow from A_0 toward A_1 or A_2. The main current must therefore flow only into the formation. The potential of the A_0 electrode is recorded at the surface as a measure of the resistivity of the formation.

Figure 5-55 represents a similar system which uses point electrodes instead of the long metallic body. It is known as the laterolog 7. The

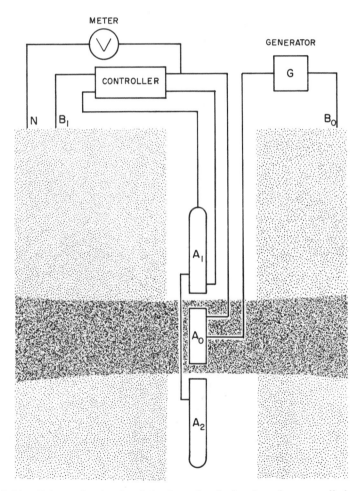

Fig. 5-54. Schematic circuit of the laterolog 3 showing the controlled current sheet. (After Doll, courtesy of the AIME.)

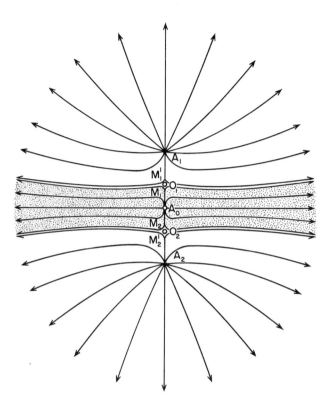

Fig. 5-55. Electrode arrangement of the laterolog 7 showing the controlled current sheet. (After Doll, courtesy of the AIME.)

potential sensing elements in this case are the electrodes M_1, M_1' and M_2, M_2'. The controller adjusts the current to the electrodes A_1 and A_2 so that the potential difference between the M electrodes and the M' electrodes is always nil. As the current to the A_0 electrode is constant, the potential of the M electrodes is a measure of the resistivity of the rock opposite the center of the device. The use of point electrodes in the laterolog 7 permits simultaneous logging of the SP and other resistivity curves; this cannot be done when elongated metallic electrodes are used because they short-circuit the mud column.

The laterolog 7 is the standard focused log run by Schlumberger. The O_1O_2 spacing is 32 in. and the A_1A_2 spacing is 80 in. The thickness of the current sheet is therefore about 32 in. The laterolog 3, which is often used in carbonates because of its finer resolution, has a current sheet that may be either 6 in. or 1 ft thick. A new device known as the conductivity laterolog is now replacing the laterolog 3 in some areas. This tool produces a 12-in. beam, focused by 5-ft guards. It differs from the laterolog 3 in the method of controlling the focusing action and in the fact that the current is allowed to vary while the potential of the electrodes is kept constant. The signal received is proportional, therefore, to the conductivity of the formation, and is recorded as such in the third track on the log. The log is also plotted on a hybrid resistivity scale in the second track; the first five divisions are linear in resistivity, and the last five divisions are linear in conductivity, although scaled in resistivity. This eliminates the need for backup curves, while still retaining sensitivity in the low-resistivity regions. The midscale value (at the fifth division) can be 20, 50, 100, or 250 ohm-meters, so that the conductivity portion of this track (divisions five to ten) would be respectively 10, 4, 2, or 0.8 mmhos per meter per division.

Bed thickness presents little difficulty in the use of the laterolog or the guard log. As long as the thickness of the current sheet is less than the bed thickness, the recorded value of the resistivity, when corrected for invasion, will be very close to the true resistivity. If the bed is thinner than the current sheet, the current will flow through the resistive and the conductive beds in parallel. In this case the parallel circuit law applies (equation 5-3), and the measured resistivity will be very close to the resistivity of the conductive bed. The minimum bed thickness that can be effectively logged with the laterolog 7 therefore is about 3 ft; the minimum thickness for the laterolog 3 is about 6 in.; and the

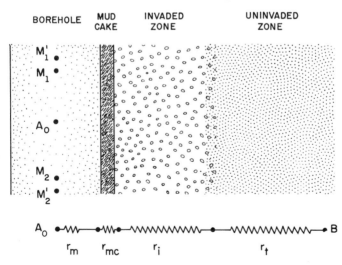

Fig. 5-56. Schematic representation of the equivalent electric circuit for current flow from a laterolog device.

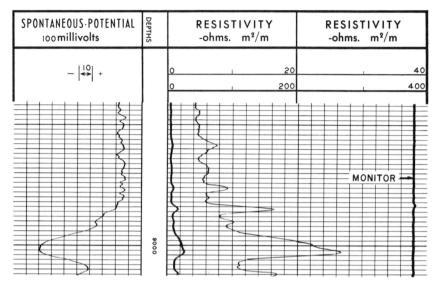

SPONTANEOUS-POTENTIAL 100 millivolts	DEPTHS	RESISTIVITY -ohms. m²/m	RESISTIVITY -ohms. m²/m

Fig. 5-57. Example of a log recorded with the laterolog 7. (Courtesy of Schlumberger Well Surveying Corporation.)

minimum thickness for the guard log is about 3 in. These figures represent a tremendous improvement over the thicknesses required for successful logging with the unfocused devices.

Figure 5-56 represents the equivalent circuit for current flow from the electrode A_0 of a laterolog. The current must flow in series through the mud column, the mud cake, the invaded zone, and the undisturbed formation. If the potential at A_0 is going to be a reasonable measure of the resistivity R_t, then it is necessary that the other resistances be kept low. The only way that this can be accomplished is by using a mud whose resistivity is as low as, or lower than, the resistivity of the formation water. The focused current log is most diagnostic, therefore, in cases where salt mud is used for the drilling fluid.

If the invaded zone should make up a significant part of the resistance of the circuit of Fig. 5-56, departure curves are available which correct for the effect of invasion and the resistivity of the invaded zone [Welex Bulletin A127 (3); Schlumberger Document No. 6 (11)]. These charts require that the resistivity of the invaded zone and the diameter of invasion are known. For the laterolog 7 the computed results of the effect of invasion can be summarized by the following approximate equation:

$$Ra = \left(0.633 \log \frac{D_i}{d}\right) R_{xo} + \left(1 - 0.633 \log \frac{D_i}{d}\right) R_t \qquad (5\text{-}41)$$

This equation can also be applied with fair accuracy for the laterolog 3 and the conductivity laterolog. In this equation R_{xo} can be determined from wall resistivity logs, or estimated from porosity logs. D_i must be estimated from local experience. The effect of the mud column itself on the reading of the laterolog is almost negligible except in cases of deep caving.

Figure 5-57 is a sample log from a laterolog 7 survey. The left-hand track on this particular log contains the SP curve, although with salt muds the γ-ray curve is often logged in this position. The entire right-hand track contains the laterolog curve plotted continuously on two scales: a 0 to 40 ohm-meter scale, and a 0 to 400 ohm-meter scale. The heavy line at the extreme right of the resistivity track is the monitor curve. This curve records the effectiveness of the controller in providing bucking current to the two electrodes, A_1 and A_2. It should appear as a straight line with small excursions where there have been large and rapid changes in resistivity. A great deal of detail on the curve indicates malfunctioning of the tool.

Schlumberger has recently introduced a new focused log which is designated as the laterolog 8 or LLs. It differs principally from the laterolog 7 in the depth of horizontal penetration. It is comparable to a short normal in its depth of investigation, and it was, in fact, designed to replace the short normal in use with the induction log in the induction-electric survey. The radial investigation characteristics of this device are shown in Fig. 5-58. It can be seen that 90 percent of the signal is from within a cylinder of 90 in. diameter, or less than 4 ft from the wall of the hole. Its measurement therefore reflects primarily R_i rather

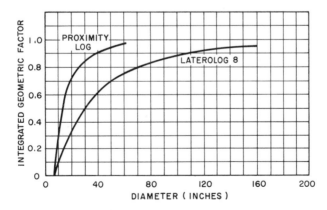

Fig. 5-58. Approximate radial investigation characteristics of the shallow laterolog (LLs) and the proximity log (PL). $d = 8$ in. (After Doll, Dumanoir, and Martin, courtesy of *Geophysics*.)

than R_t. Borehole size is not critical; calculations indicate that for borehole sizes between 6 and 12 in., the reading of the device will be within 10 percent of the formation resistivity. It also has very good vertical resolution, and if the thickness of the bed is over 5 ft, the bed thickness can generally be ignored.

The Induction Log

In 1949 a method of resistivity logging was introduced which is based on the principle of electromagnetic coupling between the logging sonde and the formations. The device was originally conceived to solve the problem of resistivity logging in oil-base muds where the ordinary methods would not work because of the lack of a conductive medium between the sonde and the formations. The effectiveness of the induction device in this service led to its adoption in 1956 for logging in fresh-water base muds also. It has now almost completely displaced electrode devices for logging except in salty muds where the laterolog and guard log are superior.

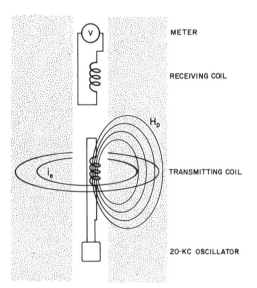

METER

RECEIVING COIL

H_p

TRANSMITTING COIL

20-KC OSCILLATOR

Fig. 5-59. Schematic representation of the principle of induction logging.

There are no electrodes used in induction logging. The sonde contains two coils of wire for energizing the formation and receiving signals from it. The transmitting coil is energized by a 20-kc oscillator, and it in turn generates an alternating electromagnetic field of this frequency which extends into the formation for a considerable distance around the tool. According to the principles outlined in Part I, an alternating field will induce a potential in any conductor cut by the field, and the direction of current flow will be at right angles to the direction of relative movement of the field and the conductor. Since the primary field produced by the transmitting coil is toroidal (doughnut-shaped), the current induced in the formation flows in a circular path around the borehole and in a plane perpendicular to the axis of the hole. In this respect the entire formation around the tool serves as a single conductor. This is illustrated in Fig. 5-59.

The eddy current set up in the formation has a magnetic field. The strength of this secondary field is proportional to the magnitude of the eddy current, which is in turn proportional to the conductivity of the formation. The receiving coil of the tool picks up the signals from both

the transmitting coil and the eddy currents. When there is no conductive medium around the tool, the voltage generated in this coil comes only from the primary field. By suitable instrumentation, the meter can be made to read zero under these conditions; then when there is a conductive medium around the tool, the reading on the meter is a direct reflection of the strength of the secondary field. Since the secondary field strength is dependent on the conductivity of the formation, the voltage induced in the receiving coil should be proportional to the conductivity. In induction logging this receiving coil voltage is displayed continuously on the log as a conductivity. As the formation resistivity is more often desired, the signal is reciprocated electronically and displayed as well in the form of a resistivity curve. A sample induction log containing both of these curves is shown in Fig. 5-3.

Not all the formation surrounding the tool contributes equally to the signal. It is usual, therefore, to divide the formation into separate "ground loops," sections of formation which are circular and concentric with the axis of the tool, and to treat the recorded signal as the sum of the contributions of these individual loops. The

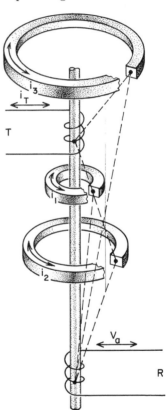

Fig. 5-60. Schematic illustration of three representative ground loops as they contribute to the induction log signal. (Duesterhoeft, Hartline, and Thomsen, courtesy of the AIME.)

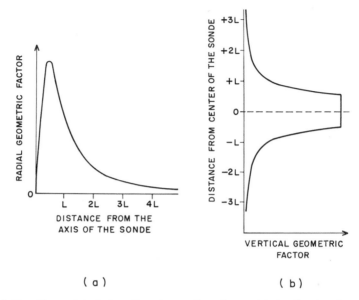

Fig. 5-61. Geometric factors for a two-coil, unfocused induction logging sonde: (a) radial and (b) vertical. (After Doll, courtesy of the AIME.)

intensity of the current in any one of the loops depends on its location with respect to the transmitting coil and on the conductivity of the formation. The contribution of a loop to the recorded signal depends also on its location relative to the receiving coil. The relative contribution of any ground loop as a result of its location with respect to the coils is called the geometric factor of that loop. Figure 5-60 shows three typical ground loops and the paths that must be taken by the primary and secondary electromagnetic waves in passing from the transmitter to the loop and then to the receiver.

In the original paper on this subject, Doll (15) reported the geometric factors for a simple two-coil sonde. These factors are presented in Fig. 5-61. The radial factor represents the contribution of a cylindrical element of formation of infinite height, unit thickness, and with a radius of l. In a formation of great thickness, this curve would represent the relative contribution of the formation at various distances from the wellbore, or more properly from the axis of the tool. The curve shows that most of the signal for a two-coil system comes from within one coil spacing L from the tool. The vertical geometric factor represents the contribution of an element of formation of unit thickness and of infinite length and width; this element is situated in a plane perpendicular to the axis of the tool. The reference point for plotting this curve is the center of the transmitter-receiver coil pair. The curve shows that almost the entire signal comes from within one coil spacing above and below the center of the sonde. Figure 5-62 shows regions of equal geometric factor with this same two-coil arrangement. The space between any two lines represents that part of the formation which is contributing one-tenth of the signal to the log. This figure really represents a combination of the two curves of Fig. 5-61.

The resistivity indicated by the induction log depends on the resistivity of the various sections of formation and on their geometric factors (also on propagation effects to be discussed later). In Fig. 5-63 a well containing mud with a resistivity of R_m penetrates a formation of resistivity R_t and forms an invaded zone of resistivity R_i; the resistivity of the adjacent formations is R_s. Because these various regions are axially symmetrical about the well, current induced in the formations by an induction logging sonde flows only in the zone in which it originates; it does not ordinarily cross from the invaded to the uninvaded zone, or from the adjacent bed to the object bed, provided that the sonde is centered in the well. The current loops are therefore flowing in parallel around the tool. For this arrangement of resistivities, the apparent resistivity recorded by the logging sonde is, by equation 5-3,

$$\frac{1}{R_a} = \frac{G_m}{R_m} + \frac{G_i}{R_i} + \frac{G_t}{R_t} + \frac{G_s}{R_s} \tag{5-42}$$

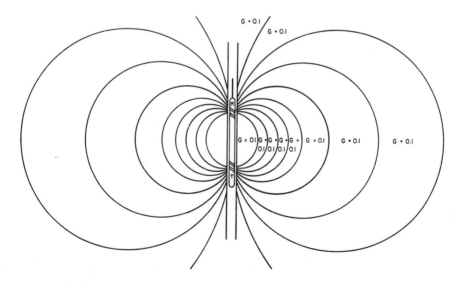

Fig. 5-62. Two-coil induction logging sonde, showing regions of equal contribution to the signal. (Doll, courtesy of the AIME.)

where the G's represent the integrated geometric factors for each region. In order for the apparent resistivity on the log to be approximately equal to the true resistivity of the formation, it is necessary to minimize the contributions of the mud column, invaded zone, and adjacent beds.

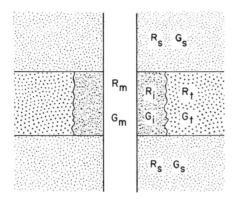

Fig. 5-63. Resistivities and geometric factors that must be considered in induction logging.

The use of a high-resistivity mud in the well reduces the magnitude of the first and second terms on the right-hand side of the equation. These two terms and the last term can also be reduced by reducing the geometric factors of these regions through the addition of auxiliary coils to the sonde. These coils are usually called "focusing coils," but their focusing action is one of providing a canceling signal, rather than

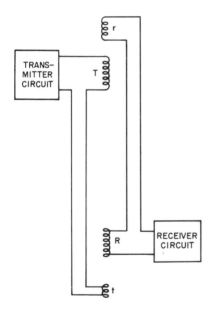

Fig. 5-64. Method of focusing the induction log through the addition of two auxiliary coils. (After Duesterhoeft, Hartline, and Thomsen, courtesy of the AIME.)

controlling the current distribution in the formation in the manner of the focusing electrodes on the laterolog.

Figure 5-64 illustrates a method of vertical focusing for an induction log. In series with the main transmitting coil T there is a second smaller coil t, and in series with the main receiving coil R there is a second smaller coil r. These auxiliary coils are both wound in the opposite sense from the main coils, and therefore any signal developed in the receiver circuit by coupling of a main coil with an auxiliary coil subtracts from the signal developed between the main coils. The signal developed between the two auxiliary coils would normally be very small because of their small size and great separation. Duesterhoeft, Hartline, and Thomsen (23) have calculated the response of such a system of coils when passing a boundary between a 50-millimho per meter (20 ohm-meters) bed and a 500-millimho per meter bed. Since the response of the instrument is the sum of the combinations of the various coil pairs, they have presented the contribution of each pair as well as the total signal. Their results are given in Fig. 5-65. In this figure the curve labeled TR represents the signal generated in the main receiving coil by coupling through the formation with the main transmitting coil, curve tR is the signal caused by coupling of the auxiliary transmitting coil and the main receiving coil, and curve Tr is the signal caused by coupling of the main transmitting coil and the auxiliary receiving coil. $Tr + tR$ represents the sum of the auxiliary signals. Since the auxiliary coils are wound in a negative sense, these signals subtract from the

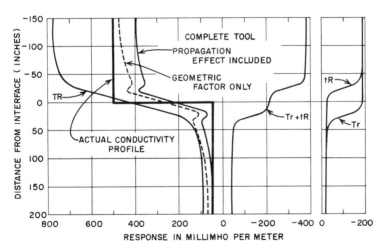

Fig. 5-65. Response of a four-coil induction sonde at the boundary between two beds with resistivities of 2 and 20 ohm-meters. (Duesterhoeft, Hartline, and Thomsen, courtesy of the AIME.)

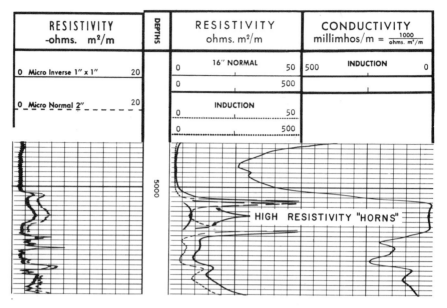

Fig. 5-66. Example of an induction log showing "horns." (Courtesy of the California Standard Co.)

TR signal, and they are therefore plotted as negative signals on the graph. The signal for the complete tool is the sum of *TR* plus *tR* and *Tr*. The reference point for the depth scale is the center of the *TR* coil pair.

The main coil pair, because of its large spacing, has a relatively large vertical and horizontal field of investigation. As the sonde pictured in Fig. 5-64 approaches the interface from the bottom, this coil pair starts to sense the change in conductivity when the reference point on the sonde is about 200 in. below the bed boundary. A long sweeping change in the signal occurs as the sonde passes from one bed to the other with the maximum rate of change taking place when the bed boundary is between the coils. The leading coil pair, *Tr*, has a smaller field of investigation, but because of its leading position, it starts to sense the more conductive bed at about the same time as the *TR* pair and starts to provide a correction signal. The maximum rate of change in signal from this auxiliary pair takes place about 25 in. before the reference point reaches the bed boundary, or 25 in. before the maximum change in the *TR* signal. For a short time, then, the *Tr* signal over-corrects the main *TR* signal, and this results in a small reversal of the curve for the complete tool just before the tool passes out of the lower bed. The *tR* coil pair, trailing the main pair, has a response to the bed boundary similar to that of the *Tr* pair, only in this case the correcting signal changes after the main signal. Again there is a slight overcorrection of the main signal, this time on the upper part of the bed boundary. The overall effect of the two auxiliary coils is to sharpen the response of the tool to the change of resistivity between the beds.

The presence of the small peaks or "horns" on the induction log when there is a sharp change in resistivity should not be misinterpreted as lithologic changes, but should be recognized merely as spurious detail that has been added by the focusing coils. Figure 5-66 shows a case where this is very pronounced. The bed from 5002 ft to 5016 ft is shown on the Microlog curves to be fairly uniform. The resistivity indicated by the 16-in. normal and the induction log at the center of the bed is about 80 ohm-meters. The induction log, however, indicates that the top of the bed has a resistivity of about 500 ohm-meters, and the bottom of the bed has a resistivity of about 150 ohm-meters. The very high resistivity indicated at the top is a combination of the effects of focusing and the thin resistive streak indicated on the microlog curves. The bottom resistivity peak results only from focusing. Notice that the horns occur about 2 ft from the bed boundary.

Figure 5-67 shows the vertical geometric factor for two Schlumberger logging sondes that are in current use. The 5FF40 is their medium depth of investigation logging tool and the 6FF40 is their deep investigation tool. Both tools have a main coil spacing of 40 in. The figure

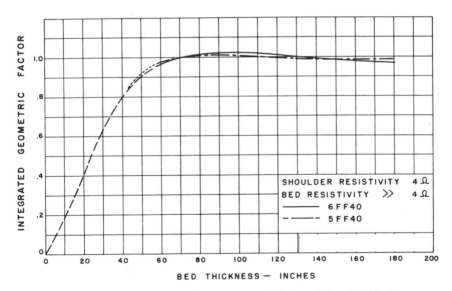

Fig. 5-67. Vertical geometric factors for the 5FF40 and the 6FF40. (Courtesy of Schlumberger Well Surveying Corporation.)

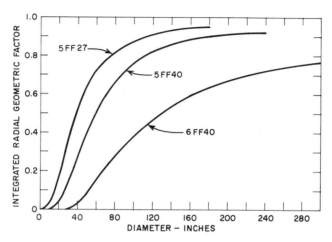

Fig. 5-68. Radial geometric factors for the 5FF27, the 5FF40, and the 6FF40. (After Doll, Dumanoir, and Martin, courtesy of *Geophysics*.)

illustrates the response of the tools to a bed of greater than 4 ohm-meters resistivity which is situated between two semi-infinite beds of 4 ohm-meters resistivity. The bed thickness is allowed to vary from zero to infinity, and the fraction of the total signal which originates from the object bed is plotted as the integrated geometric factor for the bed. As the bed thickness increases from zero to 70 in., there is a constant increase in the fraction of the signal coming from the bed. Between 70 in. and 120 to 130 in. the geometric factor exceeds unity. This anomaly is again the result of the action of the focusing coils which continue to subtract out the strong signal received from the adjacent conductive beds, thereby making the object bed appear more resistive than it actually is. When the bed is sufficiently thick, these horns would no longer affect the reading of the device (which would be taken at the bed center), but they would still appear as spurious resistive streaks on a log.

In addition to the focusing action that is included in induction logging tools to improve the vertical resolution, coils are also added in an effort to reduce the signal resulting from the mud in the borehole and from the invaded zone. The effectiveness of these additional focusing coils in accomplishing their mission can be greatly enhanced by the use of a high-resistivity mud.

Figure 5-68 shows the integrated radial geometric factor for the two Schlumberger tools mentioned in the previous paragraph, and also for the original Schlumberger tool which was designated the 5FF27. (This tool is no longer in general use.) The integrated radial geometric factor can be defined as the contribution to the total response of the tool that is received from a uniform medium enclosed within a cylinder that is coaxial with the tool as the size of the cylinder increases from zero to infinity. The figure shows that the 5FF27 receives 50 percent of its signal from within a cylinder of 40 in. diameter, and the 5FF40 receives 50 percent of its signal from within a cylinder of 60 in. diameter. The most recent tool developed by Schlumberger for induction logging, the 6FF40, receives 85 percent of its signal from outside a cylinder of 60 in. diameter; and within a cylinder of about 3 ft diameter, there is almost no geometric factor contribution to the signal.

The induction log gains its tremendous advantage over conventional logs of comparable depths of investigation because it responds only to the bed opposite the tool (as long as the bed is thicker than 5 ft), and it has a very low response to a high-resistivity invaded zone. The signal for a normal or lateral device comes from current flow in series through the various formation resistances, and it reflects the higher resistivity. The signal for the induction log comes from currents flowing in parallel through the various formation resistances, and it then tends to record the lower resistivity. It is important then that the resistivity of the invaded zone should not be too low if the induction log is to give a good value of R_t.

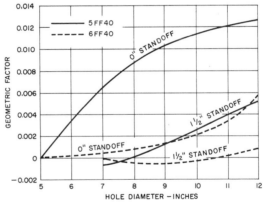

Fig. 5-69. Borehole geometric factors for the 5FF40 and the 6FF40. (Courtesy of Schlumberger Well Surveying Corporation.)

Figure 5-69 is a chart of the borehole geometric factor for the 5FF40 and for the 6FF40. Curves are plotted for zero standoff and for $1\frac{1}{2}$ in. standoff. (Standoff is the distance separating the tool from the wall of the borehole. In most cases the sonde lies against the side of the hole, i.e., zero standoff.) The hole signal for the 6FF40 for a $1\frac{1}{2}$ in. standoff can be seen to be negligible for hole sizes up to 12 in. The 6FF40 has about the same hole effect for zero standoff as the 5FF40 does with $1\frac{1}{2}$ in. standoff.

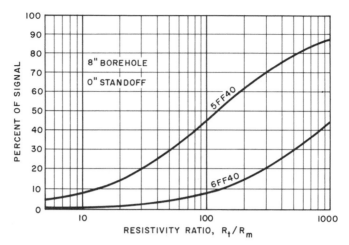

Fig. 5-70. Contribution of the borehole to the induction log signal as a function of R_t/R_m. Uninvaded beds.

The geometric factors from Fig. 5-69 were used to construct the curves of Fig. 5-70. These curves indicate the fraction of the total signal that would be received from the borehole for various ratios of R_t/R_m. The hole size is assumed to be 8 in., and the formation is uniform and uninvaded. It can be seen that when the resistivity ratio is high, the 5FF40 reading will approach a constant value that represents the borehole signal, and will not go higher than this regardless of the resistivity of the formation. The 6FF40, because of its advanced focusing action, is far superior in this respect. If the induction log is to be run in a well where there are high-resistivity formations and/or saline mud, it is desirable to make some provision to center the sonde in the hole.

An electromagnetic wave propagates through free space at the speed of light, but in a conductive medium the velocity may be reduced to less than 1 percent of this value (see equation 5-13). In a formation whose resistivity is 1 ohm-meter, the wavelength of a 20,000-cps wave is only about 75 ft. This means that there is a shift in phase of about five degrees for every foot of distance from the transmitting coil on the sonde, and the wave at a point 38 ft from the sonde is 180° out of phase with the wave at the sonde. In addition, the wave loses energy in passing through the formation because energy is required to cause the flow of the eddy currents. For a 1 ohm-meter formation, the wave loses about half of its strength for every 8 ft of travel. Both of these factors, the phase shift and the attenuation of the wave, have the effect of decreasing the signal strength in the receiving coil. An example will illustrate this point.

Consider the response of two points in the formation located equi-distant from the main coil pair as shown in Fig. 5-71. The distance from the sonde to the points is 3 ft and 5 ft respectively. The formation resistivity is 1 ohm-meter. A wave traveling from the sonde to point *a* covers a distance of 3.4 ft, and a wave traveling to *b* covers a distance of 5.3 ft. The total distance of travel of the primary and secondary magnetic waves in going from the transmitter to *a* or *b* and returning to the receiver is 6.8 ft and 10.6 ft, respectively. The wave arriving at the receiver by way of point *a* is 34° out of phase with the wave leaving the transmitter, and the wave coming from point *b* is 53° out of phase with the wave at the transmitter, or 19° out of phase with the wave from the shorter route. The waves are therefore only partially additive in causing a voltage to be generated in the receiver. In addition, the waves going by the *a* route lose 45 percent of their intensity, and the waves going by the *b* route lose 60 percent of their intensity. These figures represent the response in a 1 ohm-meter bed only. If the bed had been more conductive, the effects would have been greater, and if it were less conductive, the effects would have been less.

These propagation phenomena caused by the transfer of energy from the electromagnetic waves to the formation affect the response of an induction logging device in two ways: first, the formations distant from the tool contribute less to the signal than is indicated by geometric factor considerations only; and second, conductive beds do not contri-bute as large a signal as is indicated by consideration of the conductivity effects only, i.e., the response of the tool to conductivity is not linear nor proportional. Figure 5-72 illustrates this nonlinearity for a tool

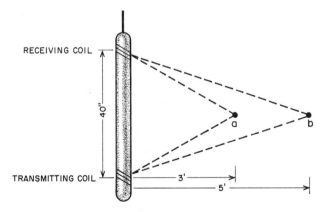

Fig. 5-71. Schematic representation of the paths traversed by primary and secondary electromagnetic waves in induction logging.

operating in a medium with a permeability of $4\pi \times 10^{-7}$ MKS at a frequency of 20,000 cps. C_a is the conductivity of the formation that would be indicated by the tool if propagation effects were neglected, and C is the true conductivity.

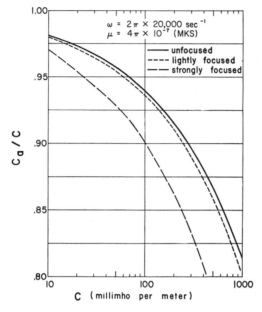

Fig. 5-72. Illustration of the nonlinear response of an induction log to changes in conductivity. (After Duesterhoeft, Hartline, and Thomsen, courtesy of the AIME.)

The combined distance and conductivity effects operate together to reduce the effect of adjacent beds on the resistivity recorded for a thin bed, particularly a thin resistive bed. This is quite strikingly illustrated by the results reported in Table 5-3. The effect can also

TABLE 5-3.   EFFECT OF PROPAGATION PHENOMENA UPON
BED THICKNESS CORRECTION

Bed Thickness, ft	Conductivity, millimhos per meter		Calculated Multiplying Factor to Obtain Thick Bed Response		Excessive Correction of Geometric Factor, percent
	Object Bed	Adjacent Bed	Based upon Geometric Factor	Based upon Propagation Effect	
33	50	500	1.54	1.03	+50
25	50	500	1.89	1.09	+75
17	50	500	6.72	1.29	400
27	500	50	1.10	0.995	+10
13	500	50	1.21	1.04	+16
7	500	50	1.48	1.21	+22

SOURCE: From Duesterhoeft, Hartline, and Thomsen (23).

be seen in the curves of Fig. 5-65, where the curve based only on geometric effects indicates the presence of other beds when the sonde is over 200 in. from the bed boundary, while including the propagation effect reduces this distance to 100 in. It can also be seen in the Schlumberger Chart B-16 (37) where this correction is referred to as "skin effect."

Wall Resistivity Logs

In the discussion of the long-spacing, deep-penetration resistivity logs, it was shown that the knowledge of the resistivity R_{xo} of the completely flushed zone is essential to the proper interpretation of the effect of invasion on those logs. It will be shown in the section on quantitative interpretation that the value of R_{xo} is also necessary in many cases if the electric log is to be used for estimating water saturation and porosity. For these reasons, tools have been developed to measure the resistivity of a small volume of the formation adjacent to the wall of the borehole. As with the long-spacing devices, some of these are focused and some are not.

Nonfocused Logs (Microlog, Contact Log, Microsurvey, Minilog). In order to limit the depth of penetration of the logging device it is necessary to use short electrode spacings. If short spacings are used, however, it is also necessary to eliminate the effect of the mud in the well, or else the log will read only the mud resistivity. This combination of requirements is effected by putting the electrodes on the face of an insulating pad and then pressing the pad tightly against the wall of the hole. One such device for doing this is the microlog, shown in Fig. 5-73. The three electrodes, A, M_1, and M_2, are small button electrodes set in the face of a fluid filled rubber pad. They are spaced 1 in. apart. The logs that are recorded are a microlateral (or microinverse), using all three electrodes with M_2 serving as the N electrode of the lateral system, and a micronormal which uses electrodes A and M_2. The two curves which are

Fig. 5-73. Microlog sonde. (Courtesy of Schlumberger Well Surveying Corp.)

recorded are referred to as the 1-in. × 1-in. microinverse and the 2-in. micronormal. The metal backup plate which presses against the opposite side of the hole serves as the B electrode.

The microinverse curve indicates the resistivity of material which is between the 1-in. and 2-in. potential surfaces. The micronormal curve indicates the resistivity of material which is outside the 2-in. potential surface. The micronormal curve, therefore, is the deeper penetration curve and is less effected by material close to the power electrode.

The readings obtained from the two microcurves are influenced by the resistivities of the mud cake, R_{mc}, the completely flushed zone, R_{xo}, the invaded zone, R_i, and even possibly the undisturbed formation, R_t. The microlateral, having less penetration, is more strongly influenced

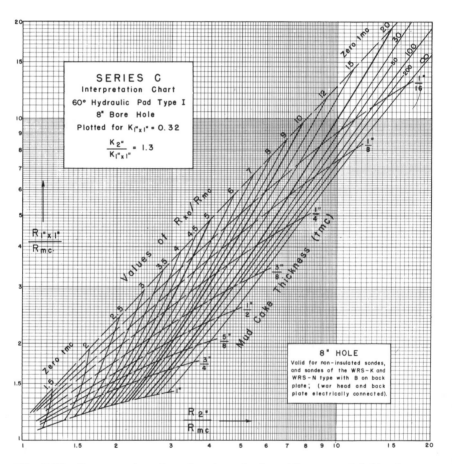

Fig. 5-74. Interpretation chart for the microlog. (Courtesy of Schlumberger Well Surveying Corporation.)

by R_{mc} than the micronormal. If the depth of invasion is greater than about 6 in., the formation beyond the flushed zone has very little effect on either curve. In the usual case, then, there will be only three parameters involved in the measurement, R_{xo}, R_{mc}, and t_{mc}. R_{mc} can usually be estimated from surface measurements. The two microcurves, therefore, give sufficient information to determine t_{mc} and R_{xo}. Interpretation is made by means of empirical departure curves such as that shown for the microlog in Fig. 5-74.

Figure 5-74 shows two things about this type of wall resistivity log. First, above a value of R_{xo}/R_{mc} of about 20, the R_{xo}/R_{mc} curves become very closely spaced. This means that the tool is losing its sensitivity to resistivity changes above this range and should not be used, at least not quantitatively. Second, as the mud cake thickness increases, the R_{xo}/R_{mc} lines again crowd together, again indicating a loss of sensitivity. In this case the device trends to read R_{mc} on both curves. Both of these limitations on the microlog result from the fact that current tends to flow preferentially in the low-resistivity mud cake rather than in the higher resistivity formation; when this occurs the determination of R_{xo} is correspondingly poor. For the microlog and similar nonfocused logs the limiting mud cake thickness is about $\frac{1}{2}$ in. and the minimum porosity of the invaded zone is about 20 percent.

The resistivity of a formation filled with mud filtrate is always higher than the resistivity of the mud cake. It might be expected, then, that $R_{2''}$ will be higher than $R_{1''\times1''}$ whenever a mud cake is present. This "positive separation" of the microlog curves may be taken, therefore, as an indication that the bed is permeable. The microlog curves of Fig. 5-75 illustrate the condition of positive separation. A word of caution is in order here. To form a mud cake, the permeability of the bed must only be greater than the permeability of the mud cake. This does not mean that it will be permeable enough to produce fluid at commercial rates.

Positive separation may occur opposite impervious beds as well if the pad is not pressed tightly against the wall of the hole. Thus, in a washed-out shale section the microinverse may read the mud resistivity while the micronormal would see some of the shale as well and would give a slightly higher reading. This false condition of positive separation can usually be recognized by comparing the resistivity readings with the mud resistivity and the resistivity measured by the short normal. In a very deep cave, of course, both microcurves would indicate the mud resistivity.

Negative separation may also occur. Figure 5-74 indicates that this

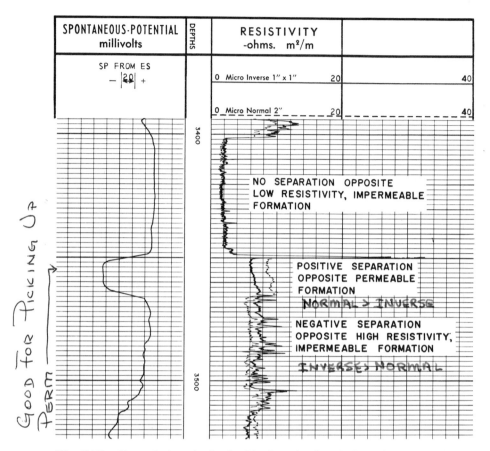

Fig. 5-75. Example log obtained with the microlog device. (Courtesy of California Standard Company.)

might be expected where there are extremely thin mud cakes, e.g., opposite shale beds, but the resistivity of shales is often so low that it is difficult to distinguish the small separations that may result. An unusual case of negative separation is encountered in the Gulf Coast area where the high vertical permeability and very saline waters cause vertical migration of the mud filtrate. This condition was illustrated in Fig. 5-24. In this case the micronormal may see beyond the invaded zone and indicate the very low resistivity of the uninvaded formation, while the microinverse reads the somewhat higher flushed zone resistivity.

Figure 5-76 summarizes the various conditions which may be found (17). In vuggy or fractured carbonate sections, where a mud cake is ordinarily not formed on the wall of the hole, porous and permeable intervals are usually indicated by the relatively low reading of both curves rather than by any condition of curve separation. A caliper log is now ordinarily run with the microlog and the presence or absence of mud cake can be substantiated from this curve.

In addition to determining R_{xo} and the presence of permeable zones, the microlog is also used to make a survey of the mud resistivity. Logging of the formations is always done on the way out of the hole. On the way in the sonde is run collapsed and both curves therefore indicate mud resistivity and allow this very important logging parameter to be measured under the actual conditions of temperature and pressure.

Because of the short spacing of the electrodes, the wall resistivity logs give an extremely detailed record of the formations. They are therefore useful as an aid to the interpretation of other logs for determining the exact location of bed boundaries and for sand counting. A modification of the microlog is also used in the dipmeter.

Focused Logs (Microlaterolog, FoRxo Log, Proximity Log). Limitations created by excessive leakage of current through the mud cake can be

MICROLOG DATA			SP	INTERPRETATION
$R_{1"x1"} > R_{lim}$				HIGHLY RESISTIVE IMPERVIOUS FORMATION
$R_{1"x1"} < R_{lim}$	$R_{2"} \ll R_{1"x1"}$			IMPERVIOUS FORMATION $R_{xo} \gg R_m$
	** $R_{2"} \simeq R_{1"x1"}$ SEPARATION SMALL OR NIL		POSITIVE	IMPERVIOUS FORMATION $R_{xo} \simeq R_m$
			NEGATIVE	PERMEABLE FORMATION * SHALLOW INVASION $R_t < R_{xo}$
	$R_{2"} > R_{1"x1"}$ LARGE POSITIVE SEPARATION			PERMEABLE FORMATION * $R_t > R_{xo}$ OR DEEP INVASION WITH $R_t < R_{xo}$
	** SPECIAL CASES : $R_{2"} \simeq R_{1"x1"} \simeq R_m$ – PROBABLE CAVED INTERNAL; $R_{2"} < R_{1"x1"}$ AND $R_{16"} \simeq R_{IND}$ PROBABLY VERY SHALLOW INVASION WITH $R_t < R_{xo}$			

* PERMEABILITY INTERPRETATION BASED ON THE INDICATED PRESENCE OF FILTER CAKE. A FILTER CAKE WILL FORM WITH GEL MUDS IF K>0.001 MD. WITH SALT MUDS THE FILTER CAKE WILL USUALLY BE TOO THIN TO INFLUENCE THE RESPONSE OF THE MICROLOG. VERY COARSE GRANULAR OR VUGGY POROSITY WILL NOT FORM A FILTER CAKE ON THE WALL OF THE BOREHOLE .

$$R_{lim} \simeq \begin{cases} 15\,R_m & \text{FOR FRESH MUD} \\ 40\,R_m & \text{FOR SALT MUD} \end{cases}$$

Fig. 5-76. Summary of rules for interpretation of the microlog. (After Doll, courtesy of the AIME.)

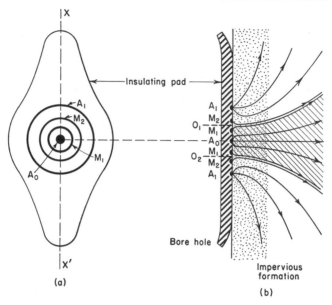

Fig. 5-77. (a) Microlaterolog device showing distribution of electrodes. (b) Vertical cross section showing the current lines issuing from the micro-laterolog. (After Doll, courtesy of the AIME.)

alleviated by using a focusing system (20) with the microlog, which is similar in principle to that used with the laterolog. The current in this case must be prevented from flowing horizontally as well as vertically, so that it is necessary to enclose the current electrode with the focusing electrode. This results in an electrode arrangement which is a series of concentric rings, as shown in Fig. 5-77. A_0 is the main current electrode, A_1 is the focusing electrode, and M_1 and M_2 are the potential electrodes. These electrodes have the same function that they do in the laterolog 7, and the tool operates the same way. In this case the current is focused into a circular tube with a gradually flaring end; the shape of the controlled current appears like the end of a trumpet, and for that reason this is sometimes called a "trumpet log."

Figure 5-78 gives the departure curves for the microlaterolog in an 8-in. hole. These curves are somewhat optimistic; however, they show that although the thickness of the mud cake is still a problem if it exceeds $\frac{3}{8}$ in., the tool is capable of successfully logging formations where the ratio of R_{xo}/R_{mc} is greater than 100. The microlaterolog can accurately log formations with a porosity of as little as 8 percent compared with a lower limit of 20 percent for the microlog. Since only one resistivity curve is recorded, it is not possible to estimate mud cake thickness from the resistivity log, and it is necessary to run a caliper log to get this parameter. The microlaterolog functions best when a salt mud is used for drilling because these muds normally have thin, low-resistivity filter cakes.

Schlumberger has recently introduced a wall resistivity device called the proximity log with an improved focusing system to overcome the deficiencies of the microlaterolog caused by the presence of thick mud cakes. The responses of these two devices are compared in Fig. 5-79. These curves indicate that the proximity log will read approximately the resistivity of the bed as long as the mud cake is thinner than $\frac{3}{4}$ in. This is true even for very high values of the ratio of R_{xo}/R_{mc}.

The radial investigation characteristic of the proximity log is greater than the microlaterolog, but it is not as penetrating as the laterolog 8. This is shown by the curves of Fig. 5-58. It can be seen from this figure that 90 percent of the geometric contribution to the signal is from within a distance of 12 in. from the wall of the hole. The vertical resolution of the proximity log is not as fine as the microlaterolog; this may or may not be considered an advantage. Vertical resolution of the

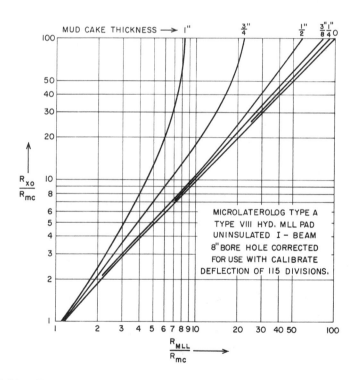

Fig. 5-78. Simplified microlaterolog departure curves. (Courtesy of Schlumberger Well Surveying Corporation.)

proximity log is about 6 in., and corrections for adjacent bed effects
are negligible if the thickness of the object bed is greater than 1 ft.

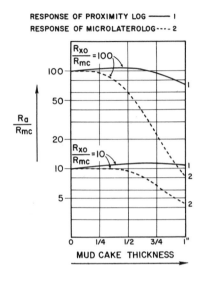

Fig. 5-79. Effect of mud cake thickness on the response of the microlaterolog and the proximity log. (Doll,
Dumanoir, and Martin, courtesy of
Geophysics.)

THE SPONTANEOUS POTENTIAL CURVE

The Source of the SP

Ever since the discovery of the existence of a natural potential in the
borehole of a rotary drilled well, there has been controversy over the
exact nature of the physical phenomena which contribute to it. In
their original reports (47, 48) on the subject, the Schlumberger brothers
and E. G. Leonardon correctly attributed the source of the potential
to both electrokinetic and electrochemical effects. It was many years
before their conclusions were accepted, however, and an even longer
period of time passed before any substantial work was done to refine
their treatment. Even now there is much to be desired in using data
from the SP curve in quantitative calculations.

The Electrochemical Potential. It was shown in Part I of this chapter
that when two solutions of different concentration are in contact, either
directly or through a charged membrane, the potential developed at
the junction can be defined by

$$E = \frac{-RT}{\mathbf{F}} \int_1^2 \sum_i \frac{t_i}{z_i} d \ln a_i \qquad (5\text{-}27)$$

and when the solutions on both sides of the junction contain only sodium chloride,

$$E = \frac{RT}{F}(2t^- - 1) \ln \frac{a_1}{a_2} \qquad (5\text{-}29)$$

The value of t^- that is used in equations 5-27 and 5-29 depends primarily on the nature of the junction.

In a well that has been drilled through salt-water bearing formations with fresh-water mud, a concentration cell is set up similar to that which led to the development of the above equations. Reference to Fig. 5-80 shows that there are two potentials developed, one through direct contact of the formation water and the mud fluid, and the other across the shale. The potential developed at the liquid boundary, where the negative transference number for a sodium chloride solution is about 0.6, is

$$E_b = 0.2 \frac{RT}{F} \ln \frac{a_w}{a_{mf}} \qquad (5\text{-}43)$$

where a_w is the activity of sodium chloride in the formation water, and a_{mf} is the activity of the sodium chloride in the mud filtrate. Since the

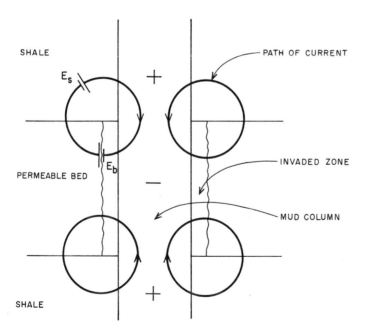

Fig. 5-80. Schematic illustration of the current flow caused by the electrochemical potential.

formation water is ordinarily more saline, and since the boundary potential is created by the higher mobility of the chloride ion relative to the sodium ion, the formation water assumes a positive charge relative to the mud filtrate. The potential developed across the shale, where the negative transference number is approximately zero, is

$$E_s = \frac{-RT}{F} \ln \frac{a_w}{a_{mf}} \tag{5-44}$$

and the formation water is negative relative to the mud filtrate. Figure 5-80 shows that these two potentials are numerically additive in a circular electrical system about the junction of the sand, shale, and borehole (more properly the invaded zone). The total electrochemical potential that is developed is therefore

$$E_c = -1.2 \frac{RT}{F} \ln \frac{a_w}{a_{mf}} \tag{5-45}$$

At 75°F this equation becomes

$$E_c \text{ (millivolts)} = -71 \log \frac{a_w}{a_{mf}} \tag{5-46}$$

The magnitude of this potential in well logging is usually less than 100 or 150 mv.

The Electrokinetic Potential.   When mud filtrate invades a porous and permeable formation, it must first flow through a negatively charged mud cake. This causes an electrokinetic, or streaming potential, with the low-pressure (formation) side of the mud cake assuming a positive charge relative to the high-pressure (borehole) side. By application of equation 5-38 to this situation, the streaming potential is

$$E_k = \frac{\zeta DPR_{mc}}{4\pi\mu} \tag{5-47}$$

This equation indicates that the streaming potential should increase in direct proportion to the pressure differential and the resistivity of the mud cake. It should also be dependent on the mud composition since ζ and D are properties of the mud system.

Experimental work that has been done supports these qualitative conclusions. In 1951 Wyllie (58) reported the results of his experiments with a wide variety of drilling muds. The average of his data is given approximately by the curve of Fig. 5-81. Hill and Anderson (32) have recently made a more extensive study of muds and have classified them

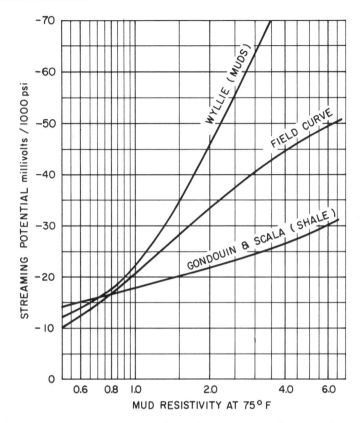

Fig. 5-81. Approximate average relationships between the streaming potential and the mud resistivity at 75°F.

according to their history of chemical treatment. Their results are shown in Fig. 5-82; these represent the best data available on the subject at the present time.

Shales are similar in composition to mud cakes, and it might be expected that streaming potentials would be observed opposite shales as well. The existence of such streaming potentials was demonstrated in the laboratory by Gondouin and Scala (27). Their results indicated that a fairly wide spread of potentials was possible, depending on the shale. The average of their data is plotted in Fig. 5-81. Comparison with the average results of Wyllie indicates that the streaming potentials for shales are probably considerably less than for muds in most cases.

Figure 5-83b illustrates the streaming potential situation which exists in the well. There is, for fresh muds, a relatively large streaming potential across the mud cake whose sign is such that it adds to the electrochemical potential. Opposite the shales there is a similar and

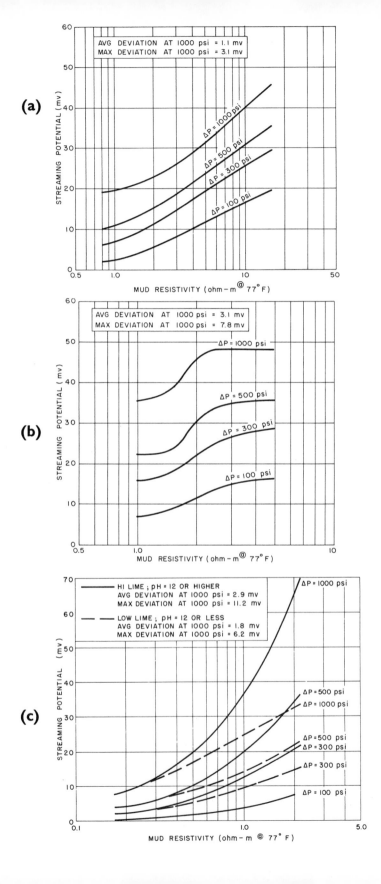

(a)

AVG DEVIATION AT 1000 psi = 1.1 mv
MAX DEVIATION AT 1000 psi = 3.1 mv

STREAMING POTENTIAL (mv)

ΔP = 1000 psi
ΔP = 500 psi
ΔP = 300 psi
ΔP = 100 psi

MUD RESISTIVITY (ohm-m @ 77°F)

(b)

AVG DEVIATION AT 1000 psi = 3.1 mv
MAX DEVIATION AT 1000 psi = 7.8 mv

STREAMING POTENTIAL (mv)

ΔP = 1000 psi
ΔP = 500 psi
ΔP = 300 psi
ΔP = 100 psi

MUD RESISTIVITY (ohm-m @ 77°F)

(c)

HI LIME ; pH = 12 OR HIGHER
AVG DEVIATION AT 1000 psi = 2.9 mv
MAX DEVIATION AT 1000 psi = 11.2 mv

LOW LIME ; pH = 12 OR LESS
AVG DEVIATION AT 1000 psi = 1.8 mv
MAX DEVIATION AT 1000 psi = 6.2 mv

STREAMING POTENTIAL (mv)

ΔP = 1000 psi
ΔP = 500 psi
ΔP = 1000 psi
ΔP = 500 psi
ΔP = 300 psi
ΔP = 300 psi
ΔP = 100 psi

MUD RESISTIVITY (ohm-m @ 77°F)

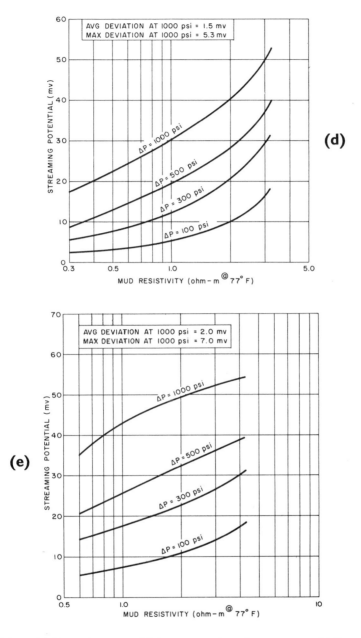

Fig. 5-82. (a) Streaming potential for untreated muds; summary. (b) Streaming potential for phosphate-treated muds; summary. (c) Streaming potential for lime-treated muds; summary. (d) Streaming potential for caustic-organic thinner muds; summary. (e) Streaming potential for soda ash-treated muds; summary. (Hill and Anderson, courtesy of the AIME.)

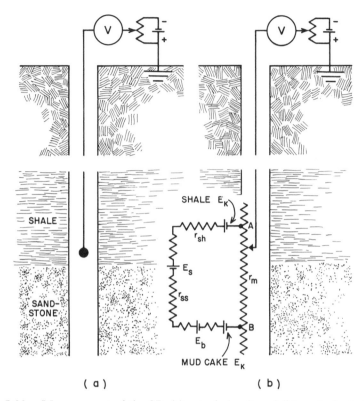

Fig. 5-83.   Measurement of the SP: (a) actual circuit and (b) equivalent electric circuit.

smaller streaming potential which opposes the electrochemical potential. There is therefore a net streaming potential equal to the difference between these two. This is additive to the electrochemical potential and makes the measured SP greater than the electrochemical component by an amount that depends on the nature and resistivity of the mud, and on the differential pressure between the mud and the formation. The field curve plotted on Fig. 5-81 has been developed from the study of the SP in a large number of wells. It seems to support this hypothesis, at least for the higher resistivity muds.

Wyllie, deWitte, and Warren (59) have argued with some merit against the conclusions of Gondouin and Scala. It is their contention that the pressure drop in the shale which causes the streaming potential extends for some distance into the shale body, and that most of the pressure drop occurs in that part of the shale which is uninvaded. Their arguments will not be developed here except to mention that they are reasonable and that they serve to point out that the contribution of the streaming potential to the SP is far from being satisfactorily explained at this time. In the absence of more exact knowledge, it is suggested that the net streaming potential be estimated from the field curve of Fig. 5-81, multiplied by a suitable correction factor developed from the data of Hill and Anderson in Fig. 5-82. Unlike the electrochemical potential, there is little or no change in the streaming potential as the temperature of the mud increases. The mud resistivity at 75°F should be used therefore for determining E_k from Fig. 5-81. When it is possible to do so without adversely affecting the mud program or the logs, the mud resistivity should be adjusted so that the streaming potential is reduced to a small value. Satisfactory electric logs can be obtained when the mud resistivity is only about four times the resistivity of the connate water. There is no advantage in logging with a very resistive mud.

Measurement of the SP

Figure 5-83a shows the circuit used in measuring the SP. The surface electrode is grounded in the mud pit or in a special mud-filled hole dug near the rig. The downhole electrode is located on the logging sonde and is a simple lead electrode approximately 2 in. in diameter and $\frac{3}{4}$ in. long. As the sonde is moved in the hole, the SP electrode measures the ohmic potential drop caused by the SP currents flowing in the mud column. The surface electrode remains at a constant potential, so the recorded voltage is the change in potential in the mud between the shales and the permeable non-shales.

Figure 5-83b shows the equivalent electric circuit involved in the measurement. The potential causing current to flow is the sum of E_s, E_b, and the net E_k. This current flows through the sandstone (resistance r_{ss}), through the shale (resistance r_{sh}), and through a portion AB of the mud column (resistance r_m). If the sum of the potentials is SSP, then

$$SSP = i(r_{ss} + r_{sh} + r_m) \qquad (5\text{-}48)$$

The potential change measured by the SP log in passing from the sandstone to the shale is

$$SP = ir_m \qquad (5\text{-}49)$$

When thick conductive beds are present, the resistance to the flow of current in the sandstone and shale is very small, and SSP = SP. In a thick bed, therefore, the measured value of the SP as read from the log is equal to the generated potential. In thin beds or highly resistive beds, the measured SP can be considerably different from the SSP.

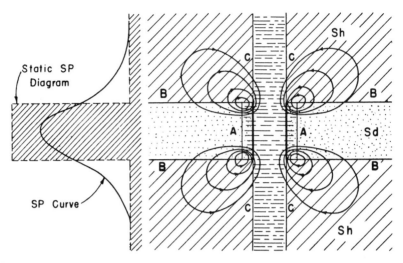

Fig. 5-84. Distribution of the SP currents in the borehole and the formations and the effect on the shape of the SP curve. (After Doll, courtesy of the AIME.)

Figure 5-84 shows the flow path of the SP current around the sandstone-shale junction. Current enters the mud column from the shale and reenters the sandstone over a considerable distance on either side of the bed boundary. The higher the formation resistivity, the more the current will spread. As the SP electrode moves from point C up toward point A, the current density in the mud increases. This means that the ohmic drop per foot of distance that the electrode travels is gradually increasing as the electrode approaches the boundary. At the boundary the current density is a maximum, and therefore the slope of the SP curve is also a maximum. As the electrode continues on to the center of the bed, the amount of current flowing in the mud gradually decreases, and the slope or the SP curve decreases until at the center of the bed the slope becomes zero and the maximum negative potential is recorded. The upper part of the curve is a mirror image of the lower part if the shales above and below the sandstone are identical, and if the sandstone contains a uniform water composition.

Since the slope of the curve is a maximum at the bed boundary, the inflection point of the SP curve may be used for determining the exact boundary location. If the shale is more resistive than the sandstone, the curve will be asymmetrical at the boundary and will tail off into the shale. If the sandstone is more resistive, the tailing off will occur primarily in the sandstone. When both beds are relatively conductive, there will be a sharp change in the SP from the one potential to the other.

In any event, the inflection point will represent the true bed boundary except in the case of very thin beds ($e < d/2$).

Actually, it is not the resistivity of the beds which controls the shape and amplitude of the SP curve, but rather the bed resistivity relative to the resistivity of the mud. This is evident from a comparison of equations 5-48 and 5-49. Figure 5-85 illustrates the effect of different values of the ratio of bed resistivity to mud resistivity on the recorded SP. For these curves it is assumed that $R_s = R_t$. The curves also show the effect of bed thickness on the amplitude and the effect of interbedding of sandstones and shales into a sandwich.

The curves of Fig. 5-86 show the magnitude of the corrections that must be made to the log value of the SP to get the SSP for thin beds. This empirical chart has been developed for hole sizes of 8 in. to 9 in. In developing the chart, corrections for average invasion conditions were incorporated. Invasion makes the effective hole size greater than the actual hole size, and since e/d is the controlling parameter, the SP corrections are greater where invasion occurs. Since invasion tends to be deeper in high-resistivity formations, and the depth of invasion

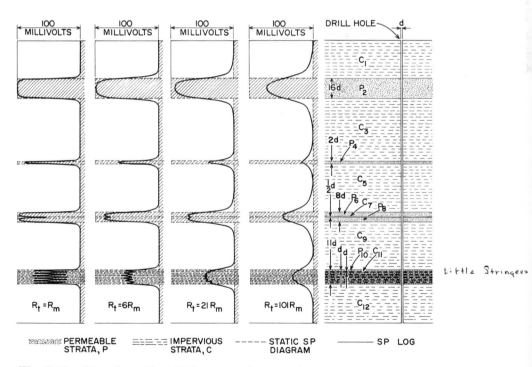

Fig. 5-85.   The effect of bed thickness and the ratio of R_t/R_m on the shape of the SP curve. (After Doll, courtesy of the AIME.)

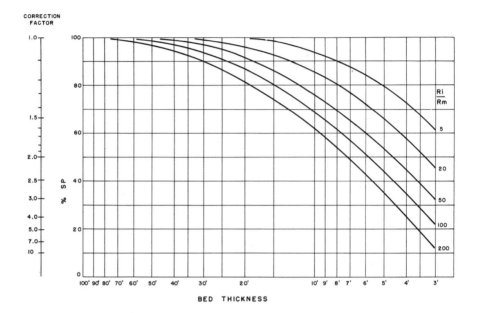

Fig. 5-86. Empirical chart for correcting the SP for bed thickness effects. (Courtesy of Schlumberger Well Surveying Corporation.)

becomes more uncertain also, the corrections necessary to the SP become subject to greater inaccuracies at high values of R_i/R_m. A thorough study of this problem has been made by Worthington and Meldau (56) through the use of an analog resistivity network. The results of their study are plotted as a series of charts of departure curves, each one for a particular relationship among the resistivity and geometry parameters which influence the magnitude of the recorded SP. Reference should be made to the original paper when the additional precision that these charts provide is desired.

Figure 5-87 shows an SP curve that has been recorded opposite a series of sandstones and shales where the formation water was saline and the mud was fairly fresh. It will be noted that over long intervals it is possible to draw a straight line through all the points of maximum positive excursion of the log. Since the previous discussion of the SP has demonstrated that the log is normally most positive opposite shales, this line is called the *shale base line*. All potential measurements are made from this line by using the scale provided at the head of the column. If the shale base line is not parallel to the grid lines of the log, the SP is measured perpendicular to the base line.

If the well passes through a series of clean sands containing the same formation water, the potential developed opposite each sand will be negative with respect to the shale base line and will be of the same magnitude. Since the shale base line is straight, it follows that a line drawn through the maximum negative points on the log will also be straight and will be parallel to the shale line. This line, of somewhat less usefulness, is called the *sand line*. Changes in the location of the sand line, relative to the shale line, indicate a change in the formation water. The failure of the potential of a particular sand in a series to reach the sand line may be the result of thin bed effects or of the presence of shaly material in the sand body.

The ideal log of Fig. 5-87 is not always realized. The SP gives a small and direct current, and as such it is prey to any stray current in the vicinity of the well. Such stray currents are particularly severe in northern Canada, where the SP may drift completely off the logging chart two or three times and total changes of the SP of as much as 1 volt may be recorded. Figure 5-88 is a log from this area. Sometimes a sudden shift in the base line will occur, as illustrated in Fig. 5-89. This is the result of a change in the nature of the shales, and as such it

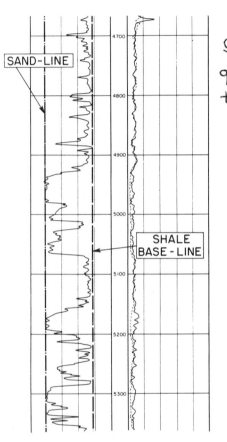

Fig. 5-87. Example of an SP curve from a sandstone-shale sequence, illustrating the sand line and the shale base line. (Courtesy of Schlumberger Well Surveying Corporation.)

serves as a good marker for correlation work. Sudden stray earth currents such as might be created by an electric railway, a power transmission line, or other electric power equipment also cause rapid changes of the SP. If difficulty of this type is experienced in an area, the stability of the SP system should be checked before logging by stopping the sonde at some point in the borehole and observing the galvanometer spot. If the spot fluctuates, it means that a valid log cannot be obtained. In areas where this difficulty is frequently encountered, it is possible to substitute a long electrode (about 100 ft) in the hole for the surface electrode. This downhole reference electrode is located at a distance of 100 or 200 ft above the sonde. The log that is recorded this way may

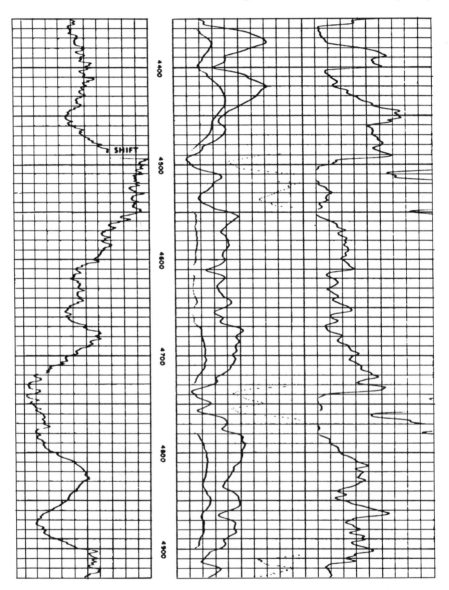

Fig. 5-88. Example of a wandering SP curve caused by stray earth currents. (Courtesy of Sinclair Canada Oil Company.)

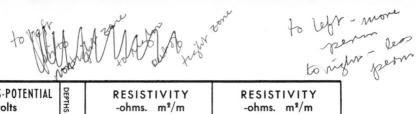

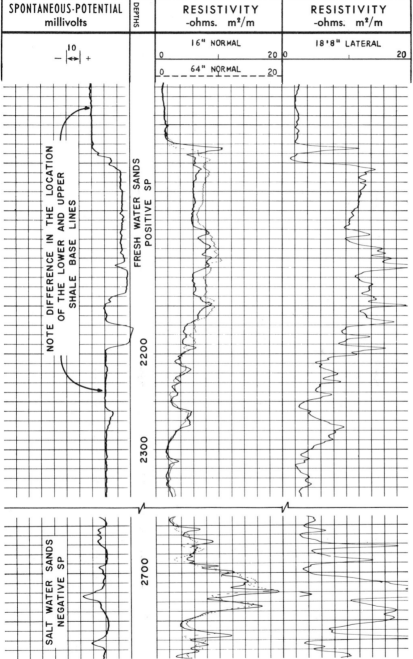

Fig. 5-89. Example of a shift in the shale base line caused by a change from a Cretaceous to a Jurassic shale. (Courtesy of the California Standard Co.)

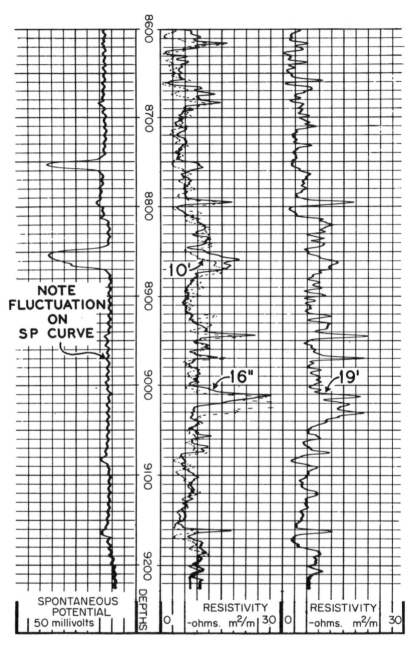

Fig. 5-90. Example of the effect of a magnetized cable drum on the SP curve. (From *Subsurface Formation Evaluation Methods* by John Walstrom. Copyright 1955 by Standard Oil Company of California. All rights reserved under the Pan-American Copyright Convention. Reproduced by courtesy of the Copyright Owner.)

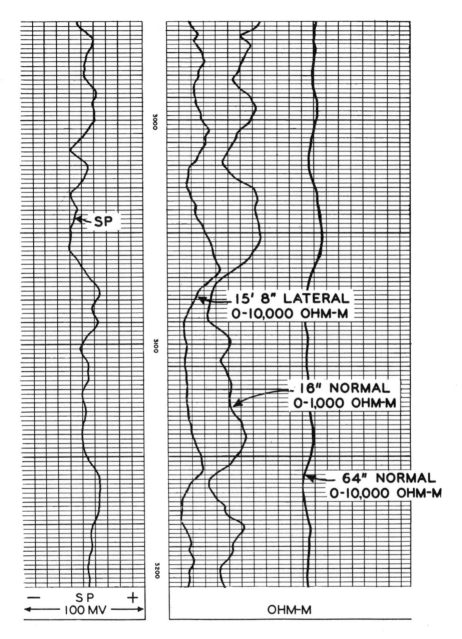

Fig. 5-91. Example of SP curve in dense, highly resistive rocks. (From *Subsurface Formation Evaluation Methods* by John Walstrom. Copyright 1955 by Standard Oil Company of California. All rights reserved under the Pan-American Copyright Convention. Reproduced by courtesy of the Copyright Owner.)

look somewhat different from the ordinary log because the reference electrode is not at a constant potential.

Other difficulties may also arise in recording the SP which are not experienced with resistivity logs. Inherent in the measurement of the SP is the potential which exists between the electrodes and the mud. Ordinarily, the same potential is created at the surface electrode and the downhole electrode, and the electrode potentials cancel. It is possible, however, that the sonde electrode may be scratched during the logging operation, thereby exposing a fresh metal surface that has a different potential from the aged surface. The surface and sonde electrodes are no longer in equilibrium, and a net potential is generated which is recorded on the log. As the scratched surface ages, this potential will gradually return to zero, and the log base line will drift back to a stable position.

Figure 5-90 shows another SP logging anomaly. This one is caused by a magnetized cable drum. As the logging cable is wound on the drum, it cuts the magnetic field and a small potential is induced. Each small fluctuation on the curve corresponds to one rotation of the drum, so the source of the extraneous potential is very easy to recognize. A similar log results if the collector rings on the drum are dirty or corroded.

In regions where salty drilling fluids are used, or where the rocks have a very high resistivity, the SP will have a wandering and indefinite appearance (see Fig. 5-91). This type of difficulty also arises occasionally when lime muds have been used. In this situation, the SP is virtually useless, whether for correlation purposes, locating bed boundaries, defining lithology, or quantitative estimations of water resistivity.

SUMMARY OF USES OF ELECTRIC LOGGING DEVICES

Determination of the Resistivity of the Completely Flushed Zone

Knowledge of the resistivity R_{xo} can be extremely useful in both qualitative and quantitative log interpretation. If the resistivity of the formation is not too high, $R_{xo}/R_{mc} < 20$, and the mud cake is less than $\frac{1}{2}$ in., a good estimate (within ± 10 percent) may be made from the microlog or contact log curves. The necessity for having a thin mud cake means that logging should be done soon after drilling is suspended. If the hole size is to be reduced, the wall resistivity log should be run first, since the smaller bit will no longer scrape the mud cake from the walls of the larger size hole during round trips.

If the resistivity of the formation is higher than the limit set for the microlog, then the microlaterolog or FoRxo log may be run to get R_{xo}. These logs work best if the thickness of the mud cake is less than $\frac{3}{8}$ in., and they are most widely used with salt muds for this reason. The depth of invasion should be greater than 6 in. or the device may be unduly influenced by the formation beyond the completely flushed zone. Since these are single curve logs, the thickness of the mud cake must be determined with a hole caliper log.

Where there is a thick mud cake, the proximity log should be used. The depth of investigation of this device is much greater than the other wall resistivity logs, however, so its reading may well be influenced by the formation beyond the R_{xo} zone. The reading of the proximity log is not considered equal to R_{xo}, but if other information is available, R_{xo} may be determined.

Other methods of determining R_{xo} with radioactivity and acoustic logs will be discussed in the following chapters.

Determination of the True Resistivity, R_t

If the drilling fluid is very conductive, the laterolog or guard log should be used. These devices can successfully log beds that are even less than 1 ft thick. Correction for the presence of the invaded zone may be made by means of equation 5-41, provided that R_{xo} has been measured and D_i can be estimated from local experience.

In all other cases the use of the induction log is recommended. This device is also focused, and so it can log beds as thin as 6 ft with accuracy. The induction log functions best if it is centered in the borehole and if the resistivity of the mud is sufficiently high so that R_{xo} is equal to or greater than R_t. When the invasion diameter is less than 8 ft, the deep induction log (6FF40) will read $1.25R_t \pm 20$ percent. When the invasion diameter is unknown, it may be determined by using other shallower penetration logs in combination with the 6FF40. The number of other logs that is necessary depends on the complexity of the problem.

Figure 5-92 gives the departure curves for the simplest case of invasion. Here it is assumed that the completely flushed zone extends out to the uncontaminated zone and then no transition zone exists between the two. Under the circumstances three resistivities are required: the deep induction log, ILd, a shorter spacing log which is primarily responsive to the invaded zone resistivity, i.e., LLs or the 16 in. normal, and a wall resistivity log to determine R_{xo}. In the example illustrated on the chart of Fig. 5-92 the ratio of R_{xo}/R_{LLs} is 1.35, and the ratio of R_{LLs}/R_{ILd} is 7.6. These determine the point M where the ratio of R_{xo}/R_t is 11.5 and

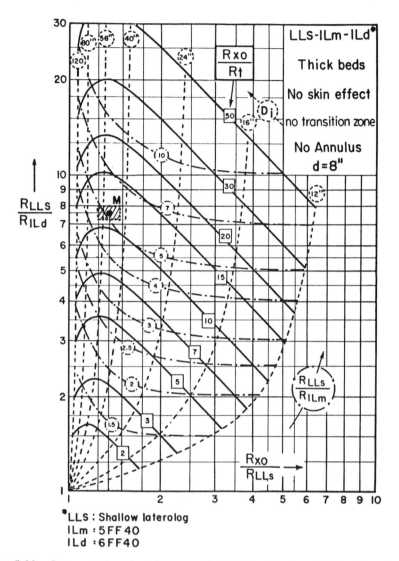

Fig. 5-92. Interpretation chart for use with the induction log, shallow laterolog, and microlog. No. transition zone, no annulus. (Doll, Dumanoir, and Martin, courtesy of *Geophysics*.)

D_i is 50 in. Since R_{xo} is known, R_t may be determined. The shaded area around point M indicates the effect of an uncertainty of ± 5 percent in the values of the ordinate and abscissa. This chart could also be used with the 5FF40 (ILm) instead of the ILd.

Figure 5-93 is a similar chart for the same invasion conditions, only this one is designed for use with the proximity log rather than an R_{xo}

device. This chart also may be used with either the ILd or the ILm. It will be observed that the charts of Figs. 5-92 and 5-93 are very much alike if the diameter of invasion is greater than 30 in. ($L_i = 11$ in.). When the diameter of invasion is less than this, the deeper penetration of the proximity log causes it to be influenced by the R_t zone. Its reading then approaches that of the LLs, i.e., R_{PL}/R_{LLs} approaches 1.0, and the sensitivity of three distinct resistivity measurements is lost.

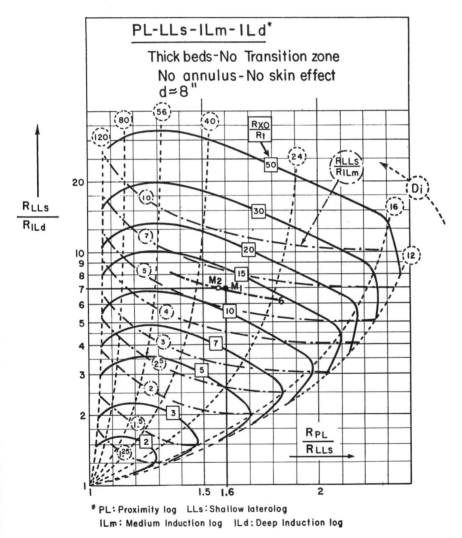

* PL: Proximity log   LLs: Shallow laterolog
ILm: Medium Induction log   ILd: Deep Induction log

Fig. 5-93. Interpretation chart for use with the induction log, shallow laterolog, and proximity log. No transition zone, no annulus. (Doll, Dumanoir, and Martin, courtesy of *Geophysics*.)

A similar effect may be noted on both figures when invasion is very deep and ILd reading approaches the LLs reading.

In the example illustrated on the chart of Fig. 5-93, four resistivity measurements were available. The fourth measurement provides a check on the solution. Point M_1 was determined by plotting the ratio R_{PL}/R_{LLs} as the abscissa and the ratio R_{LLs}/R_{ILd} as the ordinate. Point M_2 (open circle) was plotted by using the ratio R_{LLs}/R_{ILm} (the concave upward dot-dash lines) and the same ordinate as before. Since the points M_1 and M_2 do not coincide, it indicates that the model selected to represent the invasion conditions is incorrect, and a different chart should be used. When the point determined by the use of the LLs, ILm, and ILd (M_2) lies to the left of the point determined by the LLs, PL, and ILd (M_1), it indicates that the correct model should allow for a transition zone between R_{xo} and R_t as illustrated in Fig. 5-22. If the point M_2 lies to the right of point M_1 and the ratio R_{xo}/R_t is small, it indicates that the correct model should allow for the presence of annulus as illustrated in Fig. 5-23. Two departure curve charts which include the annulus effect are shown in Fig. 5-94.

The final value of R_{xo}/R_t that is selected from the appropriate departure curve chart may be checked against the SP by using the relationship of equation 5-74. The limitations of the SP in this approach should be remembered.

Only a limited number of these charts of departure curves are available at present, but additional charts to cover most practical problems are being developed. In addition, great effort is being made to design combination tools such that several devices can record simultaneously, and the number of necessary logging runs can be reduced. The combination of the microlog, microcaliper log, and proximity log is now available, and the combination of the SP, short laterolog (LLs) and deep induction log is being field tested. The final aim is to include the sonic log and the medium induction log also on these two logging runs (22).

Although the newer logs are better suited to the accurate determination of resistivity, the standard electrode arrangements still find some use, and are frequently encountered in review work. Figure 5-95 summarizes the rules for using the standard logs for determination of R_t. These rules are applicable for those conditions where a bed of a given thickness and apparent resistivity is located between two fairly thick uniform beds. In the low-resistivity range, $R_{16''}/R_m < 10$, the rules of part A are applicable. Formations having a resistivity in this range usually have fairly shallow invasion and the 64-in. normal usually provides

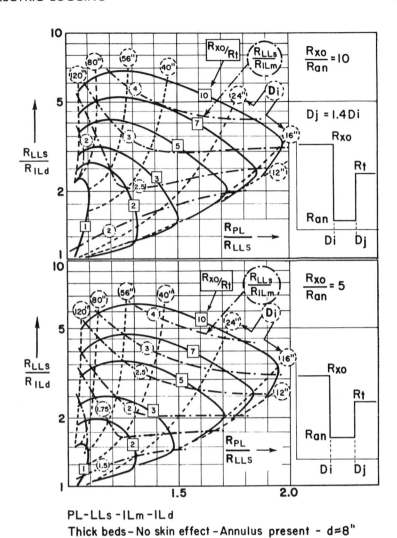

PL-LLs -ILm -ILd
Thick beds – No skin effect – Annulus present - d≠8"

Fig. 5-94. Interpretation chart for use with the induction log, shallow laterolog, and proximity log. Annulus present. (Doll, Dumanoir, and Martin, courtesy of *Geophysics*.)

sufficient penetration to get beyond the invaded zone. In the medium resistivity range, $10 < R_{16''}/R_m < 50$, the use of the long lateral becomes more important, either to confirm the reading of the long normal or to find R_t. The rules for using the lateral, shown under part B, must be observed. In the high-resistivity range, $R_{16''}/R_m > 50$, the 64-in. normal is greatly affected by invasion, and the long lateral must be used for determining R_t. The long lateral readings in this case must

R_t ESTIMATION FROM ELECTRICAL LOGS

BED THICKNESS (e)	QUALIFICATIONS	DEVICE	RESPONSE
A. IN LOW RESISTIVITY, WHEN $R_{16}"/R_m < 10$ (INVASION UP TO 2d)			
$e > 20'$ $(>4\,AM')$		Long Normal	$R_{64}" = R_t$
$e \simeq 15'$ $(\quad 3\,AM')$	$R_m \simeq R_s$ $R_{64}"/R_s \geq 2.5$	Long Normal	$R_{64}" = 2/3\ R_t$
$e \simeq 15'$ $(\quad 3\,AM')$	$R_m \simeq R_s$ $R_{64}"/R_s \leq 1.5$	Long Normal	$R_{64}" = R_t$
$e \simeq 10'$ $(\quad 2\,AM')$	$R_m \simeq R_s$ $R_{64}"/R_s \geq 2.5$	Long Normal	$R_{64}" = 1/2\ R_t$
$e \simeq 10'$ $(\quad 2\,AM')$	$R_m \simeq R_s$ $R_{64}"/R_s = 1.5$	Long Normal	$R_{64}" = 2/3\ R_t$
$5' < e < 10'$	When oil bearing and SP is $-50 - 80$ MV	Short Normal	$R_{16}" \simeq R_t$
$5' < e < 10'$	Surrounding beds homogeneous	Lateral in resistive bed	$R_t \lesssim R_{Max} \times R_s/R_{Min}$
Thin beds (in general)	Surrounding beds homogeneous	Lateral in conductive bed	$R_{19}" \simeq R_t$
$e > 3'$		Induction	$R_{IND} \simeq R_t$

B. RULES FOR USING LATERAL (AO = 18'8")

$e > 40'\ (>2.0\ AO)$ Use Mid-point Method

$e \simeq 28'\ (=1.5\ AO)$ Use 2/3 Rule

$e \simeq 24'\ (=1.3\ AO)$ Use R_{Max}

$5' < e < 10'$ Resistive bed and surrounding beds homogeneous $R_t \lesssim R_{Max} \times R_s/R_{Min}$

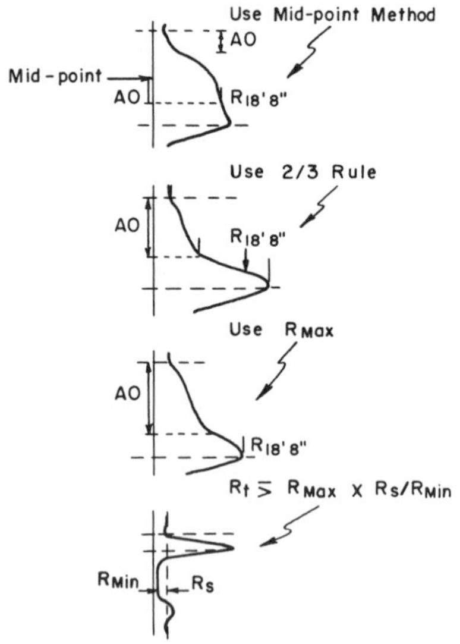

(When $R_{16}"/R_m > 50$, these values must then be corrected for the bore hole.)

Fig. 5-95. Rules for determining R_t using conventional electric logs. (Courtesy of Schlumberger Well Surveying Corporation.)

be corrected for the presence of the wellbore and the invaded zone. In some formations the depth of invasion will be so great that R_t cannot be found by any device. When the bed in question is one of a series of thin interbedded sands and shales, the rules given here do not apply. In such a case, it is necessary to use the book of analysis charts published by Hubert Guyod and John Pranglin (29). This book, which includes about 200 pages of interpretation charts, is the most complete and authoritative source of information on the determination of the true resistivity from electric log data. The charts contained in the book are the product of several years of work with a resistivity analog computer.

Determination of Lithology

The SP curve is the primary method for distinguishing between shales and permeable non-shales. The microlog can also be used for this purpose, and is particularly helpful when used in conjunction with the SP curve for detailed examination.

Determination of the Resistivity of the Formation Water

The SP curve may be used under favorable circumstances for the determination of R_w. The details of this calculation, as well as the calculation of water saturation, porosity, and permeability from the resistivity curves, are outlined in Part III of this chapter.

Correlation of Structure

Any of the electric logs may be used for this purpose, provided that they show sufficient character. In general, the long spacing and deep penetration curves and the SP are most useful in long-range correlation. The short-spacing resistivity logs and the wall resistivity logs are best for detailed correlation within a field.

Location of Bed Boundaries

The SP curve is the best method for locating the boundary between a shale and a permeable non-shale, particularly if it is supported by a wall resistivity log. When the SP does not have sufficient character, a resistivity log may be used, provided that the proper allowance is made for the effect of spacing. In oil-base muds it is necessary to depend on the induction log (the gamma-ray log and the neutron log, discussed in another chapter are also used in favorable circumstances).

Sand Counting

The determination of the number of feet of productive sandstone within a sand-shale interval is called sand counting. The primary purpose of sand counting is the estimation of the total pore volume within a reservoir, and this fact should be remembered in making a count; the basis for summing the effective feet of sand should be the same as the basis for finding the porosity.

When there are clean breaks between the sandstone and shale streaks, the points of inflection on the SP curve may be used to locate the sandstones, and the sum of these is the net sandstone thickness. The porosity that is used with this net thickness to determine the reservoir volume is the porosity of a sandstone streak. Microlog curves are very helpful in making this type of a count.

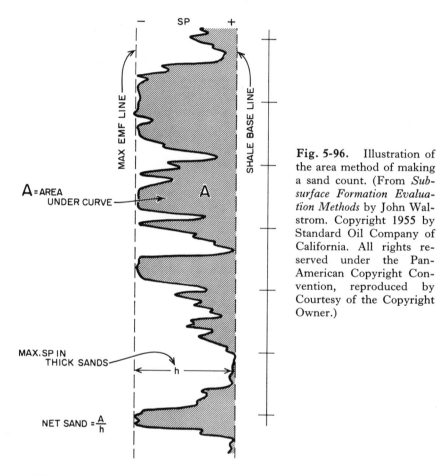

Fig. 5-96. Illustration of the area method of making a sand count. (From *Subsurface Formation Evaluation Methods* by John Walstrom. Copyright 1955 by Standard Oil Company of California. All rights reserved under the Pan-American Copyright Convention, reproduced by Courtesy of the Copyright Owner.)

When the shale and sandstone grade into each other and there are shaly sandstones present, the area method (14) is simpler and probably more accurate. This method is illustrated in Fig. 5-96. The total area between the SP curve and the shale base line is determined with a planimeter, and this is then divided by the maximum SP opposite a thick sandstone; the quotient is the net thickness. The porosity that is used in this case is the porosity at the point of the maximum SP.

This method has the limitation that the resistivity of the invaded zone must be equal to the resistivity of adjacent clean shales. If the shales are more resistive than the sandstones, the result is an upper limit of the net sand thickness. When the sandstones are more resistive than the shales (the usual case for productive intervals), the result represents a lower limit of the net sand thickness.

Part III. QUANTITATIVE INTERPRETATION OF ELECTRIC LOG DATA

Up to this point we have considered the measurements that are made by the various electrical devices. The purpose of this section is to interpret these measurements in terms of the properties of the rocks and the rock fluids. We shall begin with a study of geologic sections composed of clean sandstones (i.e., containing no disseminated conductive material such as shale) and shales. These form the simplest case and the quantitative interpretation is direct and quite good. The clean sand ideas will then be extended to the realm of shaly sandstones where the results may be anywhere from good to poor, depending on the amount of shaly material in the sandstone. Finally, we shall consider the carbonate rocks which probably present the most challenging condition. It is important that the distinction between these three categories be made in log interpretation, for the interpretation depends heavily on the nature of the formations.

CLEAN SANDSTONES AND SHALES

Empirical Relationships Between Resistivity, Porosity, and Water Saturation

The matrix material of a sandstone has an extremely high electrical resistivity, and is classified as an insulator. It follows, therefore, that any electric current passing through a formation must be conducted solely by the fluids that are contained within the pore spaces, and more particularly by the formation water, since petroleum and natural gas are also members of the insulator class.

Consider now a sandstone block as shown in Fig. 5-97a. The resistivity of the block is R_0, and the resistivity of the water in the block is R_w. This block has a porosity of ϕ, and it is 100 percent saturated with water. The length of the block is L and the cross-sectional area is A_c. Electric current is introduced into the left face of the block and flows out of the right face as shown. Now since the only conducting medium in this block is water, it is possible to draw an equivalent block of water, as shown in Fig. 5-97b, which has the same resistance as the sandstone.

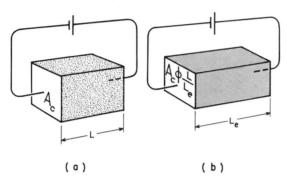

Fig. 5-97. Models illustrating the resistivity and equivalent resistivity of a sandstone block.

(a)   (b)

Current flowing through a sandstone takes a tortuous path, so the length L_e of the equivalent block is somewhat greater than the actual length L. The total amount of water in the sandstone is $\phi A_c L$. As this amount must also be in the equivalent block, its cross-sectional area is $\phi A_c L/L_e$. By equation 5-2, the resistance of the sandstone is

$$r_0 = R_0 \frac{L}{A_c} \tag{5-50}$$

and the resistance of the equivalent block of water is

$$r_w = R_w \frac{L_e^2}{L} \frac{1}{\phi A_c} \tag{5-51}$$

Since these resistances are equal,

$$R_0 = \left(\frac{L_e}{L}\right)^2 \frac{1}{\phi} R_w \tag{5-52}$$

Equation 5-52 indicates that the resistivity of a sandstone block filled with water should be directly proportional to the resistivity of the water contained within the block. The constant of proportionality depends only on the tortuosity $(L_e/L)^2$ and the porosity ϕ of the rock, and is independent of the water in the pore space.

In an experimental investigation of a large number of water-saturated clean sandstones (see Fig. 5-98), Archie (1) found that the resistivities of the sandstone and the water could be related by the equation

$$R_0 = FR_w \tag{5-53}$$

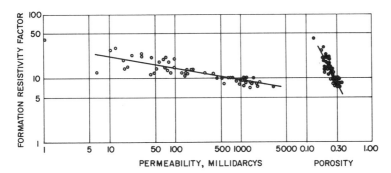

Fig. 5-98. Empirical correlations of formation factor with porosity and permeability. (Archie, courtesy of the AIME.)

where F is a constant for a particular sandstone sample. This constant is called the *formation resistivity factor*. Further investigation by Archie established that F is a function of both the porosity and permeability of the sample, as might be expected from equation 5-52. The rather slight dependence on permeability, however, led him to suggest that it would be reasonably accurate to express the relationship between F and the rock properties by

$$F = \phi^{-m} \tag{5-54}$$

The exponent m, which is called the cementation factor, has been found (61) to lie within the limits of 1.3 to 2.6. A particular value of m depends on the degree of consolidation of the formation. This is shown graphically in Fig. 5-99.

When the value of m is unknown for a particular sandstone, it may be estimated from the degree of cementation, or the Humble Oil Company formula (55) may be used.

$$F = 0.62\phi^{-2.15} \tag{5-55}$$

This equation was developed through the study of a large number of sandstone samples. It has the effect of approximating the Archie equation with $m = 1.5$ for high-porosity (usually unconsolidated) sandstones and approximating $m = 2$ for low-porosity (usually well-consolidated) sandstones. This equation has received wide acceptance among logging service companies in the development of their interpretation charts.

In addition to his work with the formation factor, Archie also examined the work of other investigators (35, 40) who had made measurements of the electrical resistivity of partially saturated sandstones. He concluded

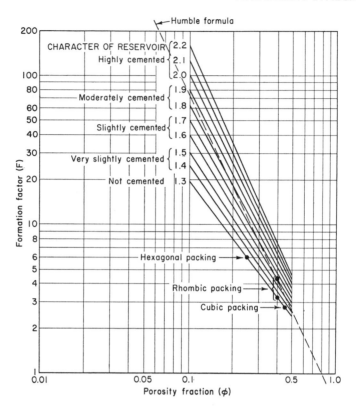

Fig. 5-99. Formation factor versus formation porosity for the Archie equation and the Humble equation. (Reproduced by permission from *Oil Reservoir Engineering*, by Sylvain J. Pirson. Copyright 1958 by McGraw-Hill Book Company, Inc.)

that their data could be expressed by a simple power relationship between the saturation and the ratio of the resistivities of the saturated and partially saturated sandstones:

$$\frac{R_t}{R_0} = I = S_w^{-n} \tag{5-56}$$

where I is known as the resistivity index, and n is the saturation exponent. The value of n lies between 1.5 and 3.0, and is more generally about 1.8 or 2.0. When the proper value of n is unknown, it is customary to choose a value of 2, simply for convenience.

Equations 5-53, 5-54 (or 5-55), and 5-56 are the three basic equations of electric logging, and form the foundation of all electric log methods and interpretation. It should be remembered in using them, or in using techniques based on them, that they are clean sand equations. They may or may not apply to shaly sandstones or carbonates. Also, while the use of the values of $m = 2$ or $n = 2$ is quite common, a fairly wide range of values is possible. When extended use of the electric log in an area warrants it, more exact values should be determined for the particular formations by means of laboratory measurements on core samples.

When reliable data are available, these equations can be used to give fairly good estimates of water saturation and porosity. F can be determined from the microlog using the relation

$$R_{xo} = FR_{mf}S_{xo}^{-n} \tag{5-57}$$

The porosity may be estimated from this value by means of equation 5-54 or 5-55. F from equation 5-57 can also be combined with R_w to form R_0. This value of R_0, and R_t as determined from a deep penetration resistivity curve, can then be used to estimate water saturation.

Permeability Determination

Another factor that is of importance in determining the commercial significance of a hydrocarbon accumulation is the permeability of the rock. Two methods based on electric logging have been developed for estimating this property, but unfortunately neither of them will give a reliable value. Both methods depend on approximate empirical relations between permeability and water saturation.

In the formation of an oil reservoir, the water which originally saturated the porous rock is gradually displaced from the trap by the upward migration of oil. This displacement process continues until the saturation of the oil becomes so high that the relative permeability of the rock to water becomes zero. (See Fig. 3-8.) At this time no more water can be removed from the rock by simple displacement processes, and an irreducible water saturation, S_{wi}, is reached. Thus, all hydrocarbon reservoirs contain some water saturation. The water saturation at which this irreducible condition occurs depends on the nature of the rock matrix and principally on the size of the sand grains of which it is composed. Smaller grains have a greater surface area per unit volume, and if the rock is water wet, the smaller grained rocks will retain more irreducible water than the large ones. Small-grained rocks also are low-permeability rocks.

It has also been known for many years that a rough correlation existed between porosity and permeability; that is, if two rocks are composed of the same size grains, the one that is more highly cemented will have the lower porosity and also the lower permeability. It might be expected, then, that the permeability of a sandstone could be expressed in terms of the irreducible water saturation, which is a measure of grain size, and the porosity, which reflects the degree of cementation. Schlumberger (37) has developed an empirical equation from field studies of porosity, permeability, and irreducible water saturation which relates these three variables:

$$K^{1/2} = 250 \frac{\phi^3}{S_{wi}} \tag{5-58}$$

The weakness of this equation arises from the fact that the permeability is dependent on the sixth power of the porosity and the second power of the water saturation. If the porosity and water saturation are determined from log data, they almost certainly will be in error by a small amount. These errors are then raised to the square and sixth powers in forming the permeability. For example, suppose the porosity of a formation is 0.2 and the irreducible water saturation is 0.3. The permeability calculated from equation 5-58 would be 44.4 md. Now suppose that the porosity and water saturation estimated from the log were 0.15 and 0.35 respectively. The estimated permeability would be 5.8 md. Thus for errors of about 25 percent in ϕ and S_{wi}, an error of an order of magnitude can be made in K. This is assuming, of course, that the empirical equation 5-58 is applicable to this particular case. This example is not meant to imply that this equation should not be used, but only that the result obtained should not be considered as more than an order of magnitude figure.

Tixier (50) has developed a method of estimating permeability which is based on the presence of a transition saturation zone in the well, (see Fig. 5-100), where the water saturation varies from the irreducible saturation at the top to 100 percent water saturation at the bottom. The length of the transition zone depends on the difference in the density of the oil and water phases and on the capillary pressure characteristics of the sand body. Since capillary pressure is related to permeability (see page 44), the rate of change of saturation through the transition zone can be used for estimating permeability. These concepts form the basis of the empirical equation presented by Tixier:

$$\left(\frac{K}{20}\right)^{1/2} = \frac{2.3}{R_0(\Delta\text{sp.gr.})} \cdot \frac{\Delta R}{\Delta h} \tag{5-59}$$

where $\Delta R/\Delta h$ is the resistivity gradient in ohm-meters per foot of depth as determined from the electric log, and $(\Delta\text{sp.gr.})$ is the difference in specific gravity between the oil and water phases. This equation does not have the apparent shortcomings of equation 5-58, and it is probably superior for estimating permeability. There are, however, three empirical relationships involved in the development of the equation, and it should therefore be used with some caution. One of these relationships is the Archie equation (5-56), so the method is necessarily limited to clean sandstones.

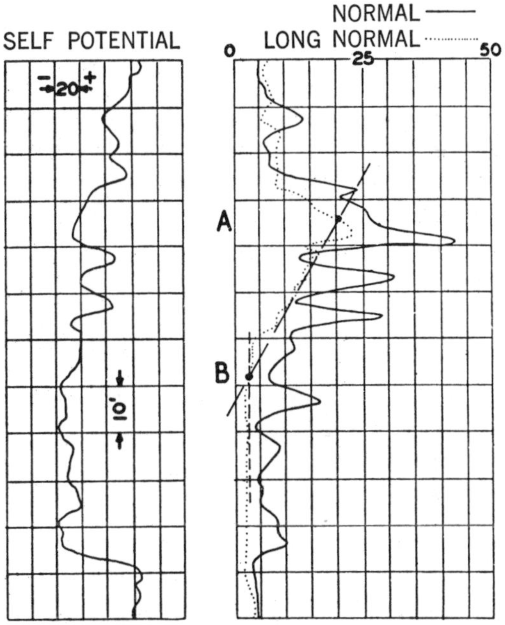

Fig. 5-100. Example of an electrical resistivity log showing a transition zone. (Tixier, courtesy of the *Oil and Gas Journal*.)

Determination of R_w from the SP Curve

It has been shown previously that the generated potential (SSP) which causes the flow of natural currents in the borehole is composed of the electrokinetic potential, E_k, and the electrochemical potential, E_c. If the SSP is obtained from the log opposite a clean sandstone, and the streaming potential can be estimated, the electrochemical potential may be obtained from the relation

$$E_c = SSP - E_k \qquad (5-60)$$

According to equation 5-46, the electrochemical potential depends on the activity of the ions in the mud filtrate and in the formation water. Since a sample of mud filtrate can be obtained at the surface, its activity may be measured. It is possible, therefore, to estimate the activity of the formation water, and from the activity to determine the resistivity.

Equation 5-46 is strictly applicable only to sodium chloride solutions. When there are other ions present in the mud filtrate or the formation water, a correction must be made for these ions according to the methods outlined in Part I. Equation 5-31 presented there is applicable only to the shale potential, but it may be extended with small error to include the total potential when put into the form of equation 5-45.

$$E_c = -1.2 \frac{RT}{F} \ln \frac{(a_{Na} + \sqrt{a_{Ca}} + a_{Mg})_w}{(a_{Na} + \sqrt{a_{Ca}} + a_{Mg})_{mf}} \qquad (5\text{-}61)$$

If the composition is known, the necessary activities can be obtained from Figs. 5-17 and 5-18. Usually, however, these are unknown quantities even for the mud, and recourse must be made to an empirical correlation chart developed from the study of logging data. For this purpose equivalent resistivity R_{we} is defined

$$R_{we} = \frac{0.073}{a_{Na} + \sqrt{a_{Ca}} + a_{Mg}} \qquad (5\text{-}62)$$

Equation 5-61 can now be rewritten

$$E_c = -71 \frac{T}{535} \log \frac{R_{mfe}}{R_{we}} \qquad (5\text{-}63)$$

where T is the absolute temperature of the formation, and R_{mfe} and R_{we} are the equivalent resistivities at the formation temperature. Sometimes the approximation is made that $R_{mfe}/R_{we} = R_{mf}/R_w$, and equation 5-63 is then written

$$E_c' = -71 \frac{T}{535} \log \frac{R_{mf}}{R_w} \qquad (5\text{-}64)$$

From an extensive study of representative formation waters from the oil-producing regions of the western hemisphere, Gondouin, Tixier, and Simard (28) have developed the empirical chart shown in Fig. 5-101 which relates the actual resistivity and the equivalent resistivity. The solid portion of these curves has been derived from laboratory data on pure sodium chloride solutions on the assumption that in very saline waters the sodium ion will completely dominate all other ions that may be present. This method of determining formation water resistivity assumes that the predominant anion is chloride. Where unusual concentrations of other anions are present, a correction should be made by using equation 5-32. If extensive logging work is to be done in an area,

TRUE Rw VS. EQUIVALENT (Rw)e

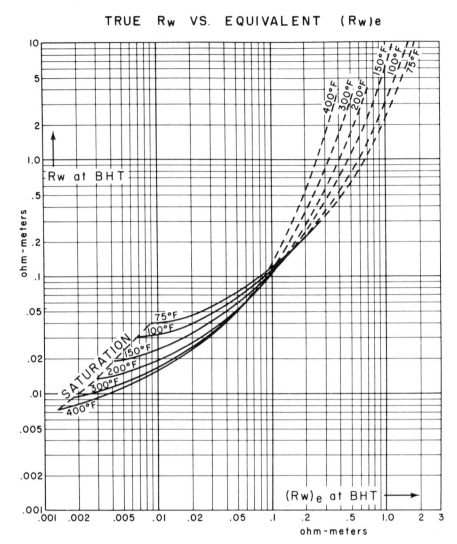

Fig. 5-101. Suggested relationship between the resistivity of a formation water and its equivalent resistivity. (Gondouin, Tixier, and Simard, courtesy of the AIME.)

an empirical chart similar to Fig. 5-101 should be developed for that area.

Example of Electric Log Interpretation in Clean Sandstones

The SP and resistivity curves of Fig. 5-3 and the microlog curves of Fig. 5-102 are from the same well and will serve as the basis of an

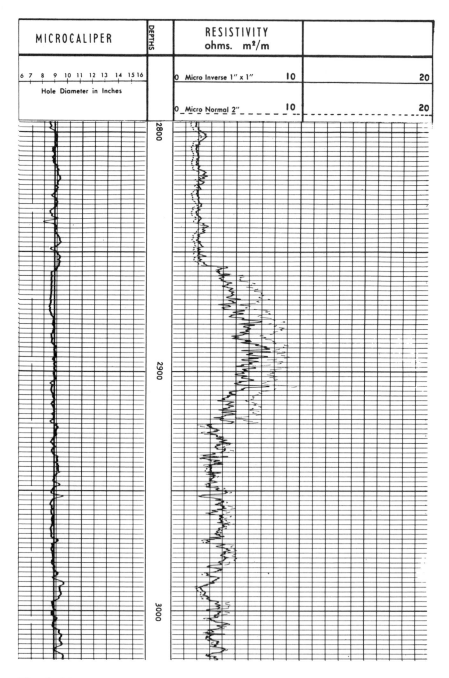

Fig. 5-102. Microlog curves for example problem. (Courtesy of Schlumberger Well Surveying Corporation.)

example of electric log interpretation. The porosity and saturation at a depth of 2885 ft will be determined. The temperature of the formation is 110°F, as determined from the known geothermal gradient for the area. (The temperature could also be estimated from the reading of the maximum recording thermometer on the logging sonde; however, such mud temperatures have been known to be as much as 50°F lower than the corresponding formation temperatures.)

The mud resistivity at this depth is estimated from the mud survey (not shown) to be 1.6 ohm-meters. Since neither the mud cake nor the mud filtrate resistivity was measured, approximate values for these parameters are obtained from the empirical correlations of Fig. 5-103. At the formation temperature,

$$R_m = 1.6 \qquad R_{mc} = 1.57 \qquad R_{mf} = 1.33$$

Mud weight = 11 lb/gal (untreated clay base)

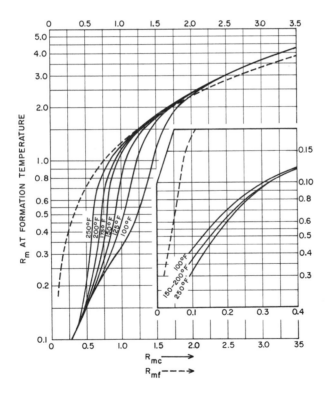

Fig. 5-103. Empirical correlation between R_m, R_{mc}, and R_{mf}. (Courtesy of Schlumberger Well Surveying Corporation.)

From the logs, the following values are read:

$$SP = -62 \text{ mv}$$

$$R_{16''} = 26 \text{ ohm-meters}$$

$$R_{\text{Ind}_.} = 23 \text{ ohm-meters}$$

$$R_{2''} = 7 \text{ ohm-meters}$$

$$R_{1 \times 1''} = 5 \text{ ohm-meters}$$

$$t_{mc} = \tfrac{1}{8} \text{ in.}$$

The ratio of the short normal to the mud resistivity is

$$\frac{R_{16''}}{R_m} = 16.2$$

This indicates that the formation is in the low end of the resistivity range and probably is fairly porous. In such a case, the invasion should be fairly shallow, and the induction log should be reading beyond the annulus. (This could be checked with appropriate departure curves.) Therefore, the resistivity R_t of the formation is 23 ohm-meters. Working with the microlog,

$$\frac{R_{2''}}{R_{mc}} = 4.46 \qquad \frac{R_{1 \times 1''}}{R_{mc}} = 3.18$$

The hole size is about $8\tfrac{1}{2}$ in., so Fig. 5-74 will suffice for determining R_{xo}. From this figure, R_{xo}/R_{mc} is 12, and therefore R_{xo} is 19.2. Some knowledge of the residual oil saturation is required at this point. Here local experience would be important. A residual oil saturation in the flushed zone of about 20 percent is fairly common, which would mean S_{xo} is 0.8. From equation 5-57, then,

$$F = \frac{R_{xo} S_{xo}^2}{R_{mf}} = \frac{19.2 \times 0.64}{1.33} = 9.24$$

By using the Humble formula, the estimated porosity is 0.285, or 28.5 percent.

In order to find the saturation, R_t and R_0 are needed. R_t was found to be 23. R_0 may be constituted from F and R_w, and R_w may be estimated from the SP curve. SP is given above as -62 mv. By using Fig. 5-5, the resistivity of the mud at 75°F is estimated to be 2.3 ohm-meters. From Fig. 5-81, E_k is -36.5 mv per 1000 psi. The formation pressure is assumed to correspond to the pressure of a salt-water column weighing 8.6 lb per gallon. The pressure differential causing invasion is

$$(11 - 8.6)\, \frac{62.4}{8.33} \times \frac{2885}{144} = 361 \text{ psi}$$

The streaming potential is therefore

$$E_k = -\,36.5 \times 361/1000 = -13.2 \text{ mv}$$

And

$$E_c = -62 + 13.2 = -48.8 \text{ mv}$$

$$= -\,71\, \frac{573}{535}\, \log\, R_{mfe}/R_{we}$$

Therefore

$$\frac{R_{mfe}}{R_{we}} = 4.38$$

By using Fig. 5-101, R_{mfe} is determined from R_{mf} to be 0.64. R_{we} is then 0.146, and R_w is 0.16. R_0 is $0.16 \times 9.24 = 1.49$, and the water saturation is

$$S_w = (R_0/R_t)^{1/2} = (1.49/23)^{1/2} = 0.255 \text{ or } 25.5\%$$

Another way in which R_0 may be determined is much simpler and probably more accurate. The small sand bodies just below the one in question probably have the same porosity and contain the same water. If this is the case, the resistivity of these sands can be taken as R_0, and it is seen that this is about 3 ohm-meters. Therefore

$$S_w = (3/23)^{1/2} = 0.36 \text{ or } 36\%$$

This does not agree too well with the previous figure, but this fact is not surprising. Many assumptions have been made in getting R_w from the SP curve, and even two assumptions are required to get R_0 directly from the log. The answers in either case indicate a probably productive zone which is worthy of further investigation and testing.

Using the SP curve is probably the poorest method of getting R_w. The best method, of course, is to obtain a sample of water from the formation in question and in the particular well. Since this requires a formation test, it would not normally be available for formation evaluation work, but if the logs were being used to determine saturation for a developed field, R_w probably could be found this way. In field development work, water samples are often available from nearby wells. In regions where the water salinity does not vary much from one place to another, water maps may be prepared for each possibly productive interval and data entered on the map each time an exploratory well is drilled and tested. Interpolation on such a map is usually quite good, even for exploratory wells that are many miles from the nearest previous well. In general such a value of R_w is far superior and can be treated with far more confidence than R_w calculated from the SP.

The factor F as determined from the microlog is usually subject to less uncertainty than R_w calculated from the SP. In addition, it may be checked by measuring the porosity with some other device (sonic log, neutron log, density log). For details of the various ramifications of this technique, reference should be made to the paper by Tixier (52).

SHALY SANDSTONES AND SHALES

Interpretation of electric logs in shaly sands is much more difficult than interpretation in clean sands, and when very large amounts of conductive material are present in the sandstones, the task can become hopeless. Log interpretation, both quantitative and qualitative, depends on the contrast in the electrical properties between the sandstones and the surrounding shales. When some shale is present in the sandstone, this electrical contrast is naturally decreased. The liquid boundary potential, E_b, becomes more like a shale potential, E_s, and instead of the potential in the sand adding to the shale potential, it begins to oppose it. The result is a decrease in the deflection of the SP. In very shaly sands, there is almost no negative excursion of the curve, even though there may be an adequate contrast between the salinity of the mud filtrate and the formation water. Electrical resistivity curves similarly lose character when there is a lot of shale present. The shale particles tend to hold large amounts of water, and even though this water is not mobile in the hydraulic sense, it is still capable of conducting electric current. Shaly sandstones with water saturations as high as 60 percent have been known to produce clean oil, i.e., water free. In this situation, the resistivity of the formation may be only two or three times that of a completely water-saturated formation. Sometimes the increase in resistivity is so slight that the bed might not even be recognized as a sandstone, much less an oil sand.

The Hill and Milburn Method of Shaly Sandstone Interpretation

The most fundamental approach yet made to the shaly sandstone problem is that of Hill and Milburn (33). At the present time their

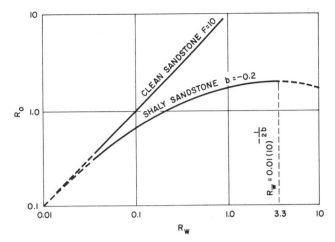

Fig. 5-104. Illustration of the relation between the resistivity of a porous formation and the formation water salinity for clean and shaly sandstones of the same porosity.

method is limited to water-saturated formations, but it represents a tremendous advance and holds great promise for an eventual solution for oil sands as well.

On logarithmic paper a plot of R_0 versus R_w for a clean sandstone is a straight line as shown in Fig. 5-104; this follows from equation 5-53. A plot of R_0 versus R_w for a shaly sandstone of the same porosity approaches the clean sand curve at the low end, but falls below it at the upper end. This indicates that the shale is acting as a conducting medium in addition to the water in the pore space. Since the ratio of R_0 to R_w varies continuously for shaly sandstones, an apparent formation factor F_a is defined.

$$F_a = \frac{R_0}{R_w} \tag{5-65}$$

The relationship between R_0 and R_w for either a clean or a shaly sandstone can be expressed by a general power series equation of the form

$$\log R_0 = A + B \log R_w + C(\log R_w)^2 + D(\log R_w)^3 + \cdots \tag{5-66}$$

In the special case of the clean sandstone, $A = \log F$, $B = 1$, and the constants for the higher degree terms are all zero.

$$\log R_0 = \log F + \log R_w \tag{5-67}$$

This is the equation of the straight line of Fig. 5-104.

For a shaly sandstone, one or more of the higher degree terms will be necessary. For a first approximation, assume that the shaly sandstone data can be described by a quadratic equation.

$$\log R_0 = A + B \log R_w + C(\log R_w)^2 \tag{5-68}$$

For convenience, let $A = \log F + 4b$. Making this substitution for A and substituting for R_0 from equation 5-65 gives

$$\log F_a = \log F + (B - 1) \log R_w + C(\log R_w)^2 + 4b \tag{5-69}$$

Now, it is known that F_a approaches F as the salinity of the formation water increases. If it is assumed that F_a is equal to F when R_w is 0.01 ohm-meters, i.e., $F_{.01} = F$, then the constants B and C that are required to satisfy the existing experimental data are: $B = 4b + 1$, and $C = b$. With these substitutions, equation 5-69 becomes

$$\log F_a = \log F_{.01} + b(\log 100\ R_w)^2$$

or

$$F_a = F_{.01}(100\ R_w)^{b \log 100 R_w} \tag{5-70}$$

where b has a negative value and is constant for a particular sample; b generally falls within the limits of 0 to -0.22. This equation was used by Hill and Milburn to correlate their resistivity measurements on shaly core samples. The equation was statistically tested with data from 450 samples (2154 individual measurements of formation factor) and found to describe the experimental data with a standard deviation of approximately ± 1 percent. R_0 calculated from this equation is

$$R_0 = F_{.01} R_w (100 R_w)^{b \log 100 R_w} \tag{5-71}$$

Differentiation of equation 5-71 with respect to R_w indicates that it goes through a maximum at

$$R_{w_{max}} = 0.01\ (10)^{-1/2b} \tag{5-72}$$

Since it is physically untenable that the resistivity of any porous rock would decrease as the water resistivity increases, this value of R_w may be considered as an upper limit of validity of equation 5-70.

As a part of their study, Hill and Milburn also measured the electrochemical potential developed between two solutions which were separated by the various core samples. Their results were not amenable to description by a simple equation, so they were presented graphically (see Fig. 5-105) by using a solution with a resistivity of 0.040 ohm-meter as

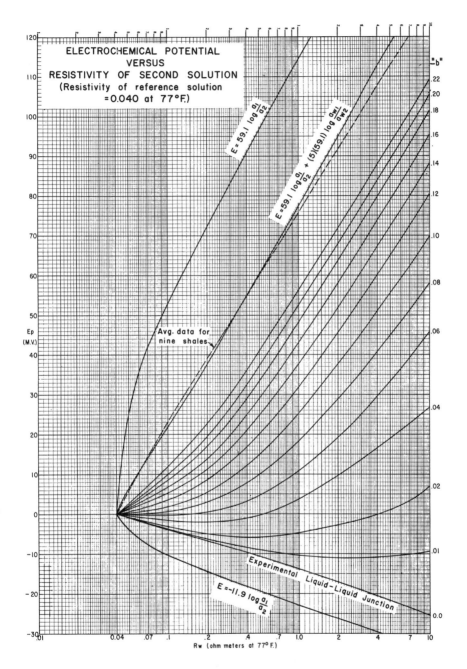

Fig. 5-105. Correlation of the electrochemical potential with the b factor. (Hill and Milburn, courtesy of the AIME.)

a reference. The factor b was found to be a suitable correlation parameter. These results again show that when the solution in the pores is concentrated, the sample tends to act like a clean sand, whereas when the solution in the pores is dilute, the sample acts more like a shale. The results of measurements on shales indicate that shales may not act like perfect membranes in the concentrated solution region, and equation 5-64 might be more appropriate for describing electrochemical behavior in this region.

Hill and Milburn tried to identify the b factor with some property of the clay in the samples. It was found that b was independent of the total clay concentration in the sample, but was directly proportional to the amount of clay that exhibited exchange ion behavior. The relation between the two properties could be satisfied approximately by the equation

$$b = -0.135 \frac{CEC}{PV} - 0.0055 \qquad (5\text{-}73)$$

where CEC/PV is the number of milliequivalents of exchangeable ion per unit volume of pore space.

Equations 5-65, 5-70, and 5-73 may be used for quantitative interpretation of shaly sandstones provided that they are water saturated. The same information is needed as for the interpretation of clean sands, and in addition the factor b must also be known. If the water resistivity is known, b may be estimated from the electrochemical potential. For example, suppose that the electrochemical potential as determined from the SP curve is -38 mv and the resistivities of the mud filtrate and the connate water are 4 and 0.3 ohm-meters respectively. By using the average shale line on Fig. 5-105, the shale potential would be

$$E_s = 48 - 108 = -60 \text{ mv}$$

This means that the boundary potential must be such as to subtract 22 mv from the potential developed across the shale. A sand with a b factor of about -0.05 would give this potential

$$E_b = 0 - 22 = -22$$

Since the boundary potential and shale potential subtract algebraically to give the total electrochemical potential,

$$E_c = -60 - (-22) = -38 \text{ mv}$$

If a core sample is available, it is possible to determine b by means of laboratory measurements of resistivity, electrochemical potential, or ion exchange capacity. It is also possible that continued study of the *b* factor will indicate some type of areal or geographical correlation that can be used.

If microlog data are available (or if the porosity is known), and the *b* factor and the water resistivity are known, the resistivity of the formation when saturated with water, R_0, may be calculated from equation 5-71. If the resistivity R_t is greater than R_0, it is an indication of the presence of hydrocarbon even though the present development of the *b* factor technique does not permit the calculation of S_w. With experience, however, it should be possible to develop empirical rules to determine when further evaluation of the formation by other means is indicated.

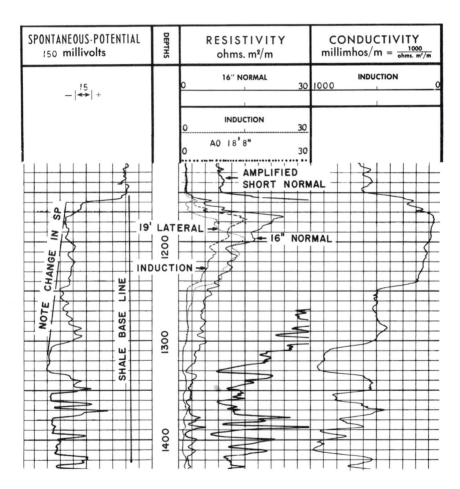

Fig. 5-106. Illustration of the effect of oil saturation on the SP curve in a shaly sandstone. (Courtesy of Schlumberger Well Surveying Corporation.)

The *b* factor concept explains some of the anomalies of electric logs recorded in shaly rocks. When oil is present, for example, the SP is always reduced as compared to the same rock saturated with water. An example of this is shown in Fig. 5-106. The resistivity curves indicate oil saturation at the top of the bed and a gradual change to complete water saturation at the bottom. The obvious trend in the SP which accompanies this change is noted on the log. The presence of oil in the pores decreases the amount of space occupied by water, and since oil is nonconducting, it should act like the sand grains. The amount of exchangeable ion is unchanged, but the effective pore volume is decreased, thereby increasing the effective magnitude of the *b* factor. The presence of oil will therefore make a shaly sand act as if it were even shalier, and the SP will decrease accordingly. This same effect will tend to reduce the resistivity of an oil sand below what might normally be expected, and therefore there will be less contrast between R_0 and R_t.

The Schlumberger Method of Interpretation of Shaly Sands

Doll (18) developed theoretical equations for the change in the resistivity and SP of a shaly sandstone by assuming that the shale and sandstone existed as a series of paper thin pure shale and clean sandstone laminations in the same proportions as existed in the actual material. Subsequently, Poupon, Loy, and Tixier (45) transformed Doll's equations into a form that was usable in terms of field logs. The resulting equation is

$$PE_c' = -K \log \frac{R_{xo}}{R_t} - 2\alpha K \log \frac{S_{xo}}{S_w} \qquad (5\text{-}74)$$

where PE_c' is the pseudo-electrochemical potential for the shaly sand (which corresponds to E_c' for a clean sand) and α is the ratio of PE_c'/E_c' (or PE_c/E_c). α is known as the *SP reduction factor*. In order to apply this equation it is desirable to have a clean, water-saturated sand as a reference. Since this case can rarely be found in a shaly sand area, it is customary to select a nearby sand which appears to be wet and which has the largest SP deflection. It is apparent that when S_{xo} equals S_w, equation 5-74 reduces to the form of equation 5-64, and for a clean sand the two are identical. Compensation for the fact that the reference sand is not clean is made by using an empirical value of K rather than the theoretical value of $71 \, T/535$.

Equation 5-74 was developed on the assumption that equation 5-64 rather than equation 5-63 expressed the electrochemical potential. In order to use equation 5-74, then, all potentials taken from the log must be changed to satisfy equation 5-64. An example will serve to clarify this procedure.

Example of Shaly Sand Interpretation of Electric Logs

The log of Fig. 5-106 will be taken as an example of this problem. It is desired to determine the water saturation at 1176 ft. The reference sand is taken as the interval from 1300 ft to 1334 ft. R_t from the induction log is 15, and the SP is -50 mv for the bed at 1176 ft. For the reference bed, SP is -65 mv and R_0 is 1.1. R_{mf} at the formation temperature of 100°F is 3.0. From microlog curves for this well, R_{xo} is known to be 32.4 at 1176 ft and 25.5 at 1322 ft. The streaming potential is assumed to be zero in order to simplify the problem.

Equations 5-63 and 5-64 are used to reconstitute the SP for the reference bed:

$$E_c = -71(T/535) \log R_{mfe}/R_{we} \qquad\qquad (5\text{-}63)$$

$$-65 = -74.4 \log R_{mfe}/R_{we}$$

$$R_{mfe}/R_{we} = 7.5$$

$$R_{mfe} = 1.0 \text{ from Fig. 5-101}$$

$$R_{we} = 0.133 \qquad R_w = 0.135$$

$$E_c' = -74.4 \log R_{mf}/R_w = -100 \text{ mv} \qquad\qquad (5\text{-}64)$$

Since $\alpha = 50/65 = 0.77$, $PE_c' = -77$ mv.

These two new potential values, -100 mv and -77 mv, are used with equation 5-74 to determine the water saturation.

For the reference bed:

$$E_c' = -K \log R_{xo}/R_0$$

$$-100 = -K \log 25.5/1.1$$

$$K = 73.2$$

For the bed at 1176 ft:

$$PE_c' = -K \log R_{xo}/R_t - 2\alpha K \log S_{xo}/S_w$$

$$-77 = -73.2 \log 32.4/15 - 2 \times 0.77 \times 73.2 \log S_{xo}/S_w$$

$$S_{xo}/S_w = 2.92$$

If the value of S_{xo} is known, it should be used here. If it is unknown, an estimate may be made by taking $S_{xo} = (S_w)^{1/5}$. Using this relationship, S_w is 0.26 or 26 percent.

A sandstone which contains shaly material acts as if it has a higher water saturation and a higher porosity than it actually does. Equation 5-74 corrects for the influence of shale on the water saturation. Poupon, Loy, and Tixier also included in their paper a graph which corrects for the influence of shale on the porosity. Figure 5-107 is a reproduction of their Fig. 6. In the present problem, R_{xo}/R_{mf} is 10.8, α is 0.77, and R_{xo}/R_t is 2.16. With these values, and a residual oil saturation of 23.5 percent, ϕ is found to be 27 percent.

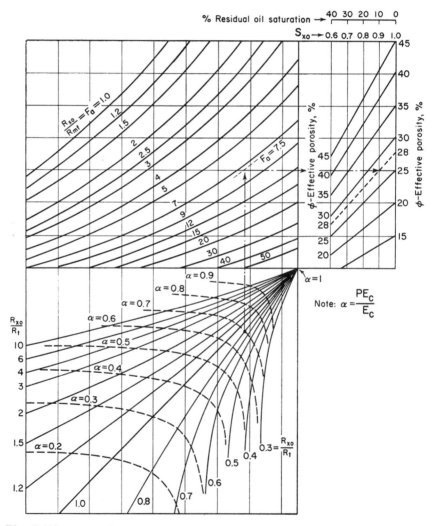

Fig. 5-107. Chart for determining porosity in a shaly sandstone. (After Poupon, Loy, and Tixier, courtesy of the AIME.)

CARBONATE ROCKS

Electric log interpretation in carbonate rocks generally follows the methods outlined for clean sandstones except that allowance must be made for the different types of porosity, and the porosity type should be known before log interpretation is attempted. Two kinds of porosity are possible in carbonates: a primary porosity which may be very fine, intergranular pores not visible under 10 × magnification, or the fine to medium intergranular, interfragmental, or interoolitic pores; and a secondary porosity composed of vugs, fractures, and intercrystalline pores. Rocks that have the coarser primary porosity (intergranular, interoolitic) can be treated the same as clean sandstones. Rocks containing fine primary porosity and secondary porosity require further classification and study.

For the purpose of electric log interpretation, we shall classify carbonate porosity into three types:[1]

Type A. Under 10 × magnification, the primary porosity is glossy to vitreous in appearance. The matrix porosity is very fine, usually amounts to 1 to 5 percent, and is almost always entirely water saturated. These rocks will not produce hydrocarbons unless secondary porosity is present. Productive Type A rocks usually have a total porosity between 5 and 15 percent and a permeability greater than 500 md. (This corresponds to Archie's Type I.)

Type C. Under 10 × magnification the primary porosity is earthy to chalky in appearance. The matrix porosity is fine, usually amounts to 20 to 40 percent, and the permeability is often less than 5 to 10 md. Water saturations are generally high, frequently greater than 40 percent. Secondary porosity is rarely present, and production must be from the low-permeability matrix material; sometimes this permeability is not sufficient for hydrocarbon production. (This type corresponds to Archie's Type II.)

Type B. This type is intermediate between Type A and Type C in all respects. Every gradation between the two principal types can occur, and some reservoirs are partly one type and partly another.

---

[1] The porosity classification given here is based on the system devised by Archie (2), but it is not nearly as complete; however, it does have the advantage of being much simpler, while still being adequate for the task of log interpretation. This classification system was developed by A. A. Brown of the California Standard Company (Calgary, Alberta, Canada).

Porosity classification can be made by visual examination of the cuttings. Primary porosity is estimated from the luster, and to this any apparent secondary porosity is added.

Figure 5-108 shows typical resistivity curves for hydrocarbon reservoirs of each type of rock. For the Type A porosity, the curve trends first to the left with increasing porosity, and then to the right. The reason for this is that in the low-porosity region, all of the porosity is primary, and it is all saturated with water. Increasing the amount of porosity therefore decreases the resistivity. When the porosity is above 5 percent, the secondary porosity becomes an increasing consideration. This exists frequently at the expense of the primary porosity, and since coarse porosity contains almost no capillary water, the resistivity increases. Rocks of the Type A porosity, therefore, are most likely to produce hydrocarbon if the resistivity is fairly high. R_t is usually above 100 ohm-meters.

Type C rocks have a relatively constant capillary water saturation, regardless of the porosity. Increasing porosity, therefore, will result in a decreasing resistivity. The best possibility of production in this type of rock is from the low-resistivity portion. Sometimes R_t will be no more than 2 to 4 ohm-meters in an oil zone.

In carbonates, as in sandstones, interpretation is based on equations

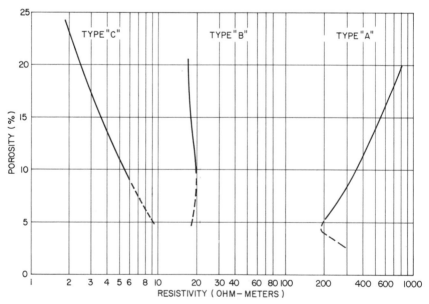

Fig. 5-108. Typical relationships between porosity and resistivity of carbonate reservoirs containing hydrocarbon. (After Archie, courtesy of the AAPG.)

5-54 and 5-56. In the case of Type A, the resistivity is controlled primarily by changes in water saturation. In the Type C reservoirs, the resistivity depends on changes of F since the water saturation is fairly independent of porosity. The type B rocks represent the intermediate condition.

The Humble equation (5-55), which was developed for sandstones, should not be used for carbonate rocks. This equation is based on the fact that a low-porosity sandstone usually has a high degree of intergranular cementation, and hence a high value of m, whereas a high-porosity sandstone usually corresponds to a low m. This is not true for carbonates and hence it is better to use the original form of the porosity-formation factor equation as proposed by Archie (equation 5-54). m lies between 1.4 and 2.6. The higher values of m correspond to the granular rocks.

Long sections of carbonate rock of uniform porosity are rare. In order to get adequate definition of thin porous intervals and still have penetration deep enough to get beyond the invaded zone, it is necessary to use focused logs. The induction log is best in the Type B rocks; Type A rocks usually are too resistive for this logging device and cause "flat-topping" of the logs (i.e., the device will record resistivities up to a certain maximum, and anything greater than this will be recorded as a constant value). Type C rocks usually give pessimistic values of water saturation with the induction log, possibly because of the formation of an annulus.

The laterolog (or guard log) is generally good provided that the mud has a low resistivity, although in very high-resistivity sections it will also flat-top. Carbonate sections are usually drilled with gyp or lime muds so the resistivity can be controlled fairly well by salt addition without increasing the mud cost significantly. For wildcat wells the mud resistivity should be controlled so that $R_{mf} = R_w$; the well is then logged with the laterolog and the microlaterolog (or the guard log and FoRxo log), and where the laterolog reads at least one and one-half to two times higher than the microlaterolog, hydrocarbon is probably present. The ratio of these two readings is $(S_{xo}/S_w)^2$. In development work where the presence of hydrocarbon is assured, and an accurate value of water saturation is desired, the mud resistivity should be adjusted to make the resistivity of the invaded zone approximately equal to the resistivity of the uninvaded zone. This assures a very good value of R_t for use in the Archie equation.

Invasion of carbonates can be particularly severe because of the high permeability of fractures and vugs. Drilling is also slow because of the dense nature of the rocks; this means that the formations will probably be exposed for long periods between logging runs. Good mud control and/or frequent logging is necessary in order to limit the depth of the invaded zone that is present during the logging operation.

REFERENCES

1. Archie, G. E., The electrical resistivity log as an aid in determining some reservoir characteristics: *Trans. AIME*, v. 146, 1942, p. 54.
2. Archie, G. E., Reservoir rocks and petrophysical considerations: *Am. Assoc. Petroleum Geologists Bull.*, v. 36, no. 2, February, 1952, p. 278.
3. *Bulletin A. 127, Application of Radiation-Guard Surveys to Carbonate Reservoirs:* Welex.
4. *Bulletin A. 132, Guyod's Electrical Well Logging:* Welex, Inc., 1944.
5. Chombart, L. G., Well logs in carbonate reservoirs: *Geophysics*, v. XXV, no. 4, August, 1960, p. 779.
6. deWitte, A. J., Influence of differential displacement in invaded oil and gas sands on the induction log: *Trans. AIME*, v. 210, 1957, p. 379.
7. deWitte, Leendert, A study of electric log interpretation methods in shaly formations: *Trans. AIME*, v. 204, 1955, p. 103.
8. *Document #2, Review of Schlumberger Well Logging and Auxiliary Methods:* Schlumberger Well Surveying Corporation, 1949.
9. *Document #3, Resistivity Departure Curves:* Schlumberger Well Surveying Corporation, 1949.
10. *Document #4, Interpretation Hand-Book for Resistivity Logs:* Schlumberger Well Surveying Corporation, 1950.
11. *Document #6, Departure Curves for Laterolog:* Schlumberger Well Surveying Corporation, 1952.
12. *Document #7, Resistivity Departure Curves, (Beds of Infinite Thickness):* Schlumberger Well Surveying Corporation, 1955.
13. *Document #8, Introduction to Schlumberger Well Logging:* Schlumberger Well Surveying Corporation, 1958.
14. Doll, H. G., The S. P. log: Theoretical analysis and principles of interpretation: *Trans. AIME*, v. 179, 1948, p. 146.
15. Doll, H. G., Introduction to induction logging and application to logging of wells drilled with oil base mud: *Trans. AIME*, v. 186, 1949, p. 148.
16. Doll, H. G., Selective SP logging: *Trans. AIME*, v. 189, 1950, p. 129.
17. Doll, H. G., The microlog—A new electrical logging method for detailed determination of permeable beds: *Trans. AIME*, v. 189, 1950, p. 155.
18. Doll, H. G., The SP log in shaly sands: *Trans. AIME*, v. 189, 1950, p. 205.
19. Doll, H. G., The laterolog: A new resistivity logging method with electrodes using an automatic focusing system: *Trans. AIME*, v. 192, 1951, p. 305.
20. Doll, H. G., The microlaterolog: *Trans. AIME*, v. 198, 1953, p. 17.
21. Doll, H. G., Filtrate invasion in highly permeable sands: *The Petroleum Engineer*, January, 1955, p. B-53.

22. Doll, H. G., Dumanoir, J. L., and Martin, M., Suggestions for better electric log combinations and improved interpretations: *Geophysics*, v. XXV, no. 4, August, 1960, p. 854.
23. Duesterhoeft, W. C., Hartline, R. E., and Thomsen, H. S., The effect of coil design on the performance of the induction log: *Annual California Regional Meeting of the AIME*, Pasadena, California, October, 1960, Paper 1558-G.
24. Dumanoir, J. L., Tixier, M. P., and Martin, M., Interpretation of the induction-electrical log in fresh mud: *Trans. AIME*, v. 210, 1957, p. 202.
25. Dunlap, H. F., and Hawthorne, R. R., The calculation of water resistivities from chemical analysis: *Trans. AIME*, v. 192, 1951, p. 373.
26. Glasstone, S., *Textbook of Physical Chemistry*, D. Van Nostrand Company, Inc., Princeton, New Jersey, second edition, 1946.
27. Gondouin, M., and Scala, C., Streaming potential and the SP log: *Trans. AIME*, v. 213, 1958, p. 170.
28. Gondouin, M., Tixier, M. P., and Simard, G. L. An experimental study on the influence of the chemical composition of electrolytes on the SP curve: *Trans. AIME*, v. 210, 1957, p. 58.
29. Guyod, H., and Pranglin, J. A., *Analysis Charts for the Determination of True Resistivity from Electric Logs:* 1959.
30. Harned, H. S., and Owen, B. B., *The Physical Chemistry of Electrolytic Solutions:* Reinhold Publishing Corporation, New York, 1943.
31. Henderson, P., Zur Thermodynamik der Flüssigkeitsketten: *Zeitschr. Physik. Chem.*, v. 59, April, 1902, p. 118.
32. Hill, H. J., and Anderson, A. E., Streaming potential phenomena in SP log interpretation: *Trans. AIME*, v. 216, 1959, p. 203.
33. Hill, H. J., and Milburn, J. D., Effect of clay and water salinity on electrochemical behavior of reservoir rocks: *Trans. AIME*, v. 207, 1956, p. 65.
34. Jordan, E. C., *Electromagnetic Waves and Radiating Systems:* Prentice-Hall, Inc., Englewood Cliffs, New Jersey, 1950, p. 131.
35. Leverett, M. C., Flow of oil-water mixtures through unconsolidated sands: *Trans. AIME*, v. 132, 1939, p. 149.
36. Lewis, G. N., and Randall, M., *Thermodynamics and the Free Energy of Chemical Substances:* McGraw-Hill Book Company, Inc., New York, 1923.
37. *Log Interpretation Charts:* Schlumberger Well Surveying Corporation, 1958.
38. Martin, J. L., and Campbell, W. M., Displacement logging—A new exploratory tool: *Trans. AIME*, v. 204, 1955, p. 233.
39. Martin, M., Relation entre la résistivité des eaux et leur composition chimique: *Inst. français pétrole Rev. et Annales combustibles liquides*, v. XIII, no. 6, June, 1958, p. 985.
40. Martin, M., Murray, G. H., and Gillingham, W. J., Determination of the potential productivity of oil bearing formations by resistivity measurements: *Geophysics*, v. III, July, 1938, p. 258.
41. Mounce, W. D., and Rust, W. M., Jr., Natural potentials in well logging: *Trans. AIME*, v. 155, 1944, p. 49.
42. Owen, J. E., and Greer, W. J., The guard electrode logging system: *Trans. AIME*, v. 192, 1951, p. 347.

43. Perkins, F. M., Brannon, H. R., and Winsauer, W. O., Interrelation of resistivity and potential of shaly reservoir rock: *Trans. AIME*, v. 201, 1954, p. 176.
44. Pirson, S. J., *Oil Reservoir Engineering:* McGraw-Hill Book Company, Inc., New York, second edition, 1958.
45. Poupon, A., Loy, M. E., and Tixier, M. P., A contribution to electric log interpretation in shaly sands: *Trans. AIME*, v. 201, 1954, p. 138.
46. Scratchard, G., Ion exchanger electrodes: *Jour. Am. Chem. Soc.*, v. 75, 1953, p. 2883.
47. Schlumberger, C., Schlumberger, M., and Leonardon, E. G., Electrical coring: A method of determining bottom-hole data by electrical measurements: *Trans. AIME*, v. 110, 1934, p. 237.
48. Schlumberger, C., Schlumberger, M., and Leonardon, E. G., A new contribution to subsurface studies by means of electrical measurements in drill holes: *Trans. AIME*, v. 110, 1934, p. 273.
49. Segesman, F., and Tixier, M. P., Some effects of invasion on the SP curve: *Trans. AIME*, v. 216, 1959, p. 138.
50. Tixier, M. P., Evaluation of permeability from electric log resistivity gradients: *Oil and Gas Jour.* v. 48, no. 6, June 16, 1949, p. 113.
51. Tixier, M. P., Electrical log analysis in the Rocky Mountains: *Oil and Gas Jour.*, v. 48, no. 7, June 23, 1949, p. 143.
52. Tixier, M. P., Porosity balance verifies water saturation determined from logs: *Trans. AIME*, v. 213, 1958, p. 161.
53. Walstrom, J. E., The quantitative aspects of electric log interpretation: *Trans. AIME*, v. 195, 1952, p. 47.
54. Winn, R. H., and Greer, W. J., A new electrical logging system: *API Drilling and Production Practice*, 1951, p. 390.
55. Winsauer, W. O., Shearin, H. M., Masson, P. H., and Williams, M., Resistivity of brine-saturated sands in relation to pore geometry: *Am. Assoc. Petroleum Geologists Bull.*, v. 36, no. 2, February, 1952, p. 253.
56. Worthington, A. E., and Meldau, R. F., Departure curves for the self-potential log: *Trans. AIME*, v. 213, 1958, p. 11.
57. Wyllie, M. R. J., A quantitative analysis of the electro-chemical component of the S.P. curve, *Jour. Petroleum Technology*, v. 1, 1949, p. 17.
58. Wyllie, M. R. J., An investigation of the electrokinetic component of the self potential curve: *Trans. AIME*, v. 192, 1951, p. 1.
59. Wyllie, M. R. J., deWitte, A. J., and Warren, J. E., On the streaming potential problem: *Trans. AIME*, v. 213, 1958, p. 409.
60. Wyllie, M. R. J., and Patnode, H. W., The presence of conductive solids in reservoir rocks as a factor in electric log interpretation: *Trans. AIME*, v. 189, 1950, p. 47.
61. Wyllie, M. R. J., and Rose, W. D., Some theoretical considerations related to the quantitative evaluation of the physical characteristics of reservoir rock from Electrical log data: *Trans. AIME*, v. 189, 1950, p. 105.
62. Wyllie, M. R. J., and Southwick, P. F., An experimental investigation of the S.P. and resistivity phenomena in dirty sands: *Trans. AIME*, v. 201, 1954, p. 43.

6

Radioactivity Logging

Radioactivity logging, like electric logging, is a wireline service. The sonde usually contains two radioactivity counters and a source of high-energy neutrons, and the surface equipment is designed to translate the counting rates into a continuous log. Two basic curves are recorded. One curve is the response of a radiation counter in the sonde to the natural atomic radiation that is present in varying amounts in all sedimentary rocks. This curve is useful for distinguishing between shales, sandstones, and limestones. It is therefore a lithology curve like the SP curve of the electric log, and is often used as a substitute for it when the SP curve lacks definition. The second recorded curve is the response of a radiation counter to the bombardment of the formations by high-energy neutrons. This neutron curve is very sensitive to the amount of hydrogen around the sonde, and hence, by inference, it is a measure of the porosity.

Although radioactivity logs have been available for the past twenty years, their rate of growth has been slow compared to other logs, primarily because they have been undependable in quantitative use. This lack of dependability stems from two factors: one, a lack of understanding and information about the various radioactive processes, and two, the difficulties which arise from the physical environment in which the logging operation must be accomplished. In the last few years there has been an intensive effort on the part of logging companies to cure these ills. In addition, other radioactivity logs have been or are being developed to make direct measurements of porosity, to estimate the amount of salt water that is present in the formations, and to measure the concentration of specific elements such as silicon, oxygen, and carbon.

ATOMIC STRUCTURE

The understanding and interpretation of radioactivity logs requires some understanding of atomic structure; and although it is too elementary for the methods of modern physics, the Rutherford-Bohr concept will be adequate for the purposes of this text.

The analogy is often drawn between the structure of the atom and our solar system. The nucleus of the atom corresponds to the sun as the center of the system, and the electrons rotate around the nucleus in fixed orbits just as the planets rotate about the sun. Here the similarity ends, for the electrons generally do not have simple, relatively circular orbits, but may exhibit orbits which vary from circular to extremely elliptical, with various orientations relative to the nucleus. In addition, each primary orbital energy level in the atom may be occupied by several electrons having slightly different energy sublevels. The shape and orientation of any electron orbit may be specified by four characteristic quantum numbers. The principal quantum number defines the primary energy shell in which the electron exists. Within each shell it is possible to have energy subdivisions based on the shape of the elliptical path (azimuthal number), the orientation relative to a magnetic field (magnetic number), and the orientation of the axial spin of the electron (spin number). With the exception of the spin number, which may be only $\pm\frac{1}{2}$, the quantum numbers must be integers; and the number of possible integers is dependent on the value of the preceding quantum number. Thus, in the lowest energy shell, the K shell, it is possible to have only two electrons; these differ in their spin orientation. In the next shell, the L shell, eight electrons are possible; the M shell may contain eighteen; and the N shell may contain thirty-two. When, for some reason, an electron moves from one energy level to a lower level, the difference in the energy between the two states is emitted as electromagnetic radiation.

The nucleus, which contains the bulk of the mass of the atom, is composed primarily of protons and neutrons. The atom must be electrically neutral, and since the electric charge on a proton is plus 1 and the charge on an electron is minus 1, the number of protons in the nucleus is exactly equal to the number of orbital electrons. The numbers of neutrons and protons in the nucleus are approximately equal in the lighter elements. In the heavy elements the number of neutrons far exceeds the number of protons.

The masses of the proton and the neutron are approximately equal and are assigned an arbitrary value of 1 mass unit. On this basis the mass of an electron is 1/1840 mass unit. The radius of an atomic nucleus is of the order of 10^{-12} cm. The radius of an atom is of the order of 10^{-8} cm, or 10,000 times larger than the nucleus. It is obvious, then that while the nucleus of an atom accounts for almost all of its mass, it is the electron cloud surrounding the nucleus which accounts for almost all of the volume; and it follows that much of the volume occupied by an atom is devoid of any matter whatsoever. On an atomic scale, apparently solid matter is actually almost empty space, and a particle which is sufficiently small is able to pass through it with little difficulty.

The number of electrons surrounding the nucleus of an element defines its chemical properties; therefore the number of protons within the nucleus also defines the chemical properties. This number is called the atomic number (Z). The sum of the number of protons and neutrons in the nucleus is the approximate mass weight of an element and is called the mass number (A). Specifying these two numbers will exactly define any isotope of any element. It is customary in considering nuclear reactions to write both numbers with the chemical symbol of the element involved, one number as a subscript, and the other as a superscript. For example, the common form of carbon contains six protons and six neutrons. The atomic number is six and the mass number is twelve, and the element is written $_6C^{12}$.

There may be more than one combination of neutrons and protons for a particular element. Hydrogen, for example, has only one proton in its nucleus, but there are two isotopes of hydrogen which have one and two neutrons as well. The three possible species of hydrogen are therefore:

Hydrogen	$_1H^1$	one proton
Deuterium	$_1H^2$	one proton and one neutron
Tritium	$_1H^3$	one proton and two neutrons

The two heavier varieties of hydrogen are of great importance in the field of military weapons. It appears that they may soon become very important as a source of neutrons for radioactivity logging.

NATURAL RADIOACTIVITY

In 1896 H. Becquerel found that salts of uranium emitted a penetrating radiation which was capable of fogging a covered photographic plate. A subsequent investigation of this phenomenon by the Curies led to the isolation of the elements polonium and radium from pitchblende ore. These two elements are daughter products of the disintegration of uranium but are much more radioactive. Radium, for example, is 10^6 times more radioactive than uranium. It was noted in these early investigations that there was not one radiation emitted, but three distinct types. At the time the true nature of these radiations was not known so they were called simply alpha (α), beta (β), and gamma (γ) rays. Ingenious experiments by Lord Rutherford established the fact that α rays were actually ionized helium atoms with a mass of 4 and a charge of plus 2. Beta rays were identified as electrons with a mass of 1/1840 and a charge of minus 1. Gamma rays were shown to be electromagnetic radiation, having zero rest mass and no electric charge.

With this knowledge of the nature of radioactivity, it is easy to show that the nucleus of an atom undergoes an actual physical change during the emission of α or β radiation, since it emits a part of its own substance. Since both of these particles are charged, the emission of either changes the charge remaining on the nucleus and therefore changes the chemical nature of the element. For example, the element radium in emitting an α particle changes into the element radon

$$_{88}Ra^{226} \rightarrow {}_{86}Rn^{222} + {}_{2}He^{4}$$

In this reaction, and in many other nuclear reactions, the new nucleus is in an excited state, having more energy than is normal for its stable condition. When such is the case, the excess energy is emitted in the form of electromagnetic radiation, or γ rays, almost immediately after the emission of the particle. The amount and wavelength of γ radiation associated with a nuclear disintegration is characteristic of the element. The radium reaction written above results in the emission of a large number of γ-ray photons. The disintegration of polonium by α emission, on the other hand, results in no γ radiation.

The radioactive disintegration of an element may be defined as a statistical process; that is, it is impossible to predict when a particular nucleus will undergo a radioactive change, but it is possible to predict when a certain fraction of a large number of nuclei will do so. The number of nuclei which undergo decay in a certain period of time is proportional to the number of nuclei that are present. This can be expressed mathematically by saying that the decay rate equals a constant λ times the number of nuclei N

$$-\frac{dN}{dt} = \lambda N \qquad (6\text{-}1)$$

or in integral form

$$N = N_0 e^{-\lambda t} \qquad (6\text{-}2)$$

where N_0 is the number of nuclei at time $t = 0$. This equation is shown graphically in Fig. 6-1. Of special interest is the time required for one-half of the original nuclei to decay. This time is known as the half-life of the element and is related to the constant λ by

$$t_{1/2} = \frac{0.693}{\lambda} \tag{6-3}$$

The half-life therefore is a measure of the disintegration rate of the species. The characteristic half-life of a radioactive element may be anywhere in the range of fractions of a second to many thousands of years.

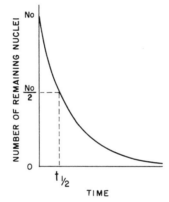

Fig. 6-1. Curve illustrating radioactive decay.

An α particle is emitted from the nucleus at speeds which range from 1.4×10^9 to 2.2×10^9 cm/sec, or less than one-tenth the speed of light. It causes extensive ionization of the material through which it passes so that its kinetic energy is rapidly consumed. As a result, its range in air is only 4 or 5 cm, and it can be stopped by as little as a sheet of paper, or 0.006 cm of aluminum. A β particle is emitted from the nucleus at speeds which range up to 0.99 times the speed of light, an average value being 2×10^{10} cm/sec. It is much less ionizing than an α particle. Its range in air is of the order of 5 ft, and it will penetrate as much as 1 mm of aluminum. A gamma ray is emitted from the nucleus at the speed of light. It has no rest mass and no charge, so that its ionizing power is very small. The ionizing power of α, β, and γ rays is approximately 10,000 to 100 to 1. The penetrating power of a γ ray is of the order of ten to one hundred times that of a beta ray, depending on its wavelength. It is obvious then, that of the natural radiation originating in the sedimentary rocks, only the γ rays are capable of traversing the formation, the borehole fluid, and the walls of the radiation detector so that they may be counted. It is from this fact that the natural radiation curve has received the name of the γ-ray curve.

There are three major groups of radioactive materials. These are known as the uranium, actinium, and thorium series. They are shown in Fig. 6-2. (The disintegrations indicated by the heavy arrows are those in which appreciable γ radiation is emitted.) The uranium series starts with uranium, $_{92}U^{238}$ and goes through a series of α and β disintegrations to become the element lead, $_{82}Pb^{206}$. The actinium series starts with a uranium isotope, $_{92}U^{235}$, and disintegrates to an isotope of lead, $_{82}Pb^{207}$. The thorium series starts with thorium, $_{90}Th^{232}$, and

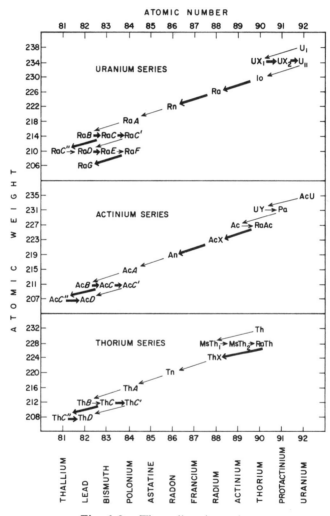

Fig. 6-2.   The radioactive series.

disintegrates to an isotope of lead, $_{82}Pb^{208}$. Natural uranium contains one part of the 235 isotope and 139 parts of the 238 species. The contribution of the actinium series to the natural radiation of sedimentary rocks is therefore negligible. In addition to the three radioactive series there is a single isotope of the element potassium which exists in nature in significant quantities and which is unstable. This isotope, $_{19}K^{40}$, undergoes a single β decay to become the stable element calcium, with the emission of γ radiation in the reaction. The relative concentration of the three types of radioelements in sedimentary rocks that is necessary to produce a given amount of countable γ ray flux is (8)

Radium and series, 1.43×10^{-10}

Thorium and series, 6.41×10^{-4}

Potassium (natural mixture), 1.0

ARTIFICIAL RADIOACTIVITY AND NUCLEAR REACTIONS

The fact that some atoms undergo a natural spontaneous disintegration led to an investigation into the possibility of causing nuclear reactions by some external means. In 1919, Rutherford noticed that when high-energy α particles from radium-C were passed through nitrogen gas, high-energy protons appeared. From the nature of the results, he concluded that there was a reaction between the α particles and the nitrogen nuclei:

$$_2He^4 + \ _7N^{14} \rightarrow \ _8O^{17} + \ _1H^1$$

Continuing experimentation indicated that similar results could be obtained from nearly all the lighter elements.

At this point the question arises of why a stable atomic nucleus should become unstable with the addition of another particle similar to those that are already present. There are two reasons for this. First, the incident α particle has a certain amount of kinetic energy which must be dissipated. Second, the weight of an element is not exactly equal to the sum of the weights of the neutrons and protons in its nucleus, but is somewhat less. This difference between the actual weight and the sum of the neutron and proton weights is called the mass defect; this is the mass that is converted into the energy that holds the nucleus together. Thus, in the reaction between an α particle and nitrogen, the sum of the masses of the reactants is approximately 0.01 mass unit greater than the mass of the intermediate element, the fluorine isotope

$_9F^{18}$. This extra mass represents about 7 Mev[1] of energy that must also be dissipated. This amount of energy is sufficient to cause the expulsion of a proton from the compound nucleus.

When a positively charged particle, such as an α particle or a proton approaches a nucleus, there is a coulombic repulsion set up between the like charges which increases as the distance between them decreases.

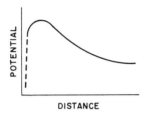

Fig. 6-3. Potential diagram for an alpha particle approaching a nucleus.

If there were no other forces present, it would be very difficult to cause many of the known reactions between positively charged particles and nuclei; but it happens that at distances of the order of 10^{-12} cm, there are very powerful, short-range, cohesive forces which cause the capture of the particle by the nucleus. These forces are illustrated in Fig. 6-3. The hump in the curve represents an energy barrier to the reaction and explains why it is necessary to supply large kinetic energies to the impinging particle to cause a reaction.

Fig. 6-4. Potential diagram for a neutron approaching a nucleus.

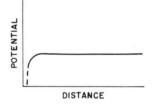

The potential energy-distance curve for a neutron approaching or leaving the nucleus is shown in Fig. 6-4. Since there is no charge on a neutron, there is no potential hump resulting from coulombic repulsion. A neutron can therefore enter and leave the nucleus more readily than a proton or an α particle, and, in fact, the smaller the kinetic energy of a free neutron, the greater is its chance of being captured by the nucleus of an element.

Neutrons do not exist in quantity in nature. They are not produced by any natural radioactivity. The first problem in neutron logging,

---

[1] Mev = million electron volts. An electron volt is the energy acquired by an electron moving under a potential drop of one volt.

then, is to provide a neutron source. The common method of doing this is by an atomic reaction known as the (α, n) reaction. It is a known fact that when certain light elements, such as beryllium, are bombarded by α particles, they emit neutrons. The source of α particles is one of the natural α-active materials such as radium, or polonium. The reactions are:

$$_{88}Ra^{226} \rightarrow {}_{86}Rn^{222} + {}_2He^4 + 10{,}000 \; \gamma\text{-ray photons}$$

$$_{84}Po^{218} \rightarrow {}_{82}Pb^{214} + {}_2He^4 + 1 \; \gamma\text{-ray photon}$$

$$_2He^4 + {}_4Be^9 \rightarrow {}_6C^{12} + {}_0n^1$$

The average energy of the neutrons produced in this reaction is 5 Mev. The high γ-ray flux associated with the disintegration of radium to produce the necessary α particles is disadvantageous, both from a safety standpoint and because of the undesirable background radiation that it produces. The polonium source, on the other hand, has a much shorter half-life (138 days) than radium (1620 years); this results in a neutron source which is changing in strength from day to day. For this latter reason the radium-beryllium source has been preferred by most logging companies for neutron logging. Recently, an actinium-beryllium source has come into use. It combines a low γ-ray flux with a long half-life. The United States government has also released some plutonium for use in neutron sources. This element has a very low γ-ray flux and a very long half-life. The plutonium source, however, must be relatively large because of the low radioactivity level of the plutonium. A plutonium source is approximately 1 in. in diameter by $3\frac{1}{2}$ in. long compared with a radium source which is approximately 1 in. in diameter by $\frac{1}{2}$ in. long.

There is a second method of producing neutrons by using deuterium and tritium. It has none of the undesirable properties of the (α, n) source. Details of the method will be discussed in a later section.

The neutron produced by the (α, n) reaction is a fast neutron with several Mev of kinetic energy. As such it may enter into many reactions. The most important of these in logging is the dissipation of energy through elastic collisions or scattering. (Since the neutron has no charge, it loses very little kinetic energy by ionization.) In this process the neutron rebounds from the nuclei of the material through which it is passing, and in the process it gives up some of its energy to those nuclei. A material which slows neutrons in this manner is called a moderator. The effectiveness of a material as a moderator varies over wide limits for the various elements, and can be determined only by

experiment. As it happens, hydrogen is the best common material for
this purpose.

The ability to moderate neutrons depends on two factors. The first
is known as the cross section. Cross section is a measure of the probability
that a reaction will occur. It is defined as

$$\sigma = \frac{N_r}{N_p \times N_t} \tag{6-4}$$

where N_r is the number of reactions or collisions occurring per unit
volume of material per second, N_p is the number of neutrons per square
centimeter of the incident beam striking the target per second, and N_t
is the number of nuclei per unit volume of target material. σ, therefore,
has units of square centimeters. The probability of a reaction occurring
is so low that it is customary to use 10^{-24} sq cm as the practical unit,
and this has been termed the *barn*. Table 6-1 gives the collision (scattering) and capture cross sections of some of the elements commonly
found in sedimentary rocks for low-energy neutrons. The element
hydrogen is obviously much better than any of the others from the
viewpoint of the probability that a neutron will collide with it.

TABLE 6-1. CROSS SECTION FOR NEUTRON CAPTURE AND SCATTERING
OF LOW-ENERGY NEUTRONS

Z	Element Symbol	Abundance, ppm	Capture, σ_a	Scattering, σ_s	Collisions Necessary to Reduce Neutron Energy from 2 Mev to 0.025 ev
1	H	1,400	0.30	20	18
4	Be		0.009	6.1	87
5	B		700	3	105
6	C	320	0.0032	4.8	115
7	N		1.88	10.0	130
8	O	466,000	0.0002	4.1	150
11	Na	28,300	0.505	3.5	215
12	Mg	20,900	0.4	3.6	227
13	Al	81,000	0.230	1.5	251
14	Si	277,000	0.13	1.7	261
16	S	520	0.53	1.5	297
17	Cl	314	31.6	10	329
19	K	25,900	2.2	1.5	362
20	Ca	36,300	0.43	9.5	371
26	Fe	50,000	2.5	11.0	514
48	Cd		2500	5.3	1028
56	Ba		1.25	8	1252

Hydrogen has a second advantage which depends on the fact that it is about the same weight as the neutron. By means of momentum and energy balances it can be demonstrated that a neutron will lose all its energy in a head-on collision with a hydrogen atom. The *maximum* possible energy loss in a collision between a neutron and any atom can be determined by the equation

$$r = \left(\frac{A - 1}{A + 1}\right)^2 \tag{6-5}$$

where r is the ratio of the energies of the neutron after and before the collision and A is the mass of the atom. For an atom with a mass of 16 (oxygen), the value of r is 0.78, or a loss of only 22 percent of the original energy. The *average* loss per collision also depends on the angle at which the neutron strikes the nucleus and is somewhat less than the maximum values indicated above. The average energy loss by elastic collision is expressed by

$$r = e^{-\xi} \tag{6-6}$$

where

$$\xi = 1 - \frac{(A - 1)^2}{2A} \ln\left(\frac{A + 1}{A - 1}\right) \tag{6-7}$$

The average energy loss per collision for hydrogen is 63 percent. The average energy loss per collision for oxygen is only 12 percent. The number of collisions necessary to reduce the neutron energy from 2 Mev to 0.025 ev is much smaller for hydrogen than for any other element. Some values for the number of collisions required for thermalization[1] are given in Table 6-1.

With both of these factors weighted heavily in favor of hydrogen, it is obvious that the range of a neutron passing through sedimentary rock is determined largely by the amount of hydrogen in the rock. This hydrogen is contained primarily in water and/or hydrocarbon. Since the concentration of hydrogen in oil and water is about the same, it does not matter to the neutron which of these is present; the moderating effect is the same. But since the water must ordinarily be contained in the pore spaces of the rock, the neutron log reflects the amount of rock porosity. If the fluid in the pores is gas, the hydrogen concentration is much lower, and the moderating effect is less pronounced. A gas-bearing formation responds like a formation of low porosity.

[1] After it has lost most of its energy to the moderator, a neutron still possesses that energy that all atoms have because of thermal agitation. This energy is temperature dependent, but corresponds to about 1/40 ev.

When a neutron has been slowed down or moderated to thermal energy levels, it is capable of entering into capture reactions with the atoms of the moderator. Two of these are of special interest. The first is the (n, γ) reaction where a neutron is absorbed by the nucleus and the excess energy is emitted as γ radiation. This reaction occurs readily with most elements; the wavelength of the emitted γ rays is characteristic of the particular element involved. The second reaction of interest is the (n, α) reaction which occurs with some elements, the most favorable being boron. In this reaction a neutron is absorbed and an α particle is emitted, with the boron changing to lithium. The reaction is used primarily in counters for counting thermal neutrons.

RADIATION MEASURING DEVICES

The devices in current use by logging companies for measuring or counting the amount of radiation fall into two classes: those depending on the ionization of a gas, and those depending on the fluorescence of a crystal to activate a photomultiplier tube. The first class may be divided into three subgroups: the ionization chamber, the Geiger-Müller counter, and the proportional counter.

Gas Ionization Counters

Ionization Chamber. A simple sketch of an ionization chamber is shown in Fig. 6-5. The body of the chamber is a metal cylinder which forms one of the electrodes. Through the center of the chamber, and insulated from it, is a rod which forms the other electrode. This central electrode is charged positively, relative to the outer one. The chamber is filled with the inert gas argon, and in order to increase the possibility of an incident ray causing ionization, the gas is usually under high pressure. When an incident γ photon passes through the chamber, there is about a 1 to 3 percent chance that it will cause ionization of the gas. The free electrons created by the ionization move under the

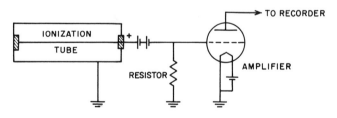

Fig. 6-5. Schematic illustration of a gas ionization type of counter.

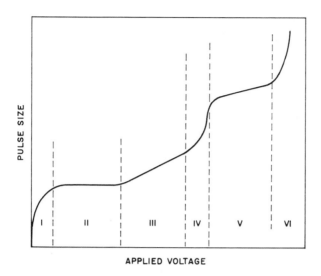

Fig. 6-6. Variation of pulse size with applied voltage for a gas ionization counter. (After *Principles of Nuclear Reactor Engineering* by S. Glasstone. Copyright 1955 by D. Van Nostrand Co.)

potential gradient toward the central electrode while the positively charged argon nuclei move toward the outer shell. If the voltage difference between the two electrodes is of the order of 100 to 300 volts, the collection efficiency will be 100 percent, but there will not be any secondary ionization within the gas. This is region II in Fig. 6-6.

The movement of the charged particles to the electrodes permits current to flow in the external circuit. This current in flowing through the resistor causes a potential drop across it. Since the current is very small, the resistance is made very large (10^{11} ohms) in order that the potential may be measurable. The potential drop from the resistor is applied to an amplifier which magnifies the signal for transmission to the recorder. The necessity for using a very high resistance which may be temperature sensitive is one of the operating drawbacks of the ionization chamber for logging. It is otherwise a very rugged instrument and functions well under the difficult conditions encountered in this service. The fact that it has such a low counting efficiency is overcome by making the chamber large, but sensitivity to formation changes is thereby lost.

Geiger-Müller Counter. The sketch of Fig. 6-5 will serve to illustrate the Geiger counter also. The potential between the electrodes is now in the 600-1000-volt region; the central wire is made very small so that the potential gradient in its vicinity is very high; and the external resistance is reduced to something of the order of 1000 ohms. The gas in the tube is at a subatmospheric pressure. Ionization of the gas is caused in the same manner as in the ionization chamber and also by recoil electrons emitted by the metal wall of the tube during the γ-ray bombardment. The free electrons formed by the ionization now move very rapidly toward the central electrode because of the high potential across the tube. The high-speed electrons reach energy levels at which they are capable of causing ionization on their own. These secondary electrons in turn cause more ionization until an avalanche results with ionization occurring over the entire length of the central electrode. The original ionization is thus multiplied many times and the current which flows through the external circuit is now of the order of 10^8 times that which flowed in the ionization chamber. The actual pulse size is sensitive to the applied voltage as indicated by region V of Fig. 6-6; therefore, the number of pulses is measured instead of the ionization current. The tube has a recovery time of approximately 2×10^{-4} sec. It can therefore count about 5000 pulses per second.

In the operation of the Geiger counter there is some danger that the tube will move into region VI where any initial ionization will cause the tube to discharge continuously and hence become ineffective as a counter. There is also a tendency for the Geiger tube to pulsate once the discharge process starts. Pulsation is caused by the positively charged ions. Because of their size and because they are moving under a lower potential gradient, these ions arrive at the outer electrode about 10^{-4} sec after the central avalanche has occurred. The positive ions can cause emission of additional electrons from the wall of the tube that will start the process over again. To prevent this it is customary to use an electronic quenching circuit, or to mix about 10 percent of a polyatomic molecular compound with the argon gas, e.g., ethyl alcohol. This quench gas must have a lower ionization potential than the main gas, it must have broad ultraviolet absorption bands, and when excited it must dissociate rather than radiate.

The Geiger counter does not have the external resistance problem of the ionization chamber, but it does have other disadvantages. Since it is operated near the continuous discharge region, it requires better voltage control, even though the counting rate is voltage insensitive. The voltage on the tube is higher, and this creates insulation problems. Its counting efficiency is of the same order as the ionization chamber (1 to 3 percent) so that it must be made large to obtain an adequate sample. The small size of the central wire makes it vibration sensitive (microphonic).

Proportional Counter.   Construction of the proportional counter is essentially the same as the Geiger counter, but it operates at a lower voltage. In logging work this tube is usually used to detect neutrons, and consequently it is filled with boron trifluoride gas enriched in the $_5B^{10}$ isotope, or with a gas containing $_2He^3$. The tube walls may be lined with boron. The ionization of the gas is accomplished by using the (n, α) reaction to form an α particle, and the α particle causes a subsequent heavy ionization. The voltage on the tube is such that an avalanche ionization occurs, but only very near the central electrode and therefore over a very small portion of the electrode. With the avalanche so restricted, a considerable amplification factor (10^5) is obtained, but the size of the avalanche is still proportional to the original number of the ion pairs formed by the α particle, hence the name proportional counter.

The size of the pulse from a proportional counter depends on the voltage which is applied to the tube. Therefore, proportional counters are usually arranged to count pulses rather than ion current. The high voltage (500 volts) is still an insulation problem, but very accurate control of the voltage is unnecessary. The small central wire used to obtain the high voltage gradients make this instrument microphonic just as in the case of the G-M tube. It has the additional disadvantage that if filled with boron trifluoride it becomes very sensitive to the temperature of the wellbore because of the high reactivity of the fluoride.

A proportional counter has a detection efficiency of about 10 percent. It is gamma insensitive, and has a recovery time of the order of 1 μsec. It can therefore count particles arriving within very short time intervals, and is at least 200 times better than a G-M counter in this respect.

Scintillation Counters

All the instruments described thus far have depended on ion pair production in a gas to translate radiation into an electric signal. One of the earliest methods of detecting radiation depended on the fact that certain materials, called phosphors, emit flashes of light when exposed to radiation. Originally, it was necessary to count these flashes with the aid of a microscope, and consequently the method was too tedious to compete with the gas ionization devices. Recent development of the photomultiplier tube has made it possible to do the counting automatically, and the discovery of a number of substances that are transparent to the light they emit, e.g., naphthalene, anthracene, diphenyl, thallium-activated sodium iodide, europium-activated lithium iodide, and calcium and magnesium tungstates, has made this the most important

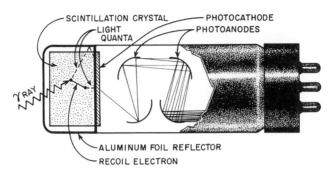

Fig. 6-7. Schematic illustration of a scintillation counter.

type of counter today. Sodium iodide crystals are replacing the G-M tube and the ionization chamber for counting γ radiation, and when shielded with cadmium, they can be used for counting thermal neutrons. Lithium iodide crystals are used for counting a combination of thermal and epithermal neutrons. The high density of the phosphor, as compared with that of gas, results in a very high efficiency for this type of counter (50-80 percent) and makes it possible to use very short counters, with a consequent improvement in formation detail. Counters with an active length of less than 8 in. are now in general use.

The operation of a scintillation counter is illustrated in Fig. 6-7. A γ ray entering the thallium-activated sodium iodide crystal interacts with electrons in the crystal and produces a flash of light. This light in turn strikes the sensitive surface of the photocathode and causes it to emit one (or more) primary electrons. This electron is drawn to the first anode, which it strikes with sufficient energy to cause the emission of five or more secondary electrons. These are then accelerated to the second anode, which is at a higher voltage, and the process is repeated. At each anode an amplification of the current occurs, so that for a tube with ten plates an amplification of about a millionfold is obtained. The current is now of sufficient strength to be handled by ordinary electronic amplifiers. The extremely short duration of the light flashes (10^{-9} to 10^{-6} sec) permits a very high counting rate. The intensity of the flash of light and the amplitude of the output from the photomultiplier are proportional. The intensity of the light flash is also proportional to the energy of the incident γ ray. This proportionality makes it possible to count only those incident rays of a given wavelength by electronically separating only those pulses of a selected strength.

Scintillation counters are expensive and very sensitive to voltage changes, as well as requiring very high voltages on the photomultiplier tube (900 volts). The big problem comes in their use at high temperatures, since the sensitive surface on the photocathode will melt at temperatures above 150°F. As a result, insulation or refrigeration is often needed. Not only should the insulation keep the tube below the melting point, but it should also maintain it at as low a temperature as possible; this eliminates much of the background noise caused by the emission of thermal electrons from the cathode.

RADIOACTIVITY LOGGING METHODS

Gamma-Ray Logging

Figure 6-8 is a schematic representation of a radioactivity logging sonde. The upper counter on the sonde is used for counting the natural

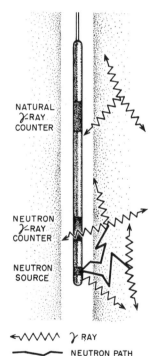

γ radiation from the formations. Since this radiation is so much less intense than the radiation induced in the formations by the neutron source, it is necessary to locate this counter several feet above the neutron logging counter. The difference in the depth reference is accounted for on the log by storing the information from the upper counter in a delaying circuit and then plotting it on the log at the reference point for the neutron system.

All rocks contain some radioactive material. The clay minerals formed during the decomposition of igneous rocks have very high absorption and ion exchange capacities. They are therefore able to absorb the heavy radioelements released during the decomposition of other minerals, as well as to hold those originally contained in the feldspars and micas from which the clays are derived. This process results in the unusually heavy concentration of radioelements in shales as compared to sandstones. Carbonate rocks are not produced by weathering, but are the result of the deposition of the skeletal remnants

Fig. 6-8. Schematic illustration of a radioactivity logging operation.

of marine organisms. Since living bodies naturally tend to eliminate radioactive elements, carbonate rocks as they are formed would normally

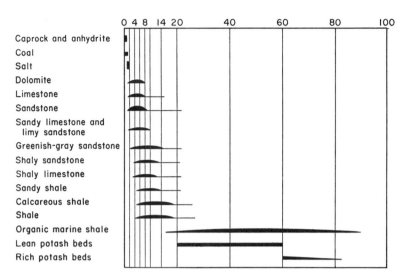

Fig. 6-9. Radioactivity levels of various sedimentary rocks. (After Russell, courtesy of AAPG.)

be expected to have a very low radioactivity level. During the formation of secondary porosity or dolomitization, solution waters can bring in and deposit some radioelements, so these sections might occasionally show a higher level of radioactivity than the undisturbed primary deposits.

Figure 6-9 shows graphically the distribution of radioactivity in various sedimentary rocks (15). The differences in radioactivity level between the limestones, dolomites, and sandstones are relatively insignificant when compared with the shales, particularly the marine shales. The principal use of the γ-ray log, then, is to distinguish between the shales and the non-shales. It is therefore a lithology log, and in many instances it is remarkably similar to the SP curve. It is especially useful in cases where the SP is not diagnostic, as for example in salty muds, oil-base muds, or in high-resistivity formations. Figure 6-10 illustrates how the different types of sedimentary rocks appear on a γ-ray log.

In certain cases the γ-ray curve may be used to estimate the amount of shale in a shaly sand; however, because of the wide possible variation in the radioactivity limit for a given shale, an empirical correlation must be determined for the particular formations under consideration. This information can be useful in interpreting other logs, such as the neutron log, the sonic log, or electric logs. The amount of shale in a carbonate section can be determined similarly, but in this case the use of the information is quite different. An argillaceous carbonate section is formed by precipitation of a very fine lime mud with the clay, and such sections do not make good carbonate reservoirs, except in a few special instances. Therefore, shaly carbonate sections can usually be discarded when considering formations for further evaluation work.

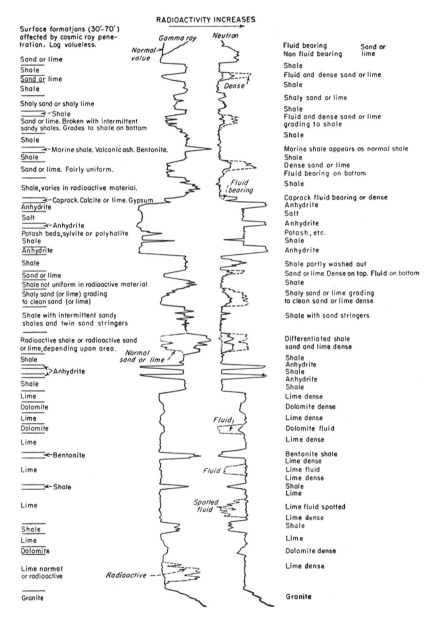

Fig. 6-10. Typical response of gamma-ray and neutron curves to various types of formations. (Courtesy of Lane-Wells Company.)

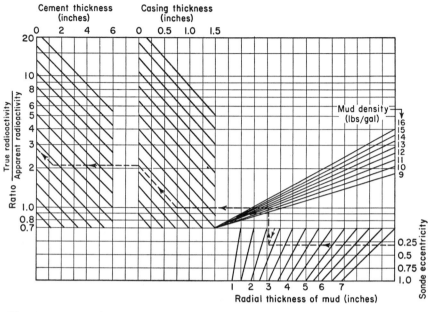

Fig. 6-11. Gamma-ray departure curves taking into account five wellbore parameters. (After Blanchard and Dewan, courtesy of *The Petroleum Engineer*.)

In attempting to use γ-ray logs quantitatively, it is important to recognize that the γ-radiation developed in the formation must pass through a section of rock, mud, and possibly casing and cement. A theoretically correct method (4) of allowing for the absorption of γ rays by these materials is shown in Fig. 6-11. Sonde eccentricity in this figure is defined as the displacement of the sonde from an axial position, expressed as a fraction of the maximum possible displacement. Thus the sonde eccentricity is zero for a centered sonde and unity for a sonde lying against the wall of the hole. Since the sonde usually rides against the wall of the hole or the casing, the eccentricity is normally unity for open holes and some lesser fraction for cased holes. Mud thickness in the figure is the average thickness of mud around the sonde. In an open hole it is equal to one-half the difference between the hole diameter and the sonde diameter. The example illustrated on the chart is for a sonde eccentricity of 0.3 in., 2.25 in. of mud, 11 lb mud weight, $\frac{3}{4}$-in. casing thickness and 1.3 in. of cement. This chart does not allow for any contribution to the signal from radioactivity in the cement or the mud, and this should be subtracted if it is known. It is apparent from the chart that the corrections would ordinarily be very small for logging in open hole.

The presence of beds of finite thickness introduces problems in radioactivity logging as well as in electric logging (12), but the problems are of a different nature. Figure 6-12 shows the response of a γ-ray counter opposite a finite bed whose radioactivity is higher than the surroundings. (a) represents the idealized condition and indicates the concentration of radioactivity within the bed. In (b) the effect of the length of the counter is taken into consideration. If a counter of a finite length were moved very slowly past the bed, and if the radiation from the bed were only in a horizontal direction, then the counter would start to indicate an increased signal when the top of the counter reached the bottom of the bed. This signal would increase directly with the movement of the counter until a full signal would be indicated when the counter was completely within the bed. The bed boundary coincides with the halfway point between the two radiation levels. The response indicated in (c) would be expected if a counter of zero length were moved very slowly past a bed where the radiation was emitted in all directions. The effect is to round the corners of the log. In actual practice, the log indicates a combination of the effects of (b) and (c). The response of (d) would occur if a counter of zero length were moved past a bed where the radiation was horizontal only, but the counter was moved at a fairly high speed. This is the result of the statistical variations in the counting rate. Some explanation of this point is in order.

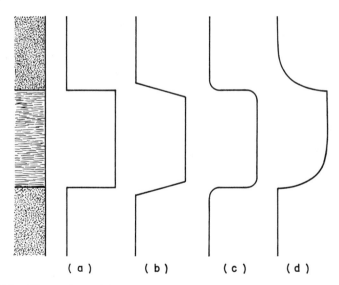

Fig. 6-12.   Illustrations of the effects of bed thickness and statistical variations on a radioactivity log.

Radioactive processes are completely random. The number of radio-active decays that will take place over a long period of time for a given element may be known with some certainty, but there is no way of knowing whether or not any will take place within a short time interval. If a counter were allowed to remain opposite a point in the formation shown in Fig. 6-12, a number of fluctuations would be observed because of the random nature of the process, although the average of these readings would be the radioactive level indicated for the bed. These random variations are known as the meaningless signal. The meaningful signal is the difference in radioactivity between the bed in question and the adjacent beds, or the difference between the average radiation levels counted at these two beds. For a good radioactivity log, the ratio of the meaningful to the meaningless variations should be between six and ten. This ratio, or quality index, can be obtained in practice by putting an adjustable averaging circuit in the recorder. Averaging, however, is accomplished at a sacrifice of speed of response, so that it is necessary to slow down the logging speed as the averaging becomes greater.

A schematic arrangement of the recording circuit is shown in Fig. 6-13. The pulses from the detector are impressed on a capacitor and build up a charge. As the charge increases, some of it is permitted to leak off through the high resistance. The voltage across the condenser is then a measure of the number of pulses being received from the counter per unit time. If there is a sudden change in the level of radioactivity, there will be a gradual change in the voltage across the condenser according to the equation

$$\Delta V = 1 - e^{-t/rC} \tag{6-8}$$

where ΔV is the fractional change in the condenser voltage from the old to the new level in the time interval t, r is the resistance of the resistor, and C is the capacitance of the condenser. The multiple rC is known as the time constant and usually is set between 1 and 10 sec.

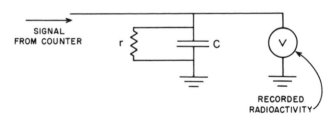

Fig. 6-13.   Circuit for averaging statistical variations.

The introduction of the time constant in the circuit to effect a time average causes a delay in the response of the recording instrument to changes in the level of radioactivity and gives a distortion of the log curves like that shown in Fig. 6-12d. If the logging speed is high, it is possible to pass a thin bed without ever recording the true value of the radiation. Also, if the bed boundaries are selected at the midpoint between the two radiation levels, the time constant effect will make the bed appear too high.

In running a radioactivity log it is customary to make a 2- or 3-minute statistical check opposite a zone where there is a high counting rate in order to establish the quality index. It is also customary to repeat 100 or 200 ft of log, preferably over the zone of most interest, as a further check on statistical variations. The time constant and the logging speed are very important in radiation logging and should always be marked on the log. The system used to correct for the time lag shown in Fig. 6-12 should also be noted on the log.

In the past commercially available γ-ray logs have been calibrated in various units. *Inches of deflection* for a standard known radiation intensity have been used by Lane-Wells, Welex, and Western; *microroentgens per hour* have been used by Pan Geo Atlas Corp. and McCullough Tool Co.; Schlumberger has used the *microgram radium equivalent per ton*. The API has recently established an empirical calibration standard at the Nuclear Logging Calibration Facility, University of Houston, Houston, Texas. The test pit contains two sections of neat cement, one of a high- and one of a low-radioactivity level. The difference in the radioactivity of the two sections is defined as 200 API γ-ray units. It is expected that all logging companies will use this standard in the future. The details of the recommended calibration procedure are outlined in API RP 33 (1).

Neutron Logging

The neutron source and the lower counter shown in Fig. 6-8 comprise the equipment for making a neutron log. The spacing between the counter and the source is 12 to 27 in. Three different types of neutron logs are possible, depending on the type of counter that is used. These are the neutron-gamma log, the neutron-thermal neutron log, and the neutron-epithermal neutron log.

Figure 6-8 illustrates schematically the principles of neutron-gamma logging. The detector in this case counts γ radiation, and so it must be shielded from the direct radiation in the source reaction. The source, located at the bottom of the tool, is capable of producing a flux of the order of 5×10^6 fast neutrons per second. These neutrons emanate in all directions, pass through the borehole fluid, and penetrate the surrounding rocks. In this process they are moderated until they reach the thermal energy level. They then diffuse for a period of time, and eventually are captured in an (n, γ) reaction. If the amount of hydrogen in the formation is high (gypsum, high porosity, or shale), the capture will take place close to the source. Since the counter is a foot or more distant, the secondary γ radiation produced in the capture reaction has very little chance of being received by the detector, and the log reading is very low. If the amount of hydrogen in the formation is low (dense limestone, hard sandstone, anhydrite), the length of the neutron path will be much greater, and the capture reaction will occur in the vicinity of the counter. The log reading in this case is high. Figure 6-14 is a section of a neutron log with the corresponding log of the porosity from the core analysis. A qualitative correspondence between the porosity and the neutron log reading is evident. There are no shales on this log,

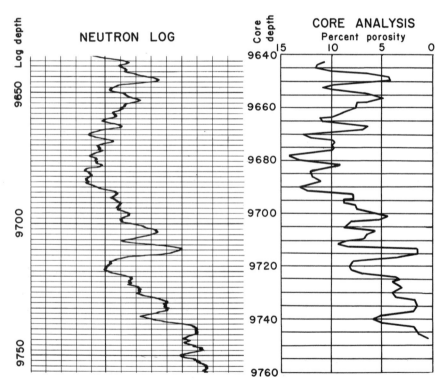

Fig. 6-14. Comparison of a neutron log with core analysis. (Courtesy of the California Standard Co.)

but a shaly section would respond as if it had a porosity of 30 to 40 percent, unless the section had been washed out; then it would correspond to 100 percent porosity.

Neutron logging systems based on the (n, γ) reaction in the formation are somewhat sensitive to the chemical constitution of the rock and the rock fluids. Table 6-1 gives the capture cross sections of various elements. Of those present in significant quantities in sedimentary formations, the cross sections range from 0.0002 for oxygen to 31.6 for chlorine. In addition to these differences in the capture cross section that influence the migration length of a neutron, there are also differences in the intensity of the emitted γ ray of capture. These two factors influence the log reading.

Neutron-neutron logs do not have the problem of shielding the counter from the γ radiation of the source reaction, since the counters used with these logs are not sensitive to γ radiation. The process of emission of fast neutrons and moderation by the borehole fluid and the formations is the same for these logs as for the neutron-gamma log, but the method of counting the number of thermal neutrons in the vicinity of the detector is different. In the neutron-thermal neutron log, the thermal neutron population may be determined with a proportional counter. This log, like the neutron-gamma log is sensitive to variations in the capture cross section of the elements in the formation, but it is not influenced by the fact that the γ rays of capture may vary.

The neutron-epithermal neutron log uses a counter that measures the population of neutrons just before they reach the thermal level. Epithermal neutrons, which have energies in the range of 50 ev to 100,000 ev, can be measured with a lithium iodide scintillation counter. This log is almost completely insensitive to variations in capture cross section, because it measures the neutron population at an energy level where the probability of a capture reaction has not yet become very large. It should be pointed out that these chemical effects are of a second order compared to the role that hydrogen plays in the neutron logging system. These small differences can be useful, however, as will be demonstrated in the section on chlorine logging.

There are a number of factors which complicate the application of the neutron curve for the measurement of porosity:

1. While hydrogen may be present in the fluid filling the pore space, it may also be present in chemically bound water (gypsum) or physically bound water (shales). The γ-ray curve can be helpful in this aspect for locating the argillaceous material. If the γ-ray curve

is less than one division off the clean formation baseline, with normal sensitivity, a shale correction is usually unnecessary.

2. The wellbore represents a condition of 100 percent porosity through which neutrons must pass before they reach the formation. This water has a very strong moderating effect, so the counting rate will reflect changes in hole size and movement of the tool from one position to another in the well. It is usually assumed that the logging sonde is lying against the wall of the hole.

3. The counting rate is sensitive to the composition of the drilling mud, but this effect is minor.

4. Gamma radiation from the source may be reflected from the formations into the counter. If a scintillation counter is used, this radiation may be eliminated by a pulse height analyzer, since it has usually lost most of its energy in transit.

5. If the neutron log detector is of the γ-ray type, it may also count natural radiation. This effect is minor.

6. The presence of casing and cement causes a shift in the γ-ray and neutron curves. While this effect is readily recognized, it does complicate the quantitative use of the neutron curve. Very often the thickness of the cement sheath around the casing is not known with certainty.

7. Design of the logging tool varies from one company to another, both in the source to detector spacing and in the strength and spectrum of the neutron source. Neutron curves from different service companies which are obtained with different tools cannot be compared directly.

8. The response of the log to changes in porosity is not linear. In addition, the theory of the processes involved in the moderation and capture of neutrons is extremely complex, and theoretical solutions may only approximate the actual condition.

A number of service companies have prepared charts which show the relation between porosity and signal strength of their neutron logging instruments for the various cases that are encountered in practice. These charts were prepared by making laboratory measurements in test pits where the rock porosities were known within close limits. If there is no other information available, these charts may be used in the field to determine porosity. If it is at all possible, however, field calibration curves should be prepared for the area and formations in which extensive logging is anticipated. The service company charts can be useful in the preparation of such curves to normalize all log readings to the same basis of borehole size, casing, cement thickness, etc.

Stick, Swift, and Hartline (16) have developed a theoretical equation for the response of a neutron log based on an approximate model which assumes diffusion of the neutrons at all energy levels. Their equation for the counting rate of the neutron logging detector is:

$$N_a = \frac{K}{S} e^{-[(\mu_H - \mu_f)S\phi + \mu_f S]} + N_t \qquad (6\text{-}9)$$

where N_a is the counting rate, N_t is that part of the response caused by neutrons reaching the detector through the tool body, S is the equivalent source to detector spacing, μ_H and μ_f are factors expressing the fast neutron transmission characteristics of the hydrogen and the formation rock, and K is a constant which includes the effects of tool design, source strength, borehole diameter, and the borehole contents. This equation assumes that all of the hydrogen that is present is in the form of fluid. When changed to the logarithmic form, the equation is:

$$\ln(N_a - N_t) = -(\mu_H - \mu_f)S\phi - \mu_f S + \ln \frac{K}{S} \qquad (6\text{-}10)$$

This equation indicates that the logarithm of the counting rate should be proportional to the porosity, a point that was clearly demonstrated in an earlier paper by Brown and Bowers (5). The *slope* of the straight line that is obtained by plotting $(N_a - N_t)$ versus ϕ on semilog paper depends only on the source to detector spacing S, and is independent of the borehole size. The porosity curves for different hole sizes plot as a series of parallel lines.

An older method of plotting calibration curves for neutron logs is based on the empirical assumption that the logarithm of the porosity is proportional to the counting rate. There is no theoretical justification for this method of plotting. It works satisfactorily in the medium porosity range, but it has been shown that very large deviations from this relation exist at high and low porosities.

In making a calibration curve for neutron logs from field data, the following procedure is suggested:

1. The available porosity data from core analysis are plotted on a linear scale of such a size that the resulting curve of core data will correspond approximately to the neutron log curve. Figure 6-14 is an example of such a plot. By using this curve as an overlay on the log, the core analysis depth scale can be adjusted to correspond to the depth scale on the log.

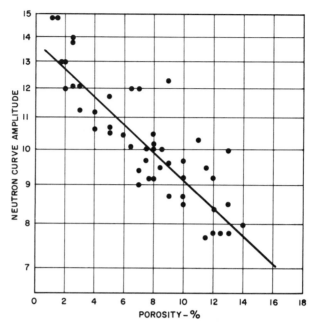

Fig. 6-15. Neutron-porosity calibration curve derived from the data of Fig. 6-14.

2. A radiation reference level is selected on the log which corresponds to a point of 100 percent porosity, e.g., a washed-out shale section. The readings on the log are now measured from this reference, using convenient units. The selection of this reference point essentially corrects for the value of N_t.

3. The data are plotted on semilog graph paper. The log readings are plotted on the logarithm scale and the porosity data from the core analysis are plotted on the linear scale. It should be possible to put a straight line through the data points. Figure 6-15 is a calibration of this type determined from the data of Fig. 6-14 for the interval from 9686 ft to 9746 ft.

4. Sometimes a better fit between the neutron log and the core data can be obtained if the core data are weighted on a 1-2-1 or 1-3-1 basis. This system of taking a weighted average allows for the fact that the formation above and below the source-detector arrangement also contributes to the reading of the log, but not so heavily as the footage directly opposite the tool.

An alternate method of plotting calibration curves has been suggested by Stick wherein the reading from the log is plotted on a linear scale and the porosity is plotted on an exponential scale. This type of plot is represented by Fig. 6-16. The advantage in this method of plotting lies in the fact that any convenient reference on the neutron log may be used; it is not necessary to determine a point corresponding to 100 percent porosity.

In an attempt to standardize different neutron logs, the API has established a Neutron Calibration Pit at the Nuclear Logging Test Facility. This pit contains three relatively pure calcium carbonate rocks of widely different porosities plus a water section. The API Neutron Unit is defined in terms of the log response in a section of Indiana limestone of 19 percent porosity. It is obvious from equation 6-9 that such a calibration will not define the response of all logging tools over the full range of operating conditions.

Figure 6-17 shows the response of a particular type of neutron-neutron logging tool, having spacings of 14 in., 18 in., and 24 in., to changes in porosity from 0 to 45 percent. (These curves are developed from Fig. 4 of the paper by Stick *et al.*) The graph shows that the short spacing curve is most sensitive to porosity changes in the high-porosity region, while the long spacing curve is most effective in the low-porosity region. It is apparent that if all three of these curves were normalized

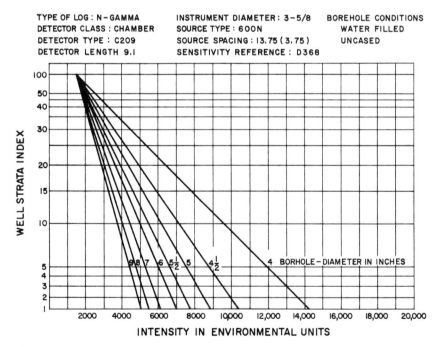

Fig. 6-16. Commercial neutron-porosity chart using an exponential porosity scale. (Courtesy of Well Surveys, Inc.)

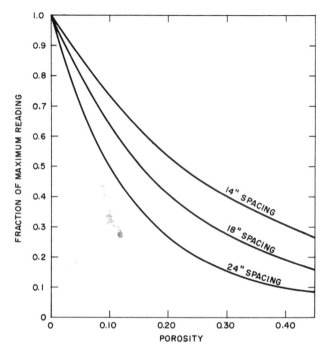

Fig. 6-17. The effect of spacing on the response of a neutron log to porosity changes.

to give the same reading at 19 percent porosity, they would not agree at the high and low ends of the scale.

NEW DEVELOPMENTS IN RADIOACTIVITY LOGGING

Density Log (14)

When γ radiation passes through matter, the rays may interact with the orbital electrons of the atoms in one of three ways. First, the γ ray may be absorbed and an electron-positron pair produced; this requires very high-energy γ radiation. Second, the γ ray may be absorbed by the electron and the electron removed from its normal orbit; this process occurs primarily with γ rays of less than 0.5 Mev. Third, the γ ray may rebound from the electron and give up some of its energy in a process known as Compton scattering; this is the process that occurs most frequently when formations are bombarded with radiation in the energy range of 0.6 to 1.3 Mev.

The probability of a γ ray colliding with an electron is proportional to the electron density. Since the ratio of the charge to mass (Z/A) is approximately 0.5 for most of the elements likely to be encountered in logging, the electron density is approximately proportional to the density of the material. This means that the decrease in the strength of a beam of γ radiation passing through matter is approximately proportional to the density of the matter. Expressed mathematically,

$$\frac{dN}{dS} = - C\rho \qquad (6.11)$$

or in integral form,

$$N = N_0\, e^{-C\rho S} \qquad (6\text{-}12)$$

where N_0 is the source strength, S is the spacing between the source and the detector, N is the counting rate, ρ is the density, and C is a constant.

Two density logging tools that are available commercially are shown schematically in Fig. 6-18. The Lane-Wells Company Densilog uses a cobalt-60 source having γ-ray energies in the range of 1.1 to 1.3 Mev with a half-life of 5.2 years. A Geiger counter is used for counting the radiation received from the source by way of the formation. The McCullough Tool Co. density logger (3) uses a cesium-137 source having γ-ray energies of about 0.6 Mev with a half-life of 30 years. A scintillation counter is used for receiving the radiation. Both the source and the counter are collimated. It is claimed for both tools that the penetration of the formation is about 6 in. The purpose of the discriminator on the McCullough tool is to limit the detected radiation to those γ rays of an energy level that correspond to the deepest penetration.

These tools have been calibrated in test pits with materials of known density. Because of the possibility of variations in the source strength and the influence of the hole diameter and borehole fluid on the readings of the devices, it is practically essential that beds of known density be available in the well so that the tool can be calibrated under field conditions. The effect of the mud cake and the roughness of the hole are particularly important in interpreting the results. These factors provide an alternate path through the mud for transmission of the γ radiation from the source to the counter, and if there is more than $\frac{1}{4}$ in. separation between the tool and the formation, a significant error in the density measurement can result. The magnitude of the error will depend on the contrast between the mud properties and the formation properties. In this vein also, the maximum logging speed is limited to about 25 ft per minute since experience has shown that higher speeds cause the sonde to lose contact with the wall of the borehole.

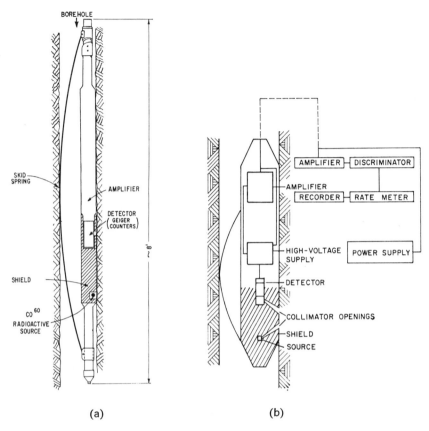

Fig. 6-18. Schematic drawings of commercial density logging tools: (a) Lane-Wells Densilog and (b) McCullough density tool. (Pickell and Heacock, courtesy of *Geophysics;* and Baker, courtesy of the AIME.)

The density of sedimentary rocks is of the order of 2.6 g/cc to 3.0 g/cc. The density of the fluid in the pore space is between 0.7 g/cc and 1.0 g/cc, and since the depth of investigation of the device is limited to the invaded zone, the fluid density will probably correspond closely to that of the mud filtrate. Some representative grain densities are given in Table 6-2. An average value of the grain density for clean sandstone is 2.65 g/cc, and the average density of shale is approximately 2.70 g/cc. The relative amounts of kaolinite, illite, and montmorillonite can have a great influence on the shale density, so experience in a given area is important for proper interpretation. The similarity of the densities of sandstone and shale allows this log to be used as a means of measuring the porosity of shaly sandstones.

TABLE 6-2.   GRAIN DENSITIES

Anhydrite	2.95 g/cc
Dolomite	2.85
Calcite	2.71
Limestone	2.70
Quartz	2.66
Kaolinite	2.63
Illite	2.76
Montmorillonite	2.00
Halite	2.17
Coal	1.00-1.80

The bulk density measured by the density logging device is a simple weighted average of the densities of the rock and the pore fluid. Once these densities are known, the porosity can be calculated from the equation

$$\phi = \frac{\rho_r - \rho_b}{\rho_r - \rho_f} \tag{6-13}$$

where ρ_r is the density of the rock matrix, ρ_f is the density of the fluid, and ρ_b is the measured bulk density. This equation is shown in Fig. 6-19 for various types of formations.

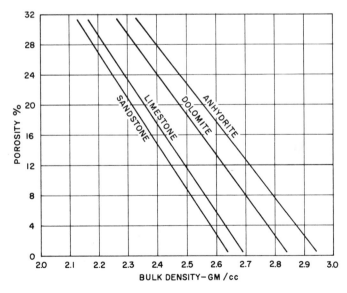

Fig. 6-19. Relation between porosity and bulk density for various sedimentary rocks.

Logging for Chlorine

It was mentioned previously that a neutron curve in which the detector measures epithermal neutrons is not sensitive to the chemical nature of the formations and therefore reflects only the amount of hydrogen that is present. The neutron-gamma curve, on the other hand, is influenced by the capture cross section of the various elements and the energy of the γ ray of capture that is emitted. Reference to Table 6-1 indicates that of the elements found in measurable quantities in the earth, the capture cross section of chlorine is several times that of any other element. Also, the energy of the capture γ ray from chlorine is of the order of 5.0 to 7.8 Mev, and this is much higher than that of many of the other elements. The combination of these two factors makes the neutron-gamma log particularly sensitive to chlorine. By running the neutron-epithermal neutron log simultaneously with the neutron-gamma log, it is possible to detect chlorine by differences in the response of the two curves.

In practice two counters are run on the sonde with a neutron source. The tool is adjusted so that the two curves are superimposed when it is opposite a porous interval which contains essentially no chlorine. Both curves will then show the same reading for zones which contain little chlorine, and the neutron-gamma curve reading will be higher than the neutron-neutron curve reading when there is much chlorine present. The amount of separation of the two curves is a measure of the amount of chlorine in the zone. (Normalization of the logs opposite a salt-water zone would be equally satisfactory; the logs would then separate opposite intervals containing oil.) If the concentration of chlorine in the formation waters is fairly uniform, the separation of the curves can be used quantitatively to estimate the oil saturation.

Figure 6-20 shows an effective method of representing data from a chlorine log. The readings from the neutron-gamma (chlorine) curve are plotted as abscissas, and the readings from the neutron-neutron (hydrogen) curve are plotted as ordinates. An approximately straight line can then be established for zones that are known to be 100 percent water saturated, and parallel to this another line is drawn through those points of known minimum water saturation (40 percent in the example). The region between these two values can then be scaled linearly in terms of water saturation. Shaly intervals will give low readings on both curves, and a shaly region on the graph may be established with the aid of the γ-ray curve. Formations which contain

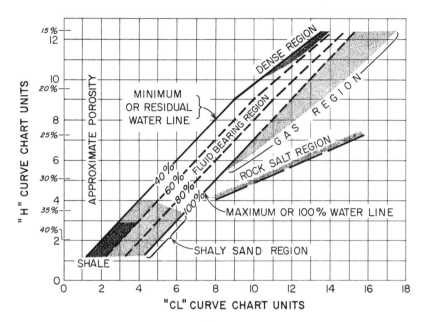

Fig. 6-20. A method for plotting chlorine log data. (After Stick, Swift, and Hartline, courtesy of the AIME.)

dry gas will give high readings on both curves because of the low concentration of hydrogen, but the chlorine curve is influenced more than the hydrogen curve; these points are high and to the right of the water-saturated line. Zones containing rock salt have very high chlorine contents, and these plot far to the right of the water-saturated line.

Chlorine logging is most effective where casing has been set and a sufficient period of time has elapsed to allow the formation fluids to replace the mud filtrate from the invaded zone; this period of time may be anywhere from a few weeks to several months. The thickness of the cement around the casing should be no more than 2 in. Unusual thickness of cement will tend to shift the data points in the direction of the minimum water saturation line. There is also a minimum water salinity beyond which the separation between the curves will not be sufficient. This minimum salinity depends on the porosity: for a porosity of 25 to 35 percent, 35,000 ppm is required; for a porosity of 15 to 25 percent, 50,000 ppm is required; for a porosity of 5 to 15 percent, 75,000 ppm is required.

Figure 6-21 is a sample chlorine log.

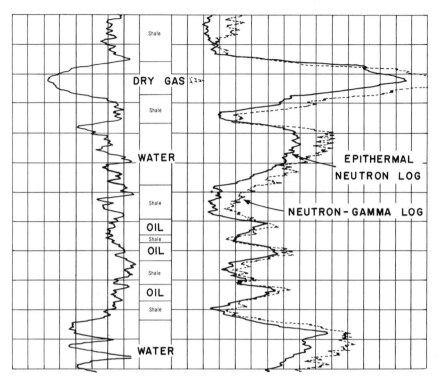

Fig. 6-21. Example of a Chlorinilog. (Courtesy of Lane-Wells Company.)

Neutron Activation Logging

In the last few years radioactivity logging service companies have been attempting to develop a compact source of high-energy neutrons that can be used in spectral or activation logging. The nuclear reaction,

$$_1H^2 + {}_1H^3 \rightarrow {}_2He^4 + {}_0n^1 \text{ (14 Mev)}$$

was known to be a suitable source of such neutrons, but the energy required for the fusion of deuterium and tritium is so great that reaction could be accomplished only with large, high-energy particle accelerators. The problem of miniaturizing such a device and making it rugged enough to operate reliably under the conditions of logging has considerably slowed the progress in the development of this type of source. One such device which is now being field tested is the Lane-Wells Accelatron (17).

The Accelatron tube contains deuterium gas under low pressure. Electrodes in one part of the tube continuously ionize the deuterium gas. The ions are then accelerated by a high-voltage source to a very high velocity, thereby giving them sufficient kinetic energy for the fusion reaction. The target for the accelerated deuterons is a titanium plate in which tritium gas has been dissolved. As the deuterons strike the target, the fusion takes place to produce monochromatic neutrons with an energy of 14 Mev. The tube is operated so as to produce 5×10^7 to 5×10^8 neutrons per second; the source is monitored and controlled continuously to assure that the neutron output is constant. The voltage required to accelerate the deuterium ions is of the order of 100,000 volts and is provided by a miniature Van de Graaff accelerator.

The source strength of the Accelatron is an order of magnitude greater than that of the (α, n) reaction source. This makes the accelerator type of log potentially superior to the ordinary neutron log, and in fact the counting rate has been determined in practice to be better by a factor of five. Also, the higher energy of the source neutrons gives greater penetration of the formation and therefore better sampling. Since the source is operated electrically, it may be turned off while it is handled at the surface so that there is no safety hazard whatever, and no special precautions are necessary for handling and storing it.

Most elements, when activated by neutron bombardment, are transmuted to unstable, γ-ray-emitting isotopes. The radiation is characteristic of the isotope and therefore characteristic of the element from which it was derived. It would appear, then, that by use of a scintillation counter and a multichannel pulse height analyzer, an analysis could be made of the elements which are present in the formation. The presence of carbon would be particularly interesting. Unfortunately, there is always a degradation of the energy of the γ radiation in its passage through the formation on the way to the counter, and the counter sees a rather continuous spectrum of energies from the theoretical value on down. In addition, many of the elements have more than one characteristic energy level. The combination of these two factors makes logging of the formations by spectral analysis an exceedingly difficult task.

A more successful logging system is activation logging, which utilizes the characteristic energy of the γ radiation and also the characteristic rate of decay of the unstable isotopes. Two elements which are of particular interest in activation logging are silicon and oxygen. When bombarded by neutrons, silicon is transmuted to $_{13}Al^{28}$, an aluminum isotope which emits β and γ radiation with a 2.3-minute half-life. Similarly, oxygen is transmuted to $_7N^{16}$, a nitrogen isotope which emits β and γ radiation with a 7.3-sec half-life. These reactions occur only with neutrons having very high energies. Gamma radiation from the silicon reaction has an energy of 1.78 Mev. The activation of oxygen gives radiation with energies of 6.1 and 7.1 Mev.

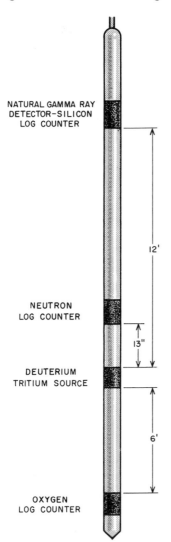

Fig. 6-22. Activation logging sonde.

NATURAL GAMMA RAY DETECTOR−SILICON LOG COUNTER

NEUTRON LOG COUNTER

DEUTERIUM TRITIUM SOURCE

OXYGEN LOG COUNTER

12'

13"

6'

An oxygen activation log is obtained by bombarding the formation with 14-Mev neutrons and then, within a few seconds, measuring the amount of γ radiation having an energy greater than 2.5 Mev. This measurement includes a large portion of the radiation from the oxygen reaction, even that which is degraded on the way to the counter, but it cuts off radiation arising from almost every other source. This is possible because the oxygen activation radiation has such a uniquely high energy. In order to log for silicon in the presence of oxygen, a period of about one minute is allowed to expire between activation and measurement. In this period of time the radiation from the oxygen disappears almost entirely (7.3-sec half-life) while that from the silicon still remains (2.3-minute half-life). The discriminator setting on the silicon log is so low that it includes radiation from the natural radioactivity of the formation. It is therefore necessary to subtract out the γ-ray log to get a true silicon log.

In practice the activation logs may be run as part of a general radioactivity survey. A special sonde is used which contains three counters, two of the γ-ray scintillation type and one a neutron counter, along with the 14-Mev neutron source. These are arranged as shown in Fig. 6-22. On the way into the hole the source is operated and the upper γ-ray counter is used to record a silicon curve. The running-in speed is set so that the time for the counter to reach the activated formation opposite the source is sufficient to allow the oxygen activation to decay. On coming out of the hole, the upper counter is used to record the standard γ-ray curve, the neutron detector records the standard neutron curve, and the lower counter records the oxygen activation log. The speed of logging is set at the optimum for the oxygen curve. (The optimum speed for activation logging can be calculated from the equation

$$V_0 = \frac{0.693L}{t_{1/2}} \tag{6-14}$$

where V_0 is the optimum speed in feet per second, L is the source to detector spacing in feet, and $t_{1/2}$ is the half-life in seconds.) Logging while coming out of the hole produces a set of curves like those shown in Fig. 6-23.

There have not been enough activation logs run to date to determine the practical value of the results. It appears that they may be useful in lithologic correlation and also in the determination of the presence of hydrocarbons when used in combination with other logs.

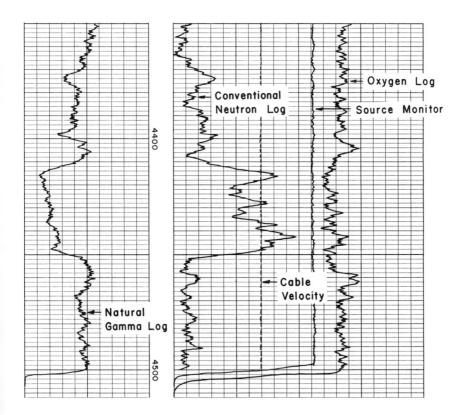

Fig. 6-23. Example of an activation log. (Youmans, Hopkinson, and Stewart, courtesy of the AIME.)

Multispaced Neutron Curves

Work in the Greater Oficina region of Venezuela (10) has indicated that gas-bearing zones can be detected by running two neutron curves with different source to detector spacings. The curves are normalized so that they have the same reading for a water-saturated zone, and then they separate opposite the gas zones. Figure 6-17 illustrates that such a separation would normally be expected. If the 24-in. spacing curve is adjusted so that it has the same reading for 30 percent porosity as the 14-in. curve, then the 24-in. curve will give a relatively higher reading when the porosity is only 10 percent. Therefore, such a separation could indicate a low-porosity zone or a high-porosity zone containing gas. The success of the multispacing technique for locating gas is dependent on all the sands having about the same porosity.

A better method of locating gas would be to run a single neutron curve and a second device which measured porosity by some other means, e.g., the acoustic velocity log, microlog, or the density log. The measurement of porosity by means of these devices is relatively insensitive to the presence of a gaseous hydrocarbon, and a difference in the response of one of these devices as compared to the neutron log would be a clear indication that gas is present.

REFERENCES

1. *API RP 33: Recommended Practice for Standard Calibration and Form for Nuclear Logs:* American Petroleum Institute, Division of Production, Dallas, Texas, 1959.
2. Baker, P. E., Neutron capture gamma-ray spectra of earth formations: *Trans. AIME*, v. 210, 1957, p. 97.
3. Baker, P. E., Density logging with gamma rays: *Trans. AIME*, v. 210, 1957, p. 289.
4. Blanchard, A., and Dewan, J. T., The calibration of gamma ray logs: *The Petroleum Engineer*, August, 1953, p. B-76.
5. Brown, A. A., and Bowers, B., Porosity determination from neutron logs: *The Petroleum Engineer*, v. 30, no. 5, May, 1958, p. B-30.
6. Bush, R. E., and Mardock, E. S., The quantitative application of radioactivity logs: *Trans. AIME*, v. 192, 1951, p. 191.
7. Fearon, R. E., Neutron well logging: *Nucleonics*, v. 4, 1949, p. 30.
8. Fearon, R. E., Gamma ray well logging: *Nucleonics*, v. 4, 1949, p. 70.
9. Glasstone, S., *Textbook of Physical Chemistry*, D. Van Nostrand Company, Inc., Princeton, New Jersey, second edition, 1946.
10. Grosmangin, M., and Walker, E. B., Gas detection by dual-spacing neutron logs in the Greater Oficina area, Venezuela: *Trans. AIME*, v. 210, 1957, p. 140.

11. Hoyer, W. A., Induced nuclear reaction logging: *Formation Evaluation Symposium*, AIME, Houston, Texas, 1960, p. III-43.
12. Kokesh, F. P., Gamma ray logging: *Oil and Gas Jour.*, v. 50, no. 12, July 26, 1951, p. 284.
13. *Lane-Wells Radioactivity Logging:* Lane-Wells Company, Houston, Texas.
14. Pickel, J. J., and Heackock, J. G., Density logging: *Geophysics*, v. XXV, no. 4, August, 1960, p. 891.
15. Russell, W. L., Well logging by radioactivity: *Am. Assoc. Petroleum Geologists Bull.*, v. 25, no. 9, September, 1941, p. 1768.
16. Stick, J. C., Swift, G., and Hartline, R., Present techniques in nuclear radiation logging: *Formation Evaluation Symposium*, AIME, Houston, Texas, 1960, p. II-15.
17. Youmans, A., Hopkinson, E. C., and Stewart, R. M., (D, T) neutron activation logging: *AIME Meeting*, Dallas, Texas, October, 1959, Paper 1304-G.

7

Acoustic Velocity Logging

A newcomer to the field of formation evaluation is the acoustic velocity log. It was originally developed as an aid in the interpretation of seismic data, but it has been found so effective in the determination of porosity that it has already become the standard wireline method of porosity estimation in many areas. The sonic device measures the time of transit of a sonic impulse through a given length of rock, usually either 1 ft or 3 ft. The rate of propagation of the compression wave through the rock depends on the elastic properties of the rock matrix and its contained fluids. Specifically, it depends on the composition of the matrix (sandstone, limestone, etc.), the particular fluid which it contains (oil, water, or gas), and the relative amounts of each that are present (porosity). When the first two of these factors are known, the porosity may be determined readily. Comparisons between the porosity calculated from the sonic log and the porosity determined by core analysis have been excellent in many cases. (See Fig. 7-1.)

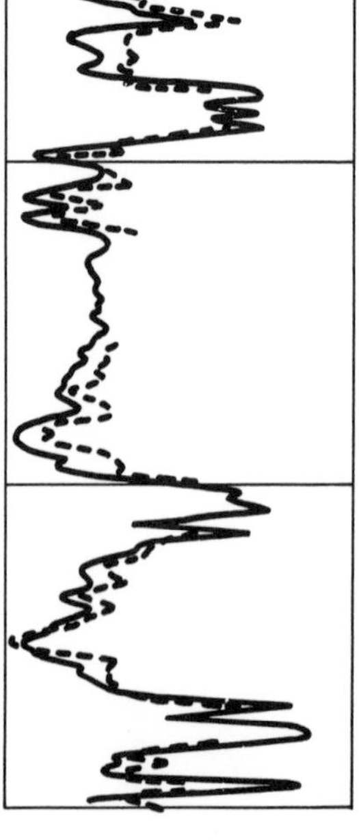

SONIC LOG

23 19 15 11 7 3 Poros.

Core
Porosities

Fig. 7-1. Comparison of the sonic log with core analysis porosity. (Tixier, Alger, and Doh, courtesy of the AIME.)

ACOUSTIC VELOCITY IN POROUS MEDIA

The speed of sound in a body is given theoretically by

$$v = \left(\frac{E + 4/3\mu}{\rho}\right)^{1/2} \tag{7-1}$$

where E is the bulk modulus (or compression modulus), ρ is the density, and μ is the modulus of rigidity (or shear modulus) of the body. This equation should be applicable to any homogeneous material and any heterogeneous material where the size of the individual components is small compared to the sonic wavelength. For a heterogeneous material, average properties must be calculated from the values of the compressibility and density of the individual components.

Equation 7-1 has been applied with moderate success to studies of unconsolidated porous materials. In an extensive study of the speed of sound in porous sedimentary rock, Wyllie, Gregory, and Gardner (8) found that their results agreed fairly well with this equation when the rock samples were unstressed. When an axial force was applied to the rock frame, however, the sonic velocity showed a marked increase. This increase in velocity continued until a pressure of several thousand psi was attained, at which time a limiting, or terminal, velocity was reached. These results are shown in Fig. 7-2 for a Berea sandstone

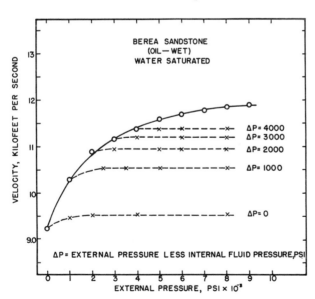

Fig. 7-2. Dependence of acoustic velocity on external pressure for a Berea sandstone. (Wyllie, Gregory, and Gardner, courtesy of *Geophysics*.)

sample. The terminal velocity far exceeded that which would be predicted by equation 7-1, but it was found that for all granular porosity rocks a much simpler empirical equation could be used.

$$\frac{1}{v_r} = \frac{\phi}{v_f} + \frac{(1-\phi)}{v_m} \qquad (7\text{-}2)$$

In this equation v_r is the measured sonic velocity, v_f is the sonic velocity of the fluid in the pore spaces, v_m is the sonic velocity of the matrix material, and ϕ is the fractional porosity. Expressed in another way, the transit time of a sound wave passing through a porous rock is the porosity weighted average of the transit time of sound in the matrix material and the transit time in the fluid which is in the pores. There is, unfortunately, little theoretical justification for this time-average equation. It has received substantial verification in field studies, but it has also been shown that in some cases (1) a velocity average may work better.

Figure 7-3 illustrates some of the results obtained by Wyllie and co-workers on materials having widely different sonic velocities. The data relating bulk velocity and pore fluid velocity for three different matrix materials, Teflon, Berea sandstone, and Alundum, follow the time average relationship, but only to that point where the bulk velocity corresponds to the velocity of the dry core. In the case of the sandstone sample, this critical fluid velocity is approximately that of water. If the pore fluid is oil or natural gas, the velocity is the same as if water were present. Therefore, equation 7-2 can be written for sandstones containing oil, gas, or water:

$$\frac{1}{v_r} = \frac{\phi}{v_w} + \frac{(1-\phi)}{v_m} \qquad (7\text{-}3)$$

where v_w is the velocity of sound in water. This is the form of the time average equation that is generally used.

When the matrix material was Teflon, the time average curve applied for all fluids that were tested. This is because the matrix velocity of Teflon is so low. When the matrix material was Alundum, the time average equation did not apply at all. The time average equation would apply for the Alundum sample only if a pore fluid could be found that has a sonic velocity greater than 11,000 ft/sec. These results seem to indicate that a slightly higher velocity than v_w should be used for interpretation in carbonate rocks, but this distinction is not made in practice.

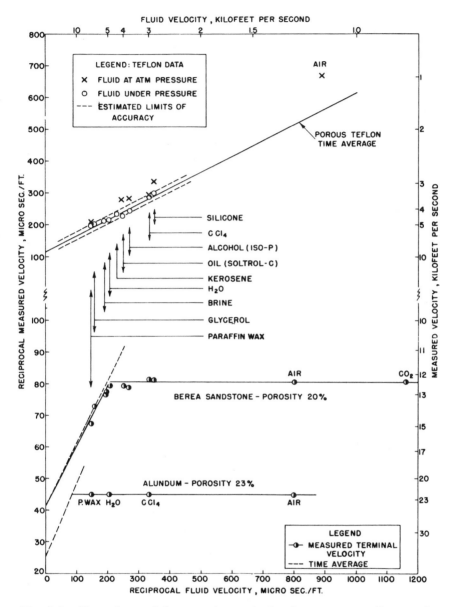

Fig. 7-3. Dependence of the acoustic transit time in a porous medium on the transit times of the matrix and the pore saturant. (Wyllie, Gregory, and Gardner, courtesy of *Geophysics*.)

Table 7-1 gives the sonic velocities of some materials which might be encountered in well logging. There is a velocity contrast here of about four times between the matrix materials and the pore fluids. This

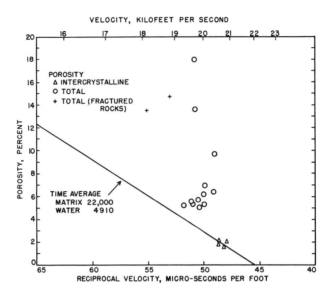

Fig. 7-4. Measured transit time in carbonate rocks showing the influence of vugs and fractures. (Wyllie, Gregory, and Gardner, courtesy of *Geophysics*.)

means that with the simple linear relationship of equation 7-3, the measured formation velocity will be very sensitive to the amount of porosity in the rock. A sonic logging device should therefore make an excellent porosity log with a high sensitivity.

TABLE 7-1

Material	Sonic Velocity, ft/sec	Transit Time, μsec/ft
Oil	4300	232
Water (mud)	5000-5300	200-189
Neoprene	5300	189
Shales	6000-16000	167-62.5
Rock salt	15000	66.7
Sandstones	up to 18000	55.6
Anhydrite	20000	50.0
Carbonates	210000-23000	47.6-43.5
Dolomites	24000	42.0

Wyllie's results for dolomitic rocks that contain both granular and secondary porosity are shown in Fig. 7-4. The samples which had only an intercrystalline porosity behaved like the sandstone samples and the data lay on the time average curve. The measured velocities for vuggy and fractured rocks, however, were all much higher than would be expected from the known porosity. Porosity, in fact, appeared to have little effect, indicating that the sound wave was bypassing the larger pores and was traveling primarily through the matrix. These anomalous results define an area where the sonic log must be used with discretion for determining the porosity. The closer the secondary porosity condition approaches the uniform porosity of a sandstone, the more nearly correct will be the porosity estimate. Large fractures which are in a plane perpendicular to the direction of propagation of the measured sound wave will show the proper porosity dependence, but these may also give spurious results, particularly in gas-bearing formations, because they effect a large attenuation of the sonic signal.

ACOUSTIC VELOCITY LOGGING METHODS

Schematic drawings of sonic logging sondes are shown in Fig. 7-5 for the single- and double-receiver types. The logging tool consists of a sound generator and one or two receivers located on a sonde body which is made of a material with a low sonic velocity and a high sonic attenuation (e.g., rubber). Contained within the sonde is instrumentation for transmitting information to the surface and the timer which controls the rate of generation of sound impulses. The sound generator may be of four possible types, a magnetostrictive alloy, a piezoelectric quartz crystal, an electric spark caused by discharging a condenser, or an electromechanical anvil and hammer arrangement. The receivers may be of either the magnetostrictive alloy or the piezoelectric crystal types.

In the operation of the single receiver type of sonic logging device, a timer starts the measured time period and simultaneously excites the sound generator, causing the brief emission of a sound pulse. The pulse travels through the mud, the sonde body, and the formation to the receiver. The first impulse to arrive at the receiver activates it and ends the timing period. This impulse usually travels by the route indicated by the arrows on the figure. Sound waves traveling through either the mud or the sonde body arrive at the receiver at a later time and consequently do not enter into the measurement. With the single-receiver type of instrument, the time lapse between generation of the signal and the first arrival measurement includes the time for the sound to pass through a section of formation approximately equal to the spacing, and twice the time for the pulse to travel from the sonde

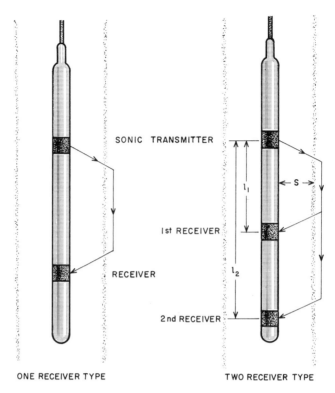

Fig. 7-5. Schematic drawing of the principles of the one- and two-receiver types of acoustic velocity logging tools.

to the formation. This mud time must be subtracted from the total time to get a correct transit time for the formation.

In the two-receiver type, the mud correction is eliminated. The timing period in this case is started not with the pulse of the generator, but by the arrival of the first pulse at the first receiver. The first arrival at the second receiver ends the time period. The first arrival pulse travels along the path indicated by the arrows. The path to the second receiver differs from the path to the first receiver by the length of formation between them. The measured elapsed time is the length of time for the sound to traverse this section of formation. It is this second type of sonde which is now being used by the Schlumberger Well Surveying Corporation for sonic logging. In their instrument the distance from the transmitter to the first receiver is 3 ft. The distance between the two receivers can be set at either 1 ft or 3 ft. In order to assure that the travel path through the mud is the same for all receivers, centralizers may be used on the sonde.

If the distance between the sonde and the borehole wall is too great, the first arrival path will be through the mud and not through the formation, and the tool will cease to function in the manner in which it was intended. The maximum standoff to spacing ratio, S/l_1, can be calculated from Snell's sine law for refracted waves.

$$\frac{S}{l_1} = \frac{1}{2}\left(\frac{1 - \beta}{1 + \beta}\right)^{1/2} \tag{7-4}$$

where β is the ratio of the mud velocity to the formation velocity, v_{mud}/v_r. On the Schlumberger tool where l_1 is 3 ft, the maximum allowable hole size is 20 in. in diameter in low-velocity formations, and 30 in. in diameter in high-velocity formations.

The generator on a sonic logging tool pulses ten times a second or once every hundred milliseconds. With this frequency of pulsing a measurement is made at least every $2\frac{1}{2}$ in. at normal logging speeds. The log is therefore continuous in appearance. The sonde usually contains an SP electrode (or it may have a γ-ray sonde attached to it) so that a direct comparison may be made with other logs. The logging speed is the same as for the electric log, except that when a γ-ray counter is used the lower logging speed of this device applies. The log is recorded as transit time (microseconds per foot of formation) with the zero on the right. Since low-porosity rocks have low transit times, the sonic log is similar in appearance to the electrical resistivity log. This simplifies the qualitative use of the combination of sonic and resistivity logs for the location of hydrocarbon-bearing zones.

Sonic logs may show a couple of anomalies: one is the effect of a caved section of hole, and the other is skipped cycles. The cave effect is shown in Fig. 7-6. With the single-receiver device, the effect of a cave can be important because it increases the length of the sound path through the mud. With the two-receiver device, the effect of a cave is insignificant as long as the maximum standoff is not exceeded; a cave influences this device only when entering and leaving the caved section because it is only at these points that the length of the sound path through the mud to the two receivers is different. A caved section therefore appears on the log as a small excursion to the right as the sonde enters the cave and another excursion of similar magnitude to the left as the sonde leaves the cave. When both receivers are within the caved section, the true transit time is measured.

Skipped cycles occur when the signal arriving at the second receiver is not strong enough to actuate it. The receiver is then actuated by a wave other than the first arrival and the measured transit time is too

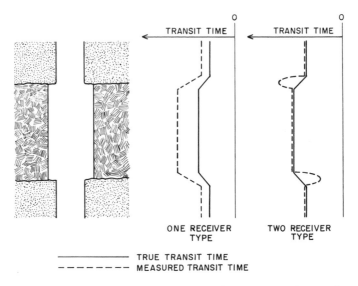

ONE RECEIVER
TYPE

TWO RECEIVER
TYPE

——————— TRUE TRANSIT TIME
— — — — — — — MEASURED TRANSIT TIME

Fig. 7-6. The effect of hole enlargement on the response of acoustic velocity logging tools: (a) single-receiver type and (b) two-receiver type.

long. As might be expected, the condition occurs more often when the longer receiver span is used. It appears to be caused by the attenuation of the signal in crossing a fracture, and therefore if skipped cycles can be recognized on the log, they may be indicative of this type of porosity. Skipping also occurs in clean unconsolidated sands, particularly if they are gas bearing. If the frequency of the generated sound pulse is known, skipping may be recognized by the fact that the apparent transit time is too long by some multiple of the reciprocal of the frequency. Thus, for a 30-kc generator, successive waves in each generated sound pulse are 33 μsec apart. If the first compression wave fails to excite the receiver, the second or third may do so, and the apparent transit time will be 33 μsec, or 67 μsec too long for the 1-ft spacing arrangement (11 μsec or 22 μsec for the 3-ft receiver spacing). (Note: This frequency of the sound wave should not be confused with the frequency with which individual sound pulses are emitted by the generator.)

The interpretation of the response of a sonic log opposite a thin bed is much simpler than for any other wireline device. A sonic log measures only the formation between the two receivers and is unaffected by the surrounding formations. Examples of the response of the log for two typical cases are given in Fig. 7-7. When the receiver span is longer than the bed thickness (Fig. 7-7a), the measured transit time is the weighted average of the transit times for the shale and the limestone.

The length of the shoulders is equal to the bed thickness and the length of the plateau opposite the limestone bed is equal to the span length minus the bed thickness. When the span is shorter than the bed thickness (Fig. 7-7b), the maximum, or plateau, value is equal to the transit time in the limestone. The length of the shoulders is equal to the span length, and the length of the plateau is equal to the bed thickness minus the span length.

APPLICATION OF ACOUSTIC VELOCITY LOGGING

The acoustic velocity log was originally developed for interpretation of geophysical data, and for this purpose an integrating circuit is incorporated into the system. This circuit adds the individual transit times and makes a record on the log for every millisecond of elapsed time. By tying this record into the data obtained from a few surface explosive shots, a complete subsurface time record can be obtained which is easy to use and which is accurate within 1 percent.

In formation evaluation work the sonic log has a number of uses. It is an excellent correlation tool, showing much character and detail, and can serve in the same manner as the electric log for the determination

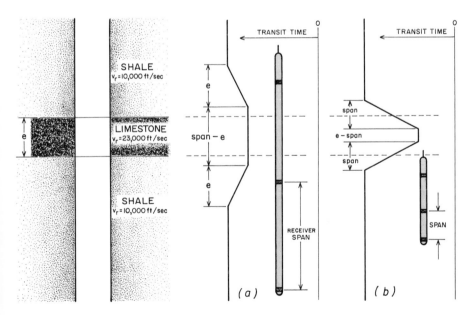

Fig. 7-7. The effect of bed thickness on the response of an acoustic velocity logging device: (a) bed thinner than the span and (b) bed thicker than the span.

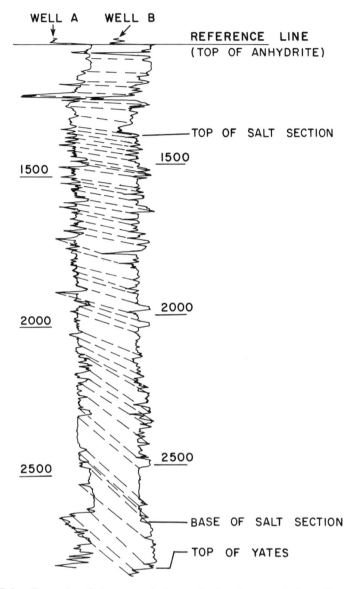

Fig. 7-8. Example of the use of the sonic log for correlation. (Courtesy of Schlumberger Well Surveying Corporation.)

of subsurface structure (see Fig. 7-8). It is also useful in locating bed boundaries accurately, for detecting thin streaks within a reservoir which might act as boundaries to fluid migration, for locating gas-oil interfaces, and for the selection of packer seats.

The acoustic velocity log has its most important use in formation evaluation as a means of estimating porosity. Figure 7-9 is a plot of the time-average equation (equation 7-3) which has been found very useful in evaluation work for porosities in the range of 5 to 30 percent. Above and below these porosity limits deviations may be expected. The values of velocity of 18,000 ft per second for sandstone, and 21,000 ft per second and 23,000 ft per second for carbonates represent average values. If it is possible, the sonic velocity for the section in question should be checked opposite a nonporous interval to determine a more pertinent velocity value, and appropriate interpolation then made on the chart. This chart is also limited to clean, well-compacted sandstones and carbonates which are moderately invaded. The chart was constructed assuming a fluid velocity of 5300 ft per second, which is the velocity of sound in water. When invasion is deep, the sound path is through a region which is almost entirely filled with mud filtrate. When invasion is shallow, there may be considerable oil or gas in the vicinity of the well, and if the sand is unconsolidated, unusually long transit times may be observed. In such cases it is suggested that the porosity obtained from the chart should be multi-

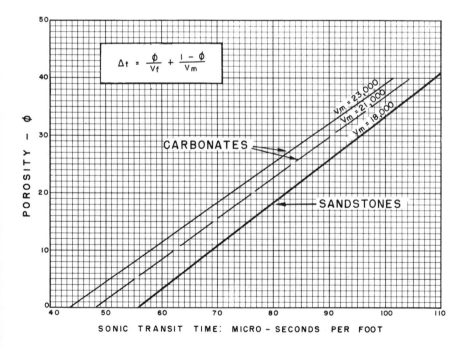

$$\Delta t = \frac{\phi}{V_f} + \frac{1 - \phi}{V_m}$$

Fig. 7-9. Porosity versus transit time. (Courtesy of Schlumberger Well Surveying Corporation.)

plied by 0.85 for oil sands and 0.70 for gas sands. This transit time anomaly is sometimes used to locate gas sands.

As was mentioned previously, equation 7-3 applies only in those cases where the compaction pressure has been sufficient to cause the sonic velocities to approach the terminal velocities. Experience indicates that this condition is satisfied approximately when the velocity in the nearby shale sections is of the order of 10,000 ft per second or greater (6). When the velocity in the shale is lower than this, an approximate empirical equation may be used to correct the porosity obtained from Fig. 7-9.

$$\phi = \phi_c \frac{100}{\Delta t_{sh} c} \qquad (7\text{-}5)$$

where ϕ_c is the porosity from Fig. 7-9, Δt_{sh} is the transit time in the nearby shale (microseconds per foot), and c is a correction factor. Very limited experience indicates that c is in the range from 0.8 to 1.2, and depends on the geographical location.

The presence of shale in a sandstone complicates the interpretation of the sonic log. The shale acts as part of the matrix, but its velocity may be several thousand feet per second slower than that of the sand grains. This results in falsely high-porosity values if the transit time of the matrix is taken equal to 18,000 ft per second. Schlumberger suggests an empirical correction for shaliness:

$$\phi = \phi_c/(2 - \alpha) \qquad (7\text{-}6)$$

where α is the ratio of PE_c to E_c that is used in electric logging. Experience with this equation is very limited. It appears that the corrections for shaliness and hydrocarbons should not be compounded. Since the presence of hydrocarbons affects the value of α used in equation 7-5, this equation tends to correct for both factors. The nomograph of Fig. 7-10 represents equation 7-3 with the corrections for hydrocarbon, compaction, and shaliness which have been suggested above.

In using the acoustic velocity log for measurement of the porosity in limestones, it should be realized that the log is making a porosity measurement and that it in no way reflects the permeability of the formation. Some evidence of permeability must be obtained from another source, as for example, the SP curve, the microlog, or the caliper log. Also, the experimental results of Wyllie indicate that the sonic log may not measure all of the porosity if it is irregular and not randomly distributed.

Since the acoustic velocity log is a method of measuring porosity, it may be used in combination with electrical resistivity logs for esti-

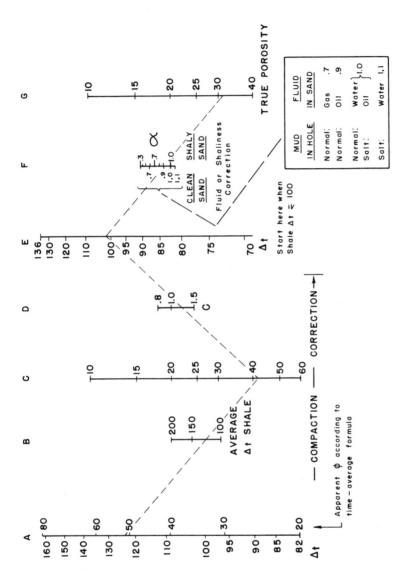

Fig. 7-10. Nomograph for correcting for hydrocarbons in unconsolidated rocks and for the presence of disseminated shales. (Courtesy of Schlumberger Well Surveying Corporation.)

mating oil or gas saturation in clean formations. Equations 5-53, 5-54, and 5-56 apply. A rapid method of analysis of a number of zones may be made by plotting the transit time (abscissas) versus the reciprocal of $R_t^{1/2}$ (ordinates). Once a line for water-saturated intervals is established on the chart, hydrocarbon-bearing intervals may be recognized readily because the data points fall below the 100 percent saturation line. This method assumes that R_w is the same for all zones.

CEMENT BOND LOG

An innovation of the sonic logging technique has been found very useful in determining the quality of cementation of casing in oil wells (3). This method of logging depends on the difference between the energy loss of a sound pulse traveling through casing that is standing free in the hole, and the energy loss of a pulse traveling through casing that is firmly bonded to a hard material of low sonic velocity, i.e., cement. The logging tool contains a sound generator and a single receiver. The receiver is instrumented so that it measures the amplitude of the pulse, rather than the transit time.

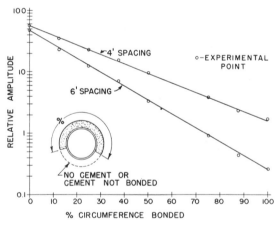

Fig. 7-11. Laboratory data showing the effect of cement bonding on the attenuation of a sonic signal in cased holes. (Grosmangin, Kokesh, and Majani, courtesy of the AIME.)

A sound pulse will travel through free casing with very little attenuation. When a cement sheath is firmly bonded to the outside of the casing, however, the sonic pulse loses energy continuously to the cement sheath and a large attenuation results. These effects are clearly shown by the experimental data of Fig. 7-11. By logging the signal amplitude, then, it is possible to locate those points in a cemented section where the cement bond to the casing is not sufficient to assure that the productive zones in the well are adequately protected from the adjacent formations. The thickness of the cement has little effect on the magnitude of the attenuation, provided that it is greater than about one-quarter of a wavelength (about $1\frac{1}{2}$ in.). This means that it is ordinarily not possible to determine whether the cement is also bonded to the formation; however, field tests with the log thus far have indicated that the cement is usually bonded to the formation when it is bonded to the casing, i.e., the conditions favorable for one are favorable for both.

Welex has recently introduced a cement bond log which they claim will make it possible to interpret the formation bond and the pipe bond separately. The service consists of three amplitude curves, one in open hole, and two in cased hole. The two cased hole signals are used to determine the effectiveness of the bond. The difference in the sonic velocity through the pipe and through the formation is used to distinguish between the casing-cement bond signal and the cement-formation bond signal. The open hole curve is used only as an aid in interpretation.

REFERENCES

1. Berry, J. E., Acoustic velocity in porous media: *Trans. AIME*, v. 216, 1959, p. 262.
2. Gassmann, F., Elastic waves through a packing of spheres: *Geophysics*. v. XVI, no. 4, October, 1951, p. 673.
3. Grosmangin, M., Kokesh, F. P., and Majani, P., The cement bond log: *Annual California Regional Meeting of the AIME*, Pasadena, California, October, 1960, Paper 1512-G.
4. Stripling, A. A., Velocity log characteristics: *Trans. AIME*, v. 213, 1958, p. 207.
5. Summers, G. C., and Broding, R. A., Continuous velocity logging: *Geophysics*, v. XVII, no. 3, July, 1952, p. 598.
6. Tixier, M. P., Alger, R. P., and Doh, C. A., Sonic logging: *Trans. AIME*, v. 216, 1959, p. 106.
7. Vogel, C. B., A seismic velocity logging method: *Geophysics*, v. XVII, no. 3, July, 1952, p. 586.
8. Wyllie, M. R. J., Gregory, A. R., and Gardner, G. H. F., An experimental investigation of factors affecting elastic wave velocities in porous media: *Geophysics*, v. XXIII, no. 3, July, 1958, p. 459.
9. Wyllie, M. R. J., Gardner, G. H. F., and Gregory, A. R., Principles underlying the interpretation of acoustic velocity logs: *Formation Evaluation Symposium*, AIME, Houston, Texas, 1960, p. II-39.

8

Drill Stem Testing

The most diagnostic method available for the evaluation of a formation is the drill stem test. This method simulates the conditions of the completed well, and thereby indicates the eventual qualitative and quantitative possibilities of the test interval. With the newer test equipment it is also possible to determine reservoir pressure (static pressure), the average formation permeability, and the degree to which the drilling technique has altered the permeability around the well bore.

A drill stem test is made by lowering a valve, a packer, and a length of perforated tail pipe on the end of the drill pipe to the level of the formation. The packer is set against the wall of the borehole so that it seals off the test interval from the mud column above. The valve is then opened. This procedure effectively reduces the pressure opposite the formation to atmospheric pressure, and the formation fluids can flow into the hole and be produced through the drill pipe. It amounts to a temporary completion of the well, and the produced fluids are therefore representative of the fluid production that may be expected if the well is eventually completed.

The simplified procedure described here is essentially that which was used in making the first drill stem tests in the late 1920s. It was soon realized, however, that better tests and more information could be obtained by the addition of other specialized devices to the string of tools. A typical test string in current use is illustrated in Fig. 8-1. The basic components of the string are the test valve, the packer, the equalizing valve, and the perforated anchor pipe. Other components such as the pressure recorders, the shut-in valve, and the choke are secondary tools that provide additional information about the test and the formation. There are also auxiliary components which are run for convenience and safety; these are the disk valve, the jars, the safety joints, and the surface control head.

In order that the functions of these components may be understood, a brief description of their construction and operation is given here.

DRILL STEM TEST TOOLS

Packer

A typical packer or bridge is shown in Fig. 8-2b. This is the heart of the drill stem tester, and in open hole it is generally responsible for the success or failure of the test. The packer is constructed of a rubber sleeve 20 or 30 in. long mounted on a steel mandrel. The rubber is vulcanized to two steel heads which are free to move relative to each other. When it is desired to set the packer, a part of the weight of the drill pipe is allowed to rest on the upper head while the bottom head is supported in a fixed position. This causes the rubber to be compressed and squeezed against the wall of the bore hole.

When the tester valve is opened, the weight of the mud column creates a pressure differential across the packer. In some cases this may be sufficient to cause the rubber to cold flow around the lower support, damaging the packer and giving a bad test. In order to alleviate this condition the clearance between the hole and the uncompressed packer is made as small as possible. If the clearance is made too small, however, there will be difficulty in running in and out of the hole, since the packer will tend to "hang up" in sections that are undersize. This will cause pressure surges or swabbing, either of which is dangerous and may

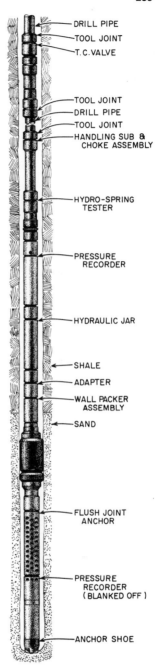

Fig. 8-1. Arrangement of tools for drill stem testing. (Courtesy of Halliburton Company.)

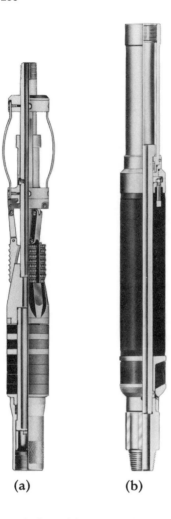

Fig. 8-2. Packer element: (a) hook wall packer and (b) open hole packer. (Courtesy of Halliburton Company.)

(a)   **(b)**

result in a blowout. The trend at the present time is to support the bottom of the packer with an expanding shoe made of metal cups or hard rubber, which limits the area open for cold flow. With this arrangement it is possible to use a packer which is 1 to $1\frac{1}{2}$ in. smaller than the hole size.

Sometimes a section of smaller sized hole (rathole) is drilled when a test is anticipated. It is then possible to make the test in the rathole with a small packer clearance and still have a large packer clearance for running in and out of the full hole above. Extensive ratholing is economically unsound, however, and drilling ahead in reduced hole should be limited only to those situations where a test is a definite possibility.

Tests conducted inside casing are run in the same manner as open hole tests, but the difficulties arising from packer failures are much less numerous. Tests inside casing are frequently run well above the bottom of the hole. In this case, two packers are used, one above and one below the interval, in what is known as a straddle test.

Anchor Pipe

In order to set the packer it is necessary to hold the bottom part stationary while weight is applied to the upper part. Where it is possible,

this is accomplished by running a perforated anchor pipe (see Fig. 8-3) to the bottom of the hole. The anchor pipe should be sufficiently sturdy to support the weight necessary to set the packer plus the weight of the mud column which rests on the packer when the test valve is open. Failure of the anchor pipe will cause the packer to slip and be damaged and will result in a bad test. It should also be ascertained that the anchor pipe rests on the true bottom of the hole and not on loose rubble which may have settled on the bottom.

When running a straddle test far off bottom, an anchor pipe, which is now blanked off, may be run to the bottom. Instead of the anchor, however, it is possible to use a set of dogs (or slips) below the lower packer. These engage the wall of the hole (or the casing wall) and provide enough support to set the packers. An equalizing line is used to connect the mud columns above and below the packers and equalize the hydrostatic pressure in these two locations. There is no net hydrostatic load on the packer system which has to be carried by the dogs.

Equalizing Valve

Fig. 8-3. Perforated anchor pipe. (Courtesy of Halliburton Company.)

The equalizing valve is usually part of a more complex tool which also houses the main test valve. It is normally open, and closes only when the tester valve opens. Its purpose is to allow mud fluid to bypass the packer through the inside of the drill pipe. This relieves the pressuring action when the packer is run into the hole and the swabbing action when it is pulled out. The most important function of the equalizing valve, however, is the equalization of pressure above and below the packer when the test is completed. If it were not for this, it would be nearly impossible to unseat the packer because the hydrostatic pressure of the mud column would tend to keep it in a compressed position.

Tester Valve

The main valve or tester valve controls the flow of fluid into the drill pipe from the anchor pipe below the packer. It is normally closed and is opened by supplying sufficient weight from the drill pipe. Since this same action is used to set the packer, some mechanical or hydraulic means is used to delay opening of the valve until the packer has been set. At the completion of a test an upward pull on the drill pipe relieves the weight on the tester valve, and allows it to close automatically. The equalizing valve opens at the same time.

Pressure Recorder

The pressure recorders may be of the spring-piston type or of the bourdon type. A stylus connected to the sensing element moves over a cylindrical chart of sensitized paper, leaving a record of the pressure fluctuations. An accurate clock is also contained within the recording instrument. This causes the chart to move at right angles to the movement of the pressure element. The result is a pressure vs time record. Modern pressure recorders have an accuracy of $\frac{1}{4}$ percent and the pressure records may be used for quantitative calculations.

At least two pressure recorders are used on a test. One is placed in the flow line so that the fluid entering the perforated anchor must flow past it. The other is located in a blanked-off section of the anchor pipe so that it is always open directly to the fluid in the wellbore. Both recorders should indicate the same pressure at all times, and differ only by the hydrostatic fluid head between them. On double shut-in pressure tests a third recorder is usually placed in the air chamber. On straddle tests a third recorder is usually placed below the bottom packer. Comparison of the various records can be very useful in analyzing the results of a test.

Choke

The choke is a small restriction placed on the flow line near the main valve to control the rate of fluid flow from the test zone. This has certain safety advantages. First, choking of the fluid causes pressure changes to be more gradual. This protects the packer and pressure recorders from the pressure shock caused by opening the tester valve.

It also maintains a back pressure against the face of the formation. This in turn helps prevent loose sand from heaving into the hole with the consequent plugging and sticking of the anchor pipe. Second, in a gas well, the surface pressure is reduced and is more easily handled.

By the proper selection of the size of the choke it is possible to obtain an accurate average production rate during the test period (1). This can be used in turn to compute the productivity index and the effective permeability of the formation. Choke sizes that are used are in the range of $\frac{3}{16}$ in. to $\frac{3}{8}$ in.

Shut-in Valve

In order to take a shut-in pressure at the end of the test, it is necessary to have a valve in the flow line that can be closed by the rotation of the pipe. This valve is located above the main tester valve and is sometimes combined in a single unit with the circulating valve.

Disk Valve

In order to ensure against the entry of mud into the drill pipe due to the accidental opening of the main valve while running into the hole, a metal disk may be placed above the other tools in the string. When the packer has been seated and the main valve opened, the disk valve is ruptured by dropping a metal bar from the surface. This use of the disk valve has been largely eliminated by the new hydraulic testers which combine the functions of the disk valve, main valve, and equalizing valve in one unit. Disk valves, however, can serve other uses in the more elegant testing techniques.

Circulating Valve

It is advantageous to remove combustible test fluids from the drill pipe before withdrawing it from the hole. The circulating valve provides a means of opening the drill pipe to the annulus a short distance above the tester. Mud pumped down the annulus can then return through the drill pipe and carry the test fluids ahead of it. The simplest type of circulating valve is a break-out plug which can be opened by a metal bar dropped at the completion of the test.

Perhaps more common at this time is the use of a combination circulation valve and shut-in valve. With this arrangement it is possible to shut in the test and simultaneously open the circulating valve simply by rotating the drill pipe a specified number of turns at the end of the flow period.

The operation of the various valves during a test is shown schematically in Fig. 8-4.

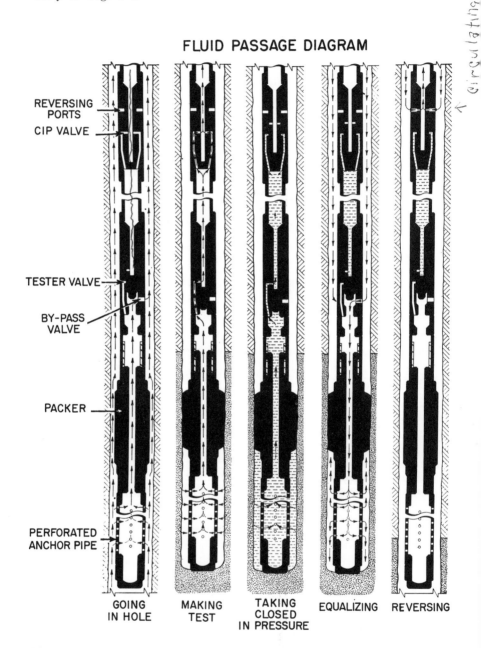

FLUID PASSAGE DIAGRAM

REVERSING PORTS

CIP VALVE

TESTER VALVE

BY-PASS VALVE

PACKER

PERFORATED ANCHOR PIPE

GOING IN HOLE   MAKING TEST   TAKING CLOSED IN PRESSURE   EQUALIZING   REVERSING

Fig. 8-4. Schematic diagram illustrating the fluid passage during a drill stem test. (Courtesy of Halliburton Company.)

Jars

If the tools should become stuck in the well, it is desirable to have a unit in the test string which can deliver a series of blows to jar the tools free. These devices are designed so that a sustained upward pull on the pipe will produce a sudden sharp blow by the jar "hammer" on the jar "anvil." The jar is then reset by slacking off on the pipe. The procedure may be repeated as necessary.

Safety Joint

It is common practice to run a safety joint in the test string just above the packer. If the jars do not succeed in freeing a stuck packer, then the safety joint may be unscrewed and the tools above it recovered. Safety joints may also be run at other locations.

Surface Control Head

In order to direct and control the fluids produced during the test, a surface control head should be used on the drill pipe. There are no firm specifications as to the mechanical arrangement of the flow head equipment. It is assembled to meet the requirements of the operating company and the operating conditions of the area.

TEST PROCEDURE

Drill stem testing is the most hazardous of all drilling operations and should therefore be conducted with the utmost care. Before beginning a test it should be determined that the hole and mud are in good condition. Mud should be circulated for at least one cycle to be sure that all cuttings have been removed; circulation should be continued until such time as the test can be run without any delay. The mud weight should be measured during this period so that the hydrostatic pressure, which will be indicated by the test recorders, may be checked.

The service company which is to conduct the test will have to know the depth of the hole, the hole size, the length of the test interval, the probable duration of the test, the mud weight, the number and type of packers, the number and type of pressure recorders, the choke size, and the type of control head, circulating valve, and jars. With this information they will be able to provide the best set of tools for the operation. When the test string has been assembled, it should be measured to check the proper location of the packer. The total length of tools and drill pipe run into the hole should also be measured so that it can be determined when bottom has been reached. This makes it possible to set down gently on the bottom and assures that the anchor is on a firm base.

In planning a test it is important that a good packer seat is selected. Examination of cores, electric logs, and caliper logs will be helpful in this regard. The packer should be set in a true-gage section of a hard formation such as a hard sandstone, nonfractured limestone, or a hard dense shale. Soft shales should be avoided as they will flow under the pressures involved, and this will result in a packer failure. If the formation is somewhat fractured, two packers adjacent to each other (dual packers) may be used to improve the chance of a successful seal. If none of the above conditions can be met, it may be necessary to set casing through the zone to get a successful test. This is true in the Gulf Coast Miocene formations where the sands are very soft and readily slough into the hole.

Before starting into the hole with the tester, the blowout preventers should be checked for proper operation. Flow lines should be installed which will carry the test fluids away from the drill floor and into a prepared tank or pit. Since it may be desirable to pump through the drill pipe if the test gets out of control, the mud line should be arranged so that it can be quickly attached to the surface control head. In regions where extreme formation pressures are expected it is well to have a cement truck on standby; the pumps on a cement truck are capable of exerting much higher pressures than the ordinary mud pumps. During the test all safety precautions should be observed in regard to smoking, open fires, exposed electric lights, and other sources of fire or explosion hazard. Power engines should be idled but should not be turned off as they may be needed in an emergency to raise or lower the drill pipe.

The speed at which the tools are run into the hole should be at least 25 percent slower than normal. The mud in the annulus should be watched continuously to see how much overflows as each stand is run in and how much the level drops when the pipe is stationary. If there is an indication that mud is being lost, the cause of the trouble should be determined and corrected before proceeding. It may be that there is a leaking joint in the drill pipe, or it may be that a weak formation has fractured from the pressure surges created during the running-in process. The two difficulties can be distinguished from one another by the fact that a leaking joint will cause air to issue from the end of the drill pipe.

When the bottom has been reached, the surface control head is connected, the packer set, and the main test valve opened. If a high-pressure hose is connected to the control head and the free end is immersed in a bucket of water, the blow of air from the drill pipe that should occur at this time can be detected immediately. The absence of a blow will indicate either a nonproductive formation, a plugged tool, or a malfunctioning tester.

The annulus mud level should be watched at all times during the test. If the mud level drops sharply at the beginning of the test, it indicates a packer failure; in this event, the tools should be picked up immediately in order to close the main test valve. A slow drop in the mud level may indicate either a leaking packer or the loss of fluid to the formations above the test interval. If the fluid loss continues after closing the shut-in valve, it indicates that the loss was to the formations.

Opening of the main test valve produces a severe pressure shock that places a strain on the recorder and packer. It may also cause the wall of the hole to collapse, and thus plug the anchor perforations or the choke, or, in severe cases, stick the anchor pipe so that it cannot be removed from the hole. In order to soften the pressure change, a back pressure is sometimes placed on the formation through the drill pipe. This pressure should be large enough to reduce the shock loading, but small enough to permit the formation to produce. The most common method of accomplishing this is with a "water cushion."

To use a water cushion, a portion of the drill pipe is filled with water as the tools are run into the hole. Opening of the test valve then drops the pressure on the formation from the pressure of the mud column to the hydrostatic pressure of the water column. There are some difficulties connected with the use of a water cushion, however. If recovery from the well is small, a water cushion may mix with the produced fluids and make interpretation of the results difficult. Also, in low-pressure wells a water cushion may inadvertently be made too great to permit production from the formation.

Where high-pressure nitrogen gas is available it is often used as a cushion instead of water. In this case the drill pipe is pressured through the control head before setting the packer, and then the pressure is bled off after the test valve is opened. This has the same effect as a water cushion without the danger of contaminating the test fluids or of making the cushion pressure too large. It is not a satisfactory substitute in certain cases, however. A water cushion may sometimes be necessary to control the initial surface pressure in a high-pressure gas well. It must also be used when testing below 7000 or 8000 ft where the hydrostatic mud pressure may be large enough to collapse an empty drill pipe.

After the tester is opened and the well is allowed to flow, an appreciable period of time will pass before the test fluids arrive at the surface. The blow of air from the drill pipe, however, will indicate that fluid is entering the pipe from the formation. If the blow stops, it may mean that the choke or anchor has plugged. It may also mean that there is insufficient formation pressure to overcome the liquid head in the pipe; in this case recovery can be improved by swabbing the drill pipe, and in some areas this practice is regularly followed.

At the completion of the flow period the shut-in valve is closed and the pressure in the wellbore opposite the formation is allowed to build up. Quantitative information about the formation can be obtained from this portion of the pressure record if the shut-in period is sufficiently long to allow the pressure in the wellbore to approach the static reservoir pressure. In general it may be said that the allotted shut-in time should be at least equal to the flow time. This is not a hard-and-fast rule, however; for a formation of high permeability containing low-viscosity fluids, a shorter period may suffice.

The double shut-in pressure test is becoming more common as a part of the general trend to obtain more quantitative information from a drill stem test. In this method of testing, the pressure of the mud on the formation is relieved at the beginning of the test without allowing a significant amount of fluid to be produced. This may be accomplished by putting a disk valve above the tester valve, thereby creating a closed air chamber in the drill pipe. The disk valve is located so that the volume of the chamber is about 10 percent of the volume of the mud trapped below the main valve. It has been found from experience that this volume is sufficient to drop the pressure in the well below the formation pressure when the main valve is opened. A small volume of fluid is produced into the air chamber, and then the pressure builds up quickly to formation pressure. After sufficient time has elapsed for static pressure to be reached, the test is continued in the conventional manner by opening the disk valve with a go-devil. (This is a bar dropped from the surface.) When a water cushion is used, the air chamber is created above the water cushion. Allowance must be made in this case for a decrease in the air volume due to the expansion of the water that is caused by heating it to the well temperature. Figure 8-5 gives a chart for rapid estimation of the volume of mud below the packer.

The use of an air chamber to relieve the pressure on the formation and obtain the reservoir pressure has not proved satisfactory in all cases. Sometimes the air chamber will inadvertently be made too small; then the pressure in the mud column opposite the formation is never

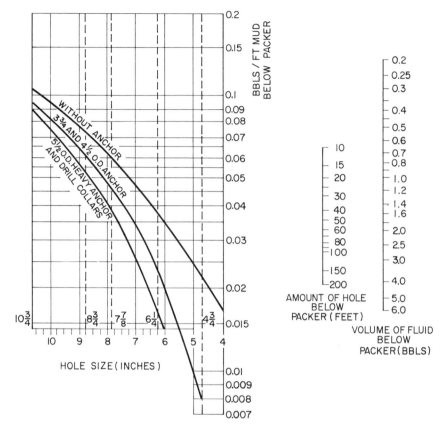

Fig. 8-5. Chart for estimating the amount of fluid below the packer. (Courtesy of Johnston Testers.)

reduced below the formation pressure and an initial shut-in value of the reservoir pressure is not obtained. On the other hand, an air chamber which was the correct size for a high-permeability formation may well prove to be too large for a low-permeability condition. There is no way of knowing at the surface when the initial shut-in period is complete. For a low-permeability formation it may be that the period of time allowed for fluid to fill the air chamber is inadequate; again, the reservoir pressure will not be measured.

Early in 1959 the Halliburton Company introduced a new tool designed to take the guesswork out of dual shut-in testing by eliminating the need for the air chamber. This device is a five-position valve run directly above the hydraulic tester valve. When the main tester valve is initially opened, the new valve is set in the open position. After a short initial flow period of 5 to 10 minutes, the valve is closed by rotation of the drill pipe through several turns to the right. This permits the initial shut-in pressure to be recorded. The initial shut-in period may range from 20 minutes to 1 hour. Additional rotation of the drill pipe through several turns to the right reopens the valve for the usual flow period. At the conclusion of this period, several more turns again close the valve for the final shut-in period. A sample pressure chart from a test run with this type of tool is shown in Fig. 8-18. In addition to the above functions, the tool also serves as a reverse circulation tool by providing communication to the annulus at the conclusion of the test.

The circulation valve may be opened at any time after the shut-in valve is closed for the final shut-in period. It is important, however, to start the mud pumps first and establish circulation to the annulus, since opening the circulating valve will allow the annulus mud to flow into the drill pipe. The greater density of the annulus mud will easily displace most of the test fluid from the pipe. The last few feet may be displaced by closing the blowout preventers and applying a pressure of 150 to 250 psi to the annulus. If the test has been conducted in open hole, caution is recommended, since excessive pressure may result in the breakdown of a weak formation and cause loss of circulation.

Test fluid may be run into a portable gaging tank to get an accurate measure of the amount of production. If only a small amount of fluid has been produced, the quantity of test fluid may be measured in the drill pipe. The recovery may be calculated as the volume of the drill pipe minus the volume of mud that had to be added to the annulus to bring the test fluid to the surface. If a knockout type of circulating valve is used, a second procedure is also possible. Several hundred feet of water may be added to the drill pipe (this is a safety measure), and the pipe pulled until the water is encountered. The pipe volume below the water is then the amount of recovery. After the pipe has been pulled to this point, the circulating valve is opened, and the test fluid is circulated into the pit.

A gas well will produce fluid in all cases. The rate of production can be determined by means of a pitot tube or an orifice meter at the exit of the gas flow line.

Withdrawing the tools from the hole at the end of a test must be done with the utmost care as the danger of a blowout and fire is very great at this time. Tests are often scheduled so that this can be done during daylight hours. The annulus mud level should be watched closely and it should be filled each time movement of the pipe stops. Any sign that there is an upward flow of mud in the casing is an indication of a blowout and should be treated as an emergency.

Below the circulating valve there will be test returns in the drill pipe. If oil has been produced during the test, these oil-filled sections of pipe should be capped as they arrive at the surface and before they are pulled up into the derrick. This will prevent oil from being sprayed into the derrick. Also, a sealed mud-saver should be used to collect the liquid as each joint is broken.

QUALITATIVE TEST INTERPRETATION

From the viewpoint of formation evaluation, the importance of drill stem testing lies in the interpretation of the test results. A qualitative interpretation can be made immediately upon completion of the test. Good quantitative interpretation, however, requires reading of test pressures on the charts with a micrometer reader. This is done at the service company office.

The most important information obtained from a drill stem test is the amount and composition of the recovered fluids, for it is on the basis of this information that completion of the well will be decided. Where there is a clear-cut case of good hydrocarbon recovery, or only salt water recovery, there is no problem. It often happens, however, that an amount of gas-cut mud or oily mud is the only recovery. The question then arises as to what the completed well may produce. Sometimes a study of the pressure charts can provide the necessary information on which to base a decision.

A typical pressure chart from a drill stem test is shown in Fig. 8-6. The five main points on the chart are indicated by the letters A, B, C, D, and E. They represent the important points in the chronological

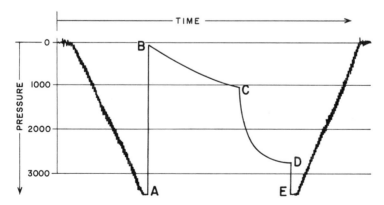

Fig. 8-6. Typical drill stem test pressure chart illustrating the five key pressure points.

sequence of events that occurs during testing. The time-pressure record starts at the upper left-hand corner. As the tools are lowered, the recorder indicates the increase in hydrostatic mud pressure. The diagonal line down to A usually has a rough or fuzzy appearance. This indicates that the pressure recorder is moving freely and responding to small pressure surges and vibrations associated with running in. Excessive oscillations on this part of the chart would indicate that pressure surges had been created by a bad hole condition. This may be important enough to qualify the test results. An example of this is shown in Fig. 8-9.

At point A the tools are at the bottom of the hole and the recorder indicates the hydrostatic pressure of the mud column. This point is known as the initial hydrostatic pressure or IHP. There may be a slight increase in pressure above this value when the packer is set, but this does not occur with a hydraulic tester tool because the equalizer valve remains open until after the packer is set.

Opening of the main tester valve relieves the pressure in the hole below the packer and causes the pressure to decrease rapidly to the point B, which is the initial flowing pressure or IFP. The pressure value at B is approximately atmospheric pressure unless a water cushion or a gas cushion has been used. As the fluids flow from the formation into the pipe, the pressure increases as shown by the line BC. The shape of the curve BC depends on the permeability of the formation, the fluid viscosity and density, and the thickness of the test interval. Point C represents the end of the flow period and so is the final flowing pressure or FFP. At point C the shut-in valve is closed, and pressure starts to build up in the wellbore. If the shut-in period, CD, is sufficiently long, the pressure at D will be the static reservoir pressure. Usually the static pressure is not reached, and point D is just the final shut-in pressure or FSIP. At point D the packer is pulled loose and the recorder then indicates the hydrostatic mud pressure at E. This final hydrostatic pressure or FHP must be equal to IHP and also to the pressure calculated from the mud weight and the depth.

Figures 8-7 to 8-15 show pressure charts that have been obtained under various test conditions. By examination of the pressure chart and a knowledge of the rate and type of fluid recovery, it is possible to determine whether or not the test was valid, and if the test failed, the reason for failure.

Along with each pressure chart, there is a record of test results and remarks about operating conditions during the test period. This portion of the record should be made as complete as possible to help others who may have to evaluate the pressure record, and who may not be present when the test is run.

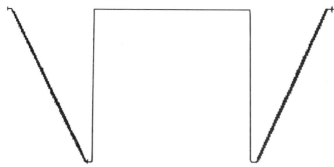

Fig. 8-7. Example of a pressure chart from a dry test. No fluid entered the hole. The pressure remained at atmospheric pressure during the entire test period.

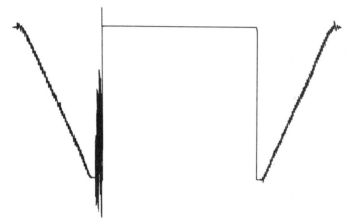

Fig. 8-8. This is an example of a pressure chart from a dry test where the anchor shoe was set on loose rubble in the bottom of the hole. When the tester valve opened, the additional weight of the mud column forced the entire tool assembly to the true bottom. The alternate sealing and failure of the packer during the period of slippage created the extremely large pressure surges at the beginning of the test period. The packer finally held, and the chart indicates a dry test as in the previous example.

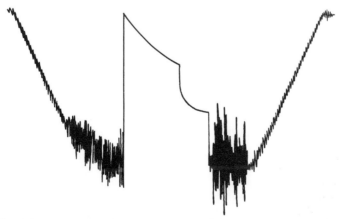

Fig. 8-9. This is an example of a bad hole condition. Normal pressure oscillations were observed as the tools were run into the hole, until the reduced hole section was reached near the bottom of the well. Large pressure surges were then created as the tools were forced on down. There is also some indication of "false bottom." The test period appears normal. At the conclusion of the test it was necessary to use the jars to free the stuck anchor pipe.

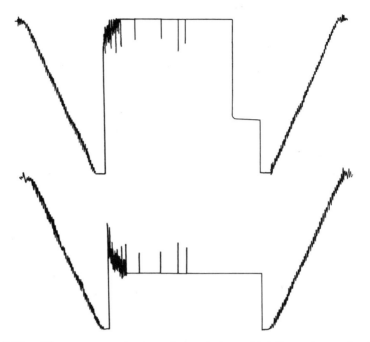

Fig. 8-10. These pressure charts are from a test on which the anchor perforations plugged. The upper chart is from the inside (flow line) recorder and the lower chart is from the outside (blanked-off) recorder. The perforations plugged almost immediately after the tool was opened. The inside recorder indicates essentially atmospheric pressure throughout the test period. The outside recorder indicates the static reservoir pressure. The small pips on both charts indicate brief periods when the anchor became unplugged. Because there was no flow, the inside recorder indicates static pressure immediately after the shut-in valve was closed.

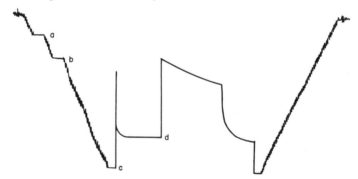

Fig. 8-11. Pressure chart from a double shut-in test with a water cushion. The steps at a and b indicate periods when the movement of the drill pipe was stopped to permit the addition of water. At point c the main valve was opened, and test fluid flowed into the air chamber. After this momentary pressure relief, the pressure built up quickly to the static pressure of the reservoir. At point d the disk valve was opened and a normal test followed.

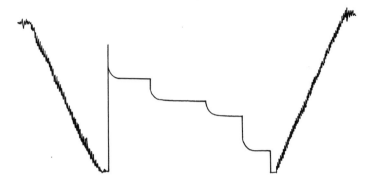

Fig. 8-12. Pressure chart from a high rate gas well. After the valve was opened, the pressure and flow stabilized quickly on a $\frac{1}{4}$-in. choke. The choke size was reduced successively to $\frac{3}{16}$-in. and $\frac{1}{8}$-in., The shut-in valve was then closed for the determination of reservoir pressure.

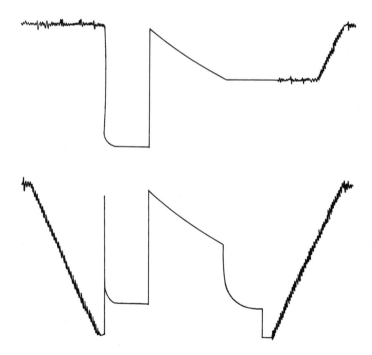

Fig. 8-13. Pressure charts from a double shut-in test. The upper chart is from the recorder that was placed in the air chamber. This chart indicates that there was no leakage into the chamber as the tools were run into the hole. The chart also shows the initial shut-in curve and the flow period. As this recorder was located above the shut-in valve, it does not show the final pressure build-up curve.

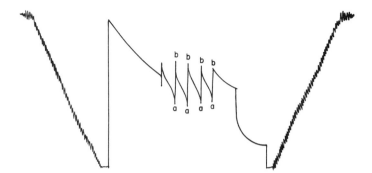

Fig. 8-14. This is a pressure chart from a well that was swabbed. The initial part of the test was conducted in the customary manner. In order to improve the recovery rate, some test fluid was removed from the pipe with a swab. Each upstroke of the swab caused a pressure reduction represented by the lines a-b. The increase of pressure from b to a is caused by the downstroke of the swab and the additional fluid flowing in from the formation.

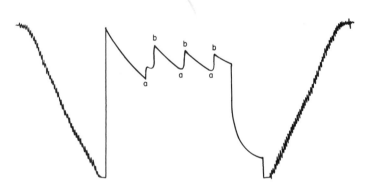

Fig. 8-15. This is a pressure chart from a well that flowed by heads. The curves b-a represent the increase in pressure resulting from flow of formation fluid into the pipe. The curves a-b represent the removal of some of this liquid from the pipe by the expansion of the gas produced with the oil.

QUANTITATIVE TEST INTERPRETATION

In addition to the qualitative information that can be obtained from the charts, a properly run test can provide quantitative information about the formation permeability, the formation pressure, and the damage that has been done to the formation during drilling. Sometimes reservoir limitations may also be determined, e.g., presence of faults.

Specific Productivity Index

Darcy's law for horizontal radial flow in the steady state is

$$q = 2\pi \frac{kh}{\mu} \frac{(P_e - P_w)}{\ln (r_e/r_w)} \tag{8-1}$$

where r_w is the radius of the wellbore, r_e is the equivalent drainage radius of the well, P_w is the pressure in the well, P_e is the reservoir pressure corresponding to r_e, h is the bed thickness, k is the permeability, and μ is the viscosity of the fluid. In practical field units, with the production, Q, in barrels of stock tank oil (STO) per day, P in psi, k in millidarcys, and h and r in feet, equation 8-1 becomes

$$Q = \frac{3.073 \times 10^{-3} hk(P_e - P_w)}{B\mu \log (r_e/r_w)} \tag{8-2}$$

In this equation B is the formation volume factor, barrels of formation fluid per barrel of stock tank oil. The group $Q/P_e - P_w)$ is known as the productivity index of the well and $Q/h(P_e - P_w)$ is the specific productivity index, SPI. If the drainage radius of the well is known, then equation 8-2 is a measure of the average flowing permeability of the formation from the wellbore to the drainage radius.

$$\bar{k} = \frac{\text{SPI } B\mu \log (r_e/r_w)}{3.073 \times 10^{-3}} \tag{8-3}$$

This average value of k includes the zone of altered permeability around the wellbore, and since most of the pressure drop $(P_e - P_w)$ occurs near the well, the average is heavily weighted toward this factor. One method of estimating formation damage is that of comparing the value of $\bar{k}$ determined from equation 8-3 with the permeability of the undamaged formation determined by another method, e.g., pressure build-up curves.

Pressure Build-up Analysis

If a formation contains a compressible fluid such as oil or gas, and this fluid is produced for a period of time, a pressure gradient will be set up in the formation which varies continuously from the wellbore pressure to the pressure at the drainage radius. When the well is shut in, the pressure in the wellbore will increase until the pressure is uniform throughout the formation. The time dependence of this pressure build-up will be similar in appearance to the curve of Fig. 8-21. If the pressure is plotted against the logarithm of the time, a much more diagnostic curve is obtained. This curve will have an appearance similar to that of Fig. 8-22. The first part of the curve has a characteristic S shape; this is followed by a straight line portion which eventually flattens out at the static pressure. All these parts do not show on every build-up curve, but so long as a reasonable part of the straight line section is present, the analysis of the data is possible.

The interpretation of pressure build-up curves is based on the mathematical model shown in Fig. 8-16. The portion of the reservoir drained by a single well is considered to be a right circular cylinder of external radius r_r, with a concentric wellbore of radius r_w. The height of the cylinder is equal to the formation thickness, h. The porosity, ϕ, and permeability, k, are assumed to be uniform throughout. Flow of fluid is assumed to be single phase and in the horizontal radial direction.

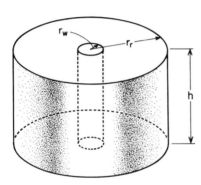

Fig. 8-16. Mathematical model for pressure build-up theory.

The viscosity of the fluid is μ, the compressibility is c, and the density is ρ. With these conditions, flow within the reservoir can be described by the differential equation,

$$\frac{\partial \rho}{\partial t} = \frac{k}{\phi \mu c} \left(\frac{\partial^2 \rho}{\partial r^2} + \frac{1}{r} \frac{\partial \rho}{\partial r} \right) \tag{8-4}$$

This equation has an infinite number of possible solutions. A unique solution can be obtained only by specifying the initial pressure (or density) distribution and the conditions that apply at each boundary, r_w and r_r.

Solution for an Infinite Reservoir. Two general groups of solutions have been developed for equation 8-4. The first assumes that flow into the wellbore is constant prior to shut in. From this fact and Darcy's law the initial pressure distribution can be calculated. The boundary conditions are set by assuming that flow into the well at r_w is zero from the instant that the well is shut in, and that the drainage radius is infinite. These assumptions were used by Horner (3), Hurst (4), and van Everdingen (17) in their solutions. The solution given by van Everdingen for the pressure in the wellbore during the drawdown or production period is

$$P_e - P_w = \frac{162.6Q\mu B}{kh} \left[\log \left(\frac{0.591 \times 10^{-3}kt_c}{\phi\mu cr_w^2} \right) + S \right] \qquad (8\text{-}5)$$

The compressibility c has the units of $1/\text{psia}$, and the time t_c is in hours. P_r is the pressure in the reservoir at the drainage radius. In order to accomplish the shut-in condition of zero flow into the wellbore, a similar equation with a negative production rate (8-6) is added to equation 8-5.

$$P_w - P_\delta = \frac{-162.6Q\mu B}{kh} \left[\log \left(\frac{0.591 \times 10^{-3}k\delta}{\phi\mu cr_w^2} \right) + S \right] \qquad (8\text{-}6)$$

The sum of equations 8-5 and 8-6 is the zero flow equation or the pressure buildup equation.

$$P_r - P_\delta = \frac{162.6Q\mu B}{kh} \left[\log \left(\frac{t_c + \delta}{\delta} \right) \right] \qquad (8\text{-}7)$$

where t_c is the total time in hours on production at the rate Q barrels STO per day, and δ is the time measured from the beginning of the shut-in period. When δ approaches ∞, $(t_c + \delta)/\delta$ approaches unity and $P_\delta = P_r$. A plot of P_δ vs $(t_c + \delta)/\delta$ on semilog paper should give a straight line with a slope m' of $162.6Q\mu B/kh$ and an intercept with the $(t_c + \delta)/\delta = 1$ line, which is equal to the static pressure of the reservoir. An example of this method of plotting data from a build-up test is shown in Fig. 8-20.

If the test of Fig. 8-20 had followed the assumptions as required in the mathematical development, all the data points would have been on a straight line. Usually, the points at the beginning of the test are below the mathematical prediction. There are two reasons for this. The first is that it is practically impossible to shut in a well at the sand face and so there is some flow into the wellbore at the beginning of the shut-in period. This afterproduction delays the build-up of pressure in the formation. When gas has been produced and the shut-in is effected at the surface, the problem is particularly serious. The second reason for the low points is the presence of the zone of altered, and usually lower permeability adjacent to the well. This effect is not as severe as afterproduction.

The term S in the van Everdingen equation 8-5 is called the skin effect. It is a measure of the additional pressure drop necessary to

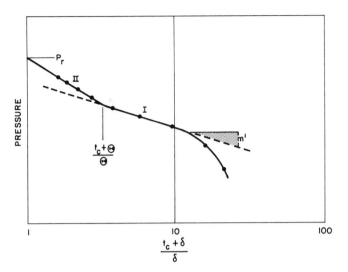

Fig. 8-17. Plot of pressure build-up data from a well, indicating a linear barrier in the formation.

overcome the flow resistance of the reduced permeability zone. A value of S greater than 10 represents serious damage around the wellbore. A value between 0 and 5 represents slight damage. Negative values of S represent improved permeability around the well.[1]

In his paper on pressure build-up theory in infinite reservoirs, Horner showed that the build-up test could also be used to indicate the presence of linear barriers, such as faults, in the vicinity of the well. When a linear barrier is present, the build-up curve shows two straight line sections, and the second of these has a slope approximately twice the slope of the first. This condition is illustrated in Fig. 8-17. The distance of the barrier from the well can be determined by the equation given by Dolan, Einarsen, and Hill (2),

$$d = 0.0121 \left(\frac{kt_c\theta}{\phi\mu c(t_c + \theta)} \right) \tag{8-8}$$

where t_c is the flowing time, and θ is the shut-in time corresponding to the intersection of the two straight line sections of the build-up curve.

---

[1] Equation 8-5 can be simplified by substituting average values of k, μ, ϕ, r_w, c, and t_c. The equation then becomes

$$S \cong \frac{P_r - P_w}{m'} - 5$$

This equation is often adequate for making an approximate estimate of the wellbore damage.

This method of detection and location of barriers should be applied with caution since an apparent break in the straight line plot may be caused by other factors, e.g., nonconstant production rate, deviations from radial flow. Where a clear case of a barrier exists, the first straight line section is used for determining the permeability, and the second for determining the reservoir pressure.

A limited reservoir condition can be detected if a dual shut-in test is run. Extrapolation of both build-up curves to infinite time should give the same value of reservoir pressure if the reservoir is infinite in extent. When the second, or final, shut-in pressure is significantly lower than the first, a limited reservoir condition is indicated. Where a test has been run with the new dual shut-in equipment which permits two flow periods, changes in the transmissibility, kh/μ, can be calculated from the slope of each of the build-up curves, m_1' and m_2'.

$$\left(\frac{kh}{\mu}\right)_1 = \frac{162.6Q_1B}{m_1'}$$

$$\left(\frac{kh}{\mu}\right)_2 = \frac{162.6Q_2B}{m_2'}$$

(8-9)

An example of this type of test is shown in Fig. 8-18. Significant differences in the transmissibility indicate the presence of a pinchout (change of h), a change in the fluid phase in the pores (change of k/μ), or a change in the formation permeability (change of k).

The method of van Everdingen is applicable to situations where the pressure disturbance caused by production from a well has not reached the drainage radius of any adjacent well or the physical limits of the reservoir. This condition is satisfied by a new well in a new field, or by a well that is being drill stem tested.

In a drill stem test, the pressure in the wellbore gradually increases throughout the flow period so that the final flowing pressure is always greater than the initial flowing pressure. This condition is the exact opposite of the pressure relation predicted by equation 8-5, and it obviously requires a nonconstant production rate. Evidence of this varying rate is the concave upward curvature of the flow line BC in Fig. 8-6. The greater the curvature of this line, the greater is the difference between the initial and final flow rates. Since the van Everdingen equations were derived on the supposition of a constant flow rate, there arises the double problem of what rate to use in the analysis, and how much of an error will be involved in the determination of reservoir pressure and permeability by this method.

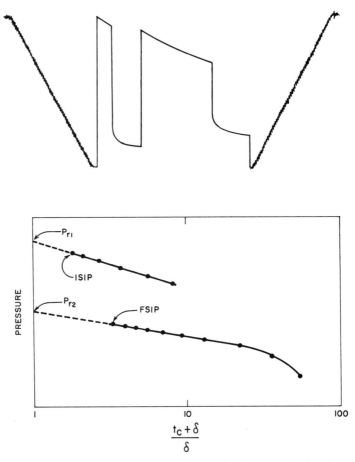

Fig. 8-18. Plot of pressure build-up data from a double flow, double shut-in test.

In his study of the application of this method of analysis to producing wells, Horner suggested the use of the average flow rate (total production divided by total time on production) in the calculations. This practice has been carried over into the analysis of drill stem tests. Dolan, Einarsen, and Hill (2) have analyzed this problem and have determined that the error involved depends on the difference between the initial and final production rates, and on how closely the final shut-in pressure comes to the reservoir pressure. In general, it may be said that the extrapolation of the build-up curve will tend to give values of the reservoir pressure which are too low; and the slope of the straight line section of the curve, when used with the average flow rate, will give values of reservoir permeability which are too high. In the great majority of the cases, the errors introduced by the nonconstant flow rate are negligible unless the difference between the initial and final rates is very large.

Solution for a Limited Reservoir.   The second method of solution to the diffusion equation was developed by Miller, Dyes, and Hutchinson (9), based on an earlier solution by Muskat (10). They also assumed steady-state flow prior to shut-in for the initial condition, and zero flow at r_w after shut-in for the one boundary condition. At the outer boundary, r_d, they made two assumptions and so obtained two solutions. One assumption is that at r_d the pressure remains constant. This might be satisfied where there is a water drive or an injection operation at adjacent wells. The other assumption is that at r_d there is zero flow. This might be satisfied by a well in a fully developed field where depletion drive is in progress.

The Miller, Dyes, and Hutchinson solution of equation 8-4 is a complex Bessel function. However, a plot of the solution on semi-logarithm paper, where pressure is plotted vs the logarithm of the shut-in time, very closely approximates a straight line. The slope, m, of the straight line is $162.6Q\mu B/kh$. Figure 8-22 is an example of this type of plot. As in the case of the infinite drainage radius, the afterproduction and permeability damage cause the points at the beginning of the shut-in period to fall below the theoretical straight line curve.

The procedure for finding the static pressure by the MDH method is more complex than that of the van Everdingen method and requires the use of generalized curves plotted as

$$ t = \frac{0.000264kt}{\phi\mu cr_d^2} \quad \text{vs} \quad \Delta P = \frac{0.00708kh(P_{ws} - P_{wt})}{Q\mu B} $$

These are shown plotted in Fig. 8-23 for the two boundary conditions assumed in the solution. Miller, Dyes, and Hutchinson state that the effects of afterproduction and permeability damage are usually diminished to a negligible amount when the generalized time has reached a value of 10^{-2}. The length of the shut-in period should be great enough, therefore, to give a value of generalized time between 10^{-2} and 10^{-1}. The shut-in time required to give quantitative information can be determined approximately in advance of the test by setting $t = 0.05$ and solving for t.

$$ t_s = \frac{190\phi\mu cr_d^2}{k} \tag{8-10} $$

Since only the approximate shut-in time is required, the values used in this expression do not have to be exact.

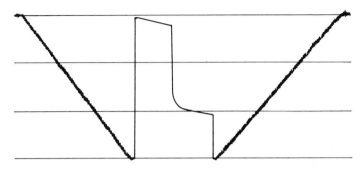

Fig. 8-19. Drill stem test chart from the example used to illustrate the van Everdingen method of analysis.

In order to determine the wellbore damage, the effective permeability calculated from the slope of the build-up curve must be compared with the average permeability calculated from the specific productivity index, equation 8-3.

Application of Build-up Analysis

Sample problems are presented on the following pages to show, step by step, how the preceding theory should be applied.

Example VE. This example demonstrates the application of the van Everdingen type of analysis to the results of a drill stem test. The test chart is shown in Fig. 8-19. The following information was obtained during the test or from the chart:

Test interval: 5000 to 5014 ft
Well diameter: 9 in. $radius = 4.5'' = r_w$
Drill pipe size: $4\frac{1}{2}$ in. O.D., 16.6 lb per foot
Mud weight: 11.6 lb per gallon
Surface temperature: 80°F
Formation temperature: 130°F
Recovery: 450 ft of 40°API oil and 60 ft of gas-cut oily mud
Gas flow rate: 244 Mcf per day; gravity = 0.81
Initial hydrostatic pressure = final hydrostatic pressure = 3000 psig
Initial flowing pressure: 20 psig
Final flowing pressure: 200 psig
Flowing time: 30 minutes
Shut-in time: 33 minutes

Solution:

1. Check of the accuracy of the pressure recorder. The mud weight multiplied by the depth should give the indicated hydrostatic mud pressures, IHP and FHP, and these must be equal to each other.

$$\frac{5000 \times 11.6 \times 7.48}{144} = 3010 \text{ psig}$$

← gals / cu. ft.

This is in satisfactory agreement with the measured value of 3000 psig.

2. Graphical determination of the reservoir pressure and the factor m'. For this determination the build-up curve is divided into eleven intervals of 3 minutes each and the pressure read from the chart at each time interval:

time since shut-in

Time, minutes	Pressure, P_δ, psig	$t_c + \delta$, minutes	$\dfrac{t_c + \delta}{\delta}$
0	200	30	∞
3	1765	33	11.00
6	1890	36	6.00
9	1934	39	4.33
12	1957	42	3.50
15	1977	45	3.00
18	1990	48	2.67
21	2000	51	2.42
24	2011	54	2.25
27	2018	57	2.11
30	2024	60	2.00
33	2028	63	1.91

A plot is made from these data of the pressure, P_δ, versus the logarithm of the dimensionless time, $(t_c + \delta)/\delta$. This plot is shown in Fig. 8-20. By extrapolating the straight line portion of this curve to a value of $(t_c + \delta)/\delta$ of 1, the reservoir pressure of 2108 is obtained. The slope m' of the straight line portion of the curve is 278 psi per cycle.

3. Determine the production rate of the reservoir fluid. (See Appendix D.)

Volume of recovered oil: $450 \times 1/70.32 = 6.40$ bbl of oil
Volume of recovered mud: $60 \times 1/70.32 = 0.85$ bbl of mud
Volume of STO produced by the formation in 30 minutes: 7.25 bbl
Rate of oil production: 348 bbl STO per day

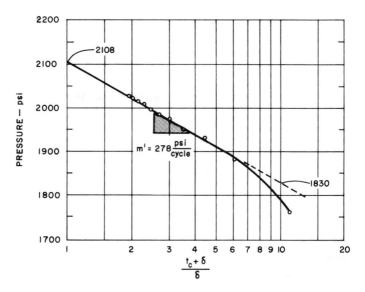

Fig. 8-20. Plot of the pressure build-up data for the example used to illustrate the van Everdingen method of analysis.

4. Determine the properties of the reservoir fluid.

Gas-oil ratio: 244,000/348 = 702 cu ft per barrel

From Standing's chart (Appendix C-2) the formation volume factor, B, is 1.37 bbl of formation oil per barrel of STO.

From Beal's charts (Appendix C-4 and C-5) the viscosity of the formation fluid is 0.68 cp.

5. Determine the undamaged reservoir permeability, k, from the equation

$$k = \frac{162.6 Q \mu B}{m'h} \tag{8-11}$$

$$= \frac{162.6 \times 348 \times 0.68 \times 1.37}{278 \times 14} = 13.5 \text{ md}$$

This is the permeability of the reservoir to oil. It may be considerably less than the specific permeability.

6. Estimate the formation damage around the wellbore from equation 8-5:

$$S = \frac{P_r - P_w}{m'} - \log\left(\frac{0.591 \times 10^{-3} k t_c}{\phi \mu c r_w^2}\right)$$

For this equation values of the porosity, ϕ, and the average compressibility, c, are needed. ϕ is estimated from sonic log data as 0.20; c is estimated as 10^{-5} psi^{-1} [1]

$$S = \frac{2108 - 200}{278} - \log \frac{0.591 \times 10^{-3} \times 13.5 \times 0.5}{0.20 \times 0.68 \times 10^{-5} \times 0.141} = 2.55$$

This value of S indicates slight damage to the formation.

Formation damage can also be expressed in terms of a "damage ratio," DR, which is the ratio of the theoretical production to the actual production. It may be determined from the skin factor by means of the equation:

$$DR = \frac{P_r - P_w}{P_r - P_w - m'S} \tag{8-12}$$

$$= \frac{1908}{1908 - 278 \times 2.55} = 1.59$$

This value of the damage ratio means that the formation could produce $1.59 \times 348 = 553$ bbl STO if the permeability to oil throughout the producing reservoir were 13.5 md. "Damage" may be the result of particle invasion from the mud, the swelling of clay in the formation when contacted by the mud filtrate, blocking by water from the mud filtrate, or even blocking by gas coming out of solution around the wellbore. The damage ratio is almost always equal to or greater than unity. Unless there is a good reason for having a condition of improved permeability around the wellbore, values of the damage ratio less then unity should be suspect. They are usually the result of taking the wrong part of the pressure build-up curve for the straight line section.

The damage ratio may also be obtained by a direct comparison of the permeability calculated from m' with the permeability calculated from the productivity index, equation 8-3.

$$k = \frac{SPI\ B\mu\ \log r_e/r_w}{3.073 \times 10^{-3}}$$

[1] The weighted average compressibility of the fluids in the pore space should be used here. For example, if the water saturation were 25 percent, then the average compressibility would be

$$c = 0.25c_w + 0.75c_o$$
$$= 0.25 \times 3 \times 10^{-6} + 0.75 \times 1.2 \times 10^{-5} \text{ (Appendix C-3 and C-7)}$$
$$= 0.975 \times 10^{-5}$$

However, the error introduced in S by using just the compressibility of oil, i.e., 1.2×10^{-5} would be only 0.08.

The effective drainage radius, r_e, for unsteady state flow in an infinite reservoir may be taken approximately as

$$r_e \cong \left(\frac{0.591 \times 10^{-3} kt_c}{\phi \mu c} \right)^{1/2}$$

$$\cong \left(\frac{0.591 \times 10^{-3} \times 13.5 \times 0.5}{0.20 \times 0.68 \times 10^{-5}} \right)^{1/2} = 54.1 \text{ ft}$$

$$\bar{k} \cong \frac{348}{1908 \times 14} \times \frac{1.37 \times 0.68 \times \log (54.1 \times 12/4.5)}{3.073 \times 10^{-3}}$$

$$\cong 8.55 \text{ md}$$

$$\text{DR} \cong 13.5/8.55 = 1.58$$

An approximate value of the damage ratio can be found quite simply with the semi-empirical equation of Dolan, Einarsen, and Hill

$$\text{DR} \cong 0.183 \frac{P_r - P_w}{m'} = \frac{0.183 \times 1908}{278} = 1.26 \qquad (8\text{-}13)$$

This equation can be obtained from equations 8-3 and 8-11 if r_e/r_w is taken as 550. Since this is a logarithm term, moderate changes in the value of the ratio will make only slight changes in the calculated value of the damage ratio. The value of the damage ratio from this equation will generally represent a lower limit.

Example MDH. This example demonstrates the application of the method of Miller, Dyes, and Hutchinson to the analysis of a pressure build-up curve from a well producing with a fixed drainage area. A pressure-time plot of the data on rectangular coordinate paper is shown in Fig. 8-21. These pressure data are given below, together with other data about the well and formation fluids that are needed to solve the problem:

Time, t, hours	Pressure, P_w, psig	Time, t, hours	Pressure, P_w, psig
0	1000	16	2175
1	1800	18	2178
2	1920	20	2181
4	2056	22	2184
6	2125	24	2187
8	2152	26	2190
10	2160	28	2192
12	2166	30	2194
14	2170		

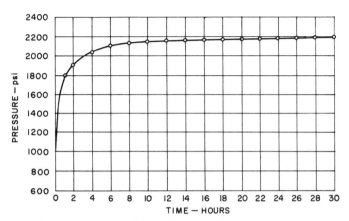

Fig. 8-21. Plot of pressure build-up data for the example used to illustrate the Miller, Dyes, and Hutchinson method of analysis.

Production interval: 6000 to 6060 ft

Hole size: 8 in.

Porosity from core analysis: 0.25

Reservoir oil compressibility from PVT analysis: 2×10^{-5}

Reservoir oil viscosity from PVT analysis: 2 cp.

Formation volume factor: 1.32 bbl of reservoir fluid per barrel of STO

Formation temperature: 170°F

Stabilized production rate prior to shut-in: 255 bbl STO per day

This well is in a developed field, and there is essentially no fluid influx over the drainage radius. Wells are located on a 40-acre spacing so that they are approximately 1320 ft apart.

Solution:

1. Graphical determination of the factor *m*. Plot the pressure data given above on semilogarithmic paper such that the pressure is plotted against the logarithm of the time. This plot is shown in Fig. 8-22. The slope of the straight line section of the curve is 73 psi per cycle.

2. Determine the undamaged reservoir permeability, k, from the equation

$$k = \frac{162.6 Q \mu B}{mh} \tag{8-14}$$

$$= \frac{162.6 \times 255 \times 2 \times 1.32}{73 \times 60} = 25 \text{ md}$$

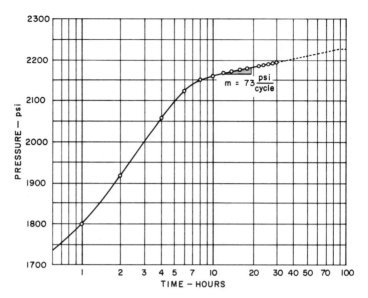

Fig. 8-22. Plot of the data of Fig. 8-21 on semilogarithmic paper.

3. Calculate the dimensionless time, t, from the equation

$$t = \frac{0.000264kt}{\phi\mu c r_d^2} \tag{8-15}$$

k in this equation has the value calculated in step 2 (25 md), t is the time at the end of the build-up period (30 hours), and r_d is the drainage radius. The drainage radius may be taken as one-half the distance between adjacent wells. For a 40-acre spacing, r_d is 660 ft.

$$t = \frac{0.000264 \times 25 \times 30}{0.25 \times 2 \times 2 \times 10^{-5} \times 4.35 \times 10^5} = 0.0455$$

This value falls in the range of 10^{-2} to 10^{-1}; therefore the proper part of the build-up curve was selected for the straight line section.

4. Determine the dimensionless pressure, ΔP, from Fig. 8-23 for the value of t determined in step 3. For the case of no fluid influx over the drainage radius, ΔP is 0.47.

5. From the definition of ΔP, determine the static pressure in the well.

$$P_{ws} = P_{wt} + \Delta P \frac{m}{1.15} \tag{8-16}$$

$$= 2194 + \frac{0.47 \times 73}{1.15} = 2224 \text{ psig}$$

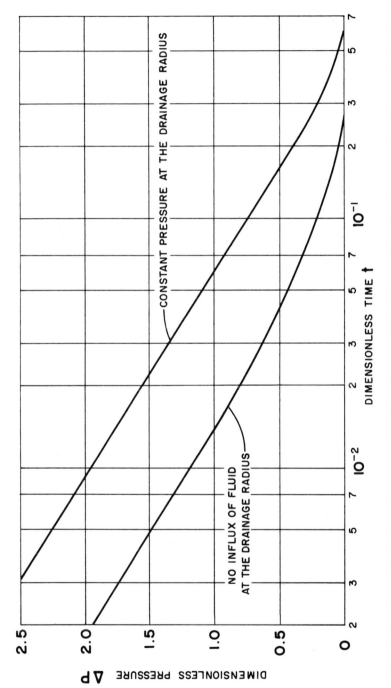

Fig. 8-23. Generalized theoretical curves of Miller, Dyes, and Hutchinson. (After Perrine, reproduced by permission from API Drilling and Production Practice, 1956.)

P_{wt} in this expression is the pressure in the wellbore corresponding to the time used in the calculation of **t**. P_{ws} is the static pressure in the wellbore. For the case where a constant pressure is maintained at the drainage radius, P_{ws} is the same as P_r. For the case where there is no influx of fluid across the drainage radius, the pressure P_{ws} is slightly lower than the pressure P_r which existed at the drainage radius during the flow period. The difference is given by

$$P_r = P_{ws} + 0.25m/1.15 \qquad\qquad (8\text{-}17)$$

6. Estimate the formation damage by comparing k calculated in step 2 with the permeability calculated from the specific productivity index.

$$k = \frac{\text{SPI } \mu B \log r_e/r_w}{3.073 \times 10^{-3}}$$

If the effective drainage radius in this equation is taken as one-half the well spacing, then the formation pressure P_e used in calculating the specific productivity index is the same as P_r for the constant pressure case and larger than P_r for the no influx case. For the case of no influx across the drainage radius, the pressure P_e is

$$P_e = P_{ws} + 0.75m/1.15 \qquad\qquad (8\text{-}18)$$
$$= 2224 + \frac{0.75 \times 73}{1.15} = 2272 \text{ psig}$$

and

$$k = \frac{255}{1272 \times 60} \times \frac{2 \times 1.32 \times \log (660 \times 12/4)}{3.073 \times 10^{-3}} = 9.45 \text{ md}$$

$$\text{DR} = \frac{25}{9.45} = 2.65$$

The significance of the damage ratio is discussed under step 6 of Example VE.

OTHER FORMATION TESTING METHODS

Halliburton Formation Sampler

The Halliburton Company is field testing a new type of formation sampler in which the packer element is a permanent part of the drill string (5). An hydraulic packer, which is part of a special drill collar, is mounted 3 ft above the bit. During normal drilling operation, the packer is deflated. In this position it is flush with the outside of the drill collar. When a test is desired, a sampling assembly consisting of sample barrels, a hydraulically operated valve, and a pressure recorder is dropped into the pipe and allowed to fall to the landing seat at the bit. After the assembly is seated, a pressure of 300 psi is applied with the mud pumps which causes the packer to expand and seal off the hole. An additional 700 psi is then applied which opens the hydraulic valve on the sampling assembly and permits the formation fluids to flow into the sample chambers through the bit. The valve is left open for a period of 10 to 20 minutes to permit the sample chambers to fill. The mud pressure is then released so that the valve closes and the packer deflates. The sampling assembly is subsequently recovered with an overshot run on a wireline.

This method of formation sampling is capable of recovering up to 25 gallons of fluid. It can also be used alternately with wireline coring by simply replacing the sampling assembly with a suitable core barrel. At present there is only one tool size available. The packer assembly has an outside diameter of $6\frac{3}{4}$-in. for use in a $7\frac{7}{8}$-in. to $8\frac{3}{4}$-in. hole. The maximum outside diameter of the sampler assembly is $2\frac{3}{4}$ in. which requires a minimum inside diameter of all drill pipe and drill collars of $2\frac{13}{16}$ in.

Lynes Inflatable Packer   *will conform to hole size*

Lynes, Inc., has marketed a hydraulic packer system that can be used for drill stem testing. The device is run to the test level on the end of tubing or internal flush drill pipe. The tubing is filled with mud and an additional pressure of about 2000 psi is applied with the mud pumps; this inflates the hydraulic packer element and creates a seal against the wall of the borehole. Check valves hold the pressure in the element once it is set. The sealing element grips the wall and holds effectively against up or down pressures without any additional support. A disk valve at the bottom of the tool is then opened by dropping a sinker bar. The mud in the tubing is swabbed out and the formation fluids then produce into the pipe. At the conclusion of the test, the packer is deflated by rotating the tubing to the right and then pulling up $1\frac{1}{2}$ ft; this allows the mud in the packer to flow out the bottom of the tool.

The Lynes tool can be used for drill stem testing, acidizing, washing, or fracturing. It can be set in any hole that is less than twice the diameter of the uninflated tool. (Available tool sizes are from $3\frac{1}{2}$ in. to $5\frac{5}{8}$ in.) It may even be left in the hole for several days with little danger of becoming stuck, and so, in a way, it is a good temporary substitute for running casing. The disadvantages in using the device for drill stem testing are that the well must be swabbed, and it is not possible to obtain quantitative information about the permeability, etc., from the test results.

By using a different type of valve and two packers, the device may also be used for straddle testing.

Schlumberger Wireline Tester

Schlumberger Well Surveying Corporation has developed a method of formation testing using a tool that is run on a wireline (6, 15). A photograph of this tool is shown in Fig. 8-24 and a schematic drawing of the mechanism is shown in Fig. 8-25.

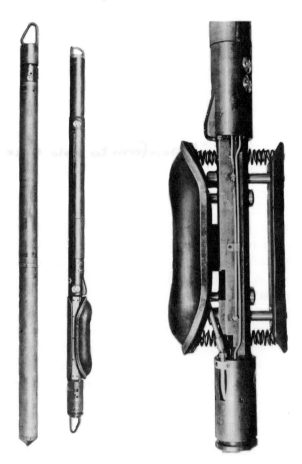

Fig. 8-24. Photograph of the Schlumberger wireline formation tester. (With permission.)

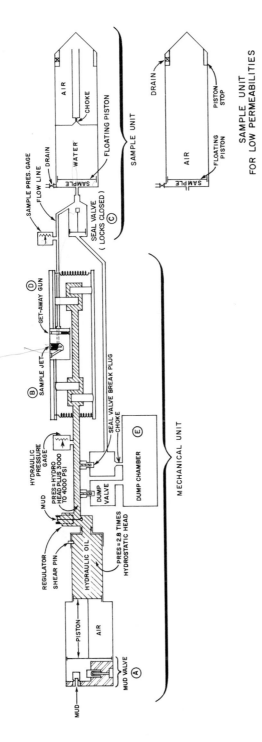

Fig. 8-25. Schematic diagram of the Schlumberger wireline formation tester. (Reproduced with permission of Schlumberger Well Surveying Corporation.)

In running a test with this device, the collapsed tool is lowered into the hole to the test depth. Exact positioning is accomplished by means of an SP electrode on the tool which may be correlated with a prior electric log survey. The mud valve (A, Fig. 8-25) is then opened electrically, and permits mud to enter the pressure intensifier and move the pistons to the right. This hydraulic pressure causes expansion of the tool and forces the seal pad and the back-up shoe against the walls of the hole. When the seal has been made between the mud column and the sample port, the sample jet, B, is fired. This creates a hole about a quarter of an inch in diameter and 6 or 8 in. deep and at the same time opens the flow line so that formation fluids can flow into the sample chamber. The sample chamber contains a water cushion which must flow through a choke during the sampling. This choking action serves the same purpose as the choke on the standard drill stem test. The sample line contains a pressure-sensitive electrical device which records the flowing pressure at the surface with an accuracy of ±50 psi.

At the end of the flow period, the seal valve break plug is fired; this permits the hydraulic pressure to close the seal valve, C. The valve automatically locks closed, and the remaining hydraulic pressure is gradually relieved by flowing through the choke into the dump chamber, E. With the relief of the hydraulic pressure the springs collapse the tool. Usually the pressure differential between the mud column and the formation in front of the seal pad is sufficient to continue to hold the pad against the formation even after the tool is collapsed. At this point a get-away gun, D, is fired; this makes a fluid connection between the front and back of the pad so that the pressure is equalized and the tool falls free. (A second getaway shot is available as a safety measure.)

When the sample has been brought to the surface, a pressure gage, gas separator unit, and gas flow meter are connected to the upper drain of the sample chamber, and the fluids are removed and analyzed. Gas-oil ratio, gas gravity, and oil gravity can all be measured. If water is recovered, its resistivity can be measured to determine whether it is formation water or mud filtrate. The sample chambers can even be arranged to separate the first and last fluid produced into the chamber into two parts which may be analyzed separately.

The wireline tester contains measuring elements which record at the surface all the events during the test. Three curves are recorded as shown in Fig. 8-26. Curve 1 gives the pressure in the hydraulic system; this indicates the mechanical action of opening and closing of the seal pad and back-up shoe. Curve 2 gives a record of the electrical functions which cause the operation of the tool. Curve 3 is a record of the pressure

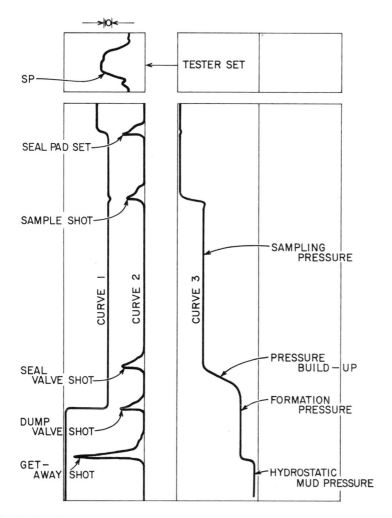

Fig. 8-26. Typical curves indicating the operation of the tester and fluid pressures during a wireline formation test.

in the flow line leading from the sample port to the sample chamber. The chart is driven electrically and each horizontal division line represents either 1 sec or 5 sec, depending on the selected time scale. In addition to these three curves, a short section of the SP curve used to position the tester is shown.

When it is desired to obtain a pressure build-up curve with this tool, a slight modification is made in the operation procedure. Before lowering the tool into the hole, the choke between the seal valve system and the dump chamber is closed off. Then when the seal shot is fired, the pressure remains in the hydraulic system and the tool remains set. When the surface recorder indicates that the build-up is complete, a dump valve shot is fired and the tool collapses. To improve the accuracy of the pressure measurements, an additional carrier is being developed to house a bourdon tube type of pressure recorder below the sample chamber.

The wireline tester can be used in open holes having diameters between $7\frac{7}{8}$ in. and 12 in. and in cased holes between 7 in. and $12\frac{1}{4}$ in. The hole should be circulated and conditioned before the test. A caliper log should be run if possible to help in selecting a uniform-sized section of hole for the seal; variations in hole size of as little as $\frac{1}{2}$ in. are sufficient to cause pad failure. About one-third of the tests are failures unless a caliper log is used; the use of a caliper log can cut this failure ratio by a factor of two.

The necessary clearance between the test depth and the bottom of the hole is 10 ft if a 1-gallon reservoir is used, and 20 ft if the larger samplers (2.75 gallons and 5.5 gallons) are used. A mud pressure of at least 400 psi is necessary to set the tool against the spring pressure.

REFERENCES

1. Black, W. M., A review of drill-stem test techniques and analysis: *Symposium on Formation Evaluation*, AIME, Houston, Texas, 1955, p. 98.
2. Dolan, J. P., Einarsen, C. A., and Hill, G. A., Special applications of drill-stem test pressure data: *Trans. AIME*, v. 210, 1957, p. 318.
3. Horner, D. R., Pressure build-up in wells: *Proceedings of the Third World Petroleum Congress*, Section II, 1951, p. 503.
4. Hurst, W., Establishment of the skin effect and its impediment to fluid flow in a well bore: *The Petroleum Engineer*, October, 1953, p. B-6.
5. Hyde, W. E., New formation sampler reduces operational costs: *World Oil*, v. 149, September, 1959, p. 63.
6. Lebourg, M., Fields, R. Q., and Doh, C. A., A method of formation testing on logging cable: *Trans. AIME*, v. 210, 1957, p. 260.
7. Matthews, C. S., Analysis of pressure buildup and flow test data: *Formation Evaluation Symposium*, AIME, Houston, Texas, 1960, p. IV-1.
8. Milburn, J. D., and Howell, J. C., Formation evaluation with wireline formation tester: *Formation Evaluation Symposium*, AIME, Houston, Texas, 1960, p. IV-39.
9. Miller, C. C., Dyes, A. B., and Hutchinson, C. A., Jr., The estimation of permeability and reservoir pressure from bottom hole pressure build-up characteristics: *Trans. AIME*, v. 189, 1950, p. 91.
10. Muskat, M., *Flow of Homogeneous Fluids Through Porous Media*, McGraw-Hill Book Co., New York, 1937, p. 641.

11. Nisle, R. G., The effect of a short term shut-in on a subsequent pressure build-up test on an oil well: *Trans. AIME*, v. 207, 1956, p. 320.
12. Nisle, R. G., The effect of partial penetration on pressure build-up in oil wells: *Trans. AIME*, v. 213, 1958, p. 85.
13. Perrine, R. L., Analysis of pressure build-up curves: *API Drilling and Production Practice*, 1956, p. 482.
14. Stegemeier, G. L., and Matthews, C. S., A study of anomalous pressure build-up behavior: *Trans. AIME*, v. 213, 1958, p. 44.
15. *Supplement No. 1, Schlumberger Formation Tester:* Schlumberger Well Surveying Corp., 1959.
16. Thomas, G. B., Analysis of pressure build-up data: *Trans. AIME*, v. 198, 1953, p. 125.
17. van Everdingen, A. F., The skin effect and its influence on the productive capacity of a well: *Trans. AIME*, v. 198, 1953, p. 171.
18. Van Poollen, H. K., Status of drill-stem testing techniques and analysis: *Formation Evaluation Symposium*, AIME, Houston, Texas, 1960, p. IV-21.

9

Other Evaluation Methods

This chapter includes those tools which are currently of secondary importance in formation evaluation, and which cannot be properly included with one of the other methods reviewed in the preceding chapters. Included here are: temperature logging, caliper logging, casing collar locators, nuclear magnetism logging, and the determination of the dip of subsurface formations.

TEMPERATURE LOGGING

It is a known fact that the temperature of the earth increases with depth. Except for the first hundred feet or so, which are influenced by partial fluid saturation and the seasonal variations in the air temperature, the rate of temperature increase with depth is approximately linear. This temperature increase is known as the *geothermal gradient*. The geothermal gradient varies from place to place on the earth, but averages about one degree Farenheit per 100 ft of depth. Small variations in the geothermal gradient occur with depth because of the differences in the thermal conductivity of the various types of rock.

The temperatures in the drill hole of a rotary drilled well are not in equilibrium with the temperatures of the surrounding rocks because of the circulation of the drilling mud; in fact, the temperatures measured on the ordinary logging surveys may be as much as fifty degrees different from the rock temperatures. These facts limit the use which can be made of temperature logs for evaluation work. At present they are used primarily for locating the top of cement behind casing, and for locating an interval which is producing gas during actual production operations.

When cement sets, it releases considerable heat, so that an easily recognizable temperature change occurs at the top of a cemented section. Also, the amount of heat generated, and hence the temperature, is higher in those locations where there is more cement behind the casing. The temperature log therefore should correlate with the hole caliper log. For this reason temperature sensing elements may be used on gun perforators for depth control (see Chapter 10).

When gas is produced into a well, the expansion of the gas may cause a temperature drop of as much as twenty degrees. The amount of the cooling anomaly is related to the pressure drop that occurs in the formation, and if the formation properties and the pressures are known, the cooling effect can be used to estimate the amount of production from a given horizon. The method is particularly useful for calculating the relative production rates from several gas stringers producing into a single well.

Temperature logs are made with a resistance thermometer (an element whose electrical resistance changes with changes in temperature). The variations in the resistance of the thermometer are transmitted electrically to the surface and are displayed on a strip log in the same manner as logs from other wireline tools. Logging is done while running into the hole because passage of the sonde disturbs the existing temperature conditions. If another run is to be made, an intervening period of time of several hours must be allowed so that the undisturbed conditions can be re-established. Logging speeds may range up to 5000 ft per hour.

CALIPER OR SECTION GAGE LOGGING

The caliper log is a measurement of the size of the borehole. It can be run as a separate survey (section gage), or as part of the wall resistivity log survey (microlog caliper). The principle of measurement is the same in both cases.

Figure 9-1 is a schematic drawing of the section gage. On the body of the instrument are fastened three large flexible springs which ride against the wall of the borehole. These three springs are attached to a movable rod at the bottom of the tool. The position of this rod in the tool body is governed by the size of the hole. The position of the rod also governs the amount of inductive coupling between the current coil and the pickup coil in the tool body. Changes in the borehole size are therefore reflected in changes in the voltage induced in the pickup coil, and these voltages are logged at the surface. The instrument can record hole diameters up to 36 in.

The microcaliper log operates with two contact surfaces rather than three, and the distance between the outer faces of the two pads on the microlog tool is recorded as the hole diameter. The microcaliper log is ordinarily recorded in the left-hand track of the microlog survey.

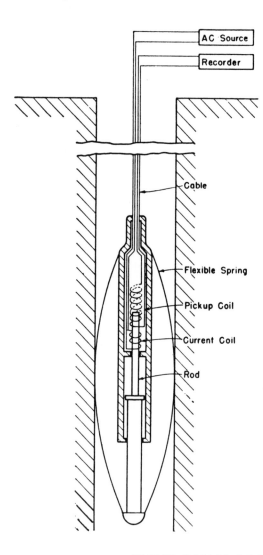

Fig. 9-1. Schematic drawing of a section gage. (Courtesy of Schlumberger Well Surveying Corporation.)

CASING COLLAR LOCATORS

A casing collar locator is a device that is run with cased hole radio-activity logs for the purpose of correlating the formation depths with the position of the casing collars. Each collar then becomes a depth reference point for the precise depth control that is often needed in gun perforating operations.

Two types of collar locators are available. One type employs metal feelers which contact the inside of the casing and detect the change in the pipe size that occurs at a joint. A superior type of locator measures the magnetic properties of the casing, and these, of course, change when a collar is present. This second type of device is also sensitive to changes in the casing caused by perforating.

NUCLEAR MAGNETISM LOGGING

A new logging method (1, 2, 5), based on measurements of the nuclear magnetic properties of the hydrogen contained in formation fluids, has been introduced recently on an experimental basis by Byron Jackson. Based on limited field experience, it appears that the log can successfully represent the amount of pore space containing fluid that is free to move, and in some cases it can distinguish between oil and water. Two logging runs are necessary to get the maximum information. The free fluid log is made as a continuous log over the length of the hole. Points of interest are then selected for the second type of measurement which requires stopping the instrument for short periods of time and obtaining the nuclear magnetic relaxation curves.

Fundamental Properties of Nuclei

Nuclear Angular Momentum. In order to account for various atomic phenomena, it is necessary to postulate the existence of angular momenta for the atomic particles, electrons, protons, and neutrons. Two kinds of angular momentum are possible. The first is an orbital momentum caused by the rotation of a particle about the common center of mass of the atom. The second is a spin momentum that results from the particle rotating about its own axis. The total angular momentum of the atom is the vector sum of the momenta of the various particles.

Angular momentum can exist only in discrete levels that are integral or half-integral multiples of $h/2\pi$ ($= \hbar$), where h is Planck's constant (6.6242×10^{-27} erg-sec). The spin component of the angular momentum for any particle can have a magnitude of only $\frac{1}{2}\hbar$, and can be only positive or negative with respect to a given direction. The orbital angular momentum can be any integral multiple of $\hbar$.

Nuclear Magnetism. Each of the three subatomic particles has a magnetic field associated with it. A composite particle, such as an atom, molecule, or nucleus has a field which is the vector sum of the fields of the individual particles. These fields have the properties of a bar magnet, and the strength of the field is defined in terms of the magnetic moment.[1]

The magnetic field of the electron has been computed theoretically on the assumption that the movement of the electron in its orbit is equivalent to the flow of electric current. From this result for the electron it has been deduced that the magnetic moment of a proton in the nucleus should be

$$\mu_N = \frac{e\hbar}{2M_p c} \tag{9-1}$$

where e is the charge on the proton, M_p is the mass of the proton, and c is the speed of light. μ_N is called the nuclear magneton. It has a value of 5.0493×10^{-24} erg per gauss. It has been found experimentally that the proton (or hydrogen nucleus) has a moment which is actually much larger than this, being equal to 2.793 nuclear magnetons, or 14.105×10^{-24} erg per gauss.

It has been determined also that the magnetic moment of a particle is directly related to its angular momentum. The magnetic moment can therefore be expressed in terms of a multiple of the momentum quantum number.

$$\mu_J = J\gamma_J\hbar \tag{9-2}$$

where γ_J is the gyromagnetic ratio and J is the angular momentum number. The gyromagnetic ratio is the ratio of the absolute magnetic

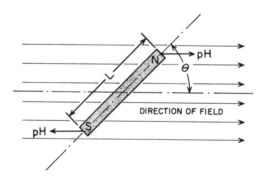

[1] The figure shows a bar magnet having a pole strength of p which is placed in a magnetic field of an intensity of H. The intensity of the field is defined as the force experienced by a unit pole located in the field. The force acting on each pole of the magnet is therefore Hp, and the torque that this creates about the center of the magnet is

$$\text{Torque} = HpL \sin \theta$$

The multiple, pL, is called the magnetic moment of the magnet.

dipole moment in ergs per gauss to the absolute angular momentum in erg-seconds. It has a specific value for each element.

The Gyroscope

A simple spherical gyroscope is pictured in Fig. 9-2a. The mass of the gyroscope is rotating about the x axis with a speed of ω revolutions per second. This creates an angular momentum which can be represented, as in Fig. 9-2b, by an arrow on the x axis. The length of this arrow is proportional to the product of the moment of inertia of the mass, I, and the speed of rotation. The direction of the arrow is the direction of travel of a right-hand screw having the same motion as the gyroscope. Now, if forces F are applied to the gyroscope in an attempt to turn it about the y axis, these forces will create a torque that can be represented by a vector in the negative y direction. If the torque is applied for an interval of time dt, the magnitude of the torque impulse acting on the system will be $T\,dt$. This impulse must change the momentum of the gyroscope by an equal amount. From the figure it is obvious that

$$T\,dt = I\omega \tan d\phi \qquad (9\text{-}3)$$

Since $d\phi$ is a very small angle, $\tan d\phi = d\phi$, and

$$T = I\omega \frac{d\phi}{dt} = I\omega\omega' \qquad (9\text{-}4)$$

$d\phi/dt$ is the rate of change of position of the axis of the gyroscope and represents the velocity with which it rotates about the z axis as the result of a torque applied about the y axis. This motion is called precession.

When the gyroscope is precessing, it has an additional angular momentum of $I\omega'$, which may be represented by a vector in the positive

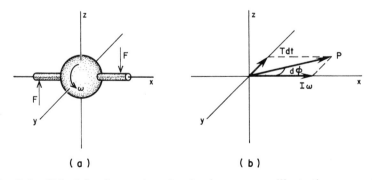

(a)   (b)

Fig. 9-2. Principle of operation of a simple gyroscope illustrating precession.

z direction. This momentum is negligibly small, and in the case of nuclear spins it is nonexistent.

Interaction of the Nucleus with an External Field

Consider the single proton, shown schematically in Fig. 9-3a. It has a spin of $\frac{1}{2}\hbar$, and is aligned with a weak magnetic field that lies in the direction of the x axis. Suppose now that a very strong field is applied with an electromagnet in the direction of the z axis. Because of the magnetic properties of the proton, a torque is applied to it that tends to align its magnetic field with the stronger field. This torque causes a precession about the z axis, as illustrated in Fig. 9-3b.

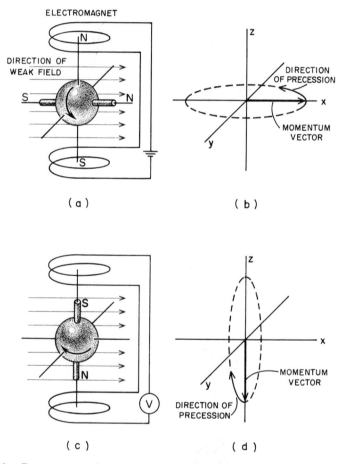

Fig. 9-3. Proton precessing in a magnetic field: (a, b) effect of placing a strong field on a proton originally in a weak field; (c, d) effect of releasing the strong field.

The angle that a magnet makes with a magnetic field is a measure of its potential energy with respect to that field. In order for the proton to realign itself with the new field, it is necessary for it to give its potential energy to the surrounding atoms, and this energy appears as an increased thermal motion of the system. The length of time required for the proton to reach a new equilibrium position in alignment with the new field depends on the efficiency of the energy exchange among the atoms.

After a period of time, the proton will align itself with the electromagnetic field. Suppose that the strong field is now removed instantaneously, but that the weak field is still present, as illustrated in Fig. 9-3c. The weak field now puts a torque on the proton which causes it to precess about the x axis. Since the precessing proton represents a rotating magnetic field, and since this field is cutting the coils of the now inactive electromagnet, an alternating voltage is induced in the coils. If the strength of the weak field is known, the frequency of this signal can be computed by means of the Larmor equation.

$$2\pi\nu = \frac{\mu_p}{\hbar/2} H \qquad (9\text{-}5)$$

where ν is the frequency, μ_p is the magnetic moment of the proton, and H is the strength of the magnetic field. For a proton precessing in a magnetic field of $\frac{1}{2}$ gauss (approximate strength of the earth's field) the frequency is 2.14 kc.

A fluid sample, of course, contains many protons. The degree of alignment, or polarization, that can be obtained with available field strengths is very small, equivalent to a preferential orientation of perhaps one proton in a million. Thermal agitation causes a random arrangement of the others.

The magnitude and direction of the net preferential orientation of the protons in a sample can be represented by a vector, and this vector can be resolved into two components, one perpendicular to the axis of precession (transverse component), and one parallel to the axis of precession (thermal component). The transverse component is a maximum at the start of precession and decreases to zero; the thermal component, when represented by a vector in the direction of the new field, is zero at the start of precession and increases to a maximum. Since the precession around the axis is represented by the transverse component, it is this component which determines the strength of the signal that is generated in the receiving coil.

The process by which the proton polarization arrives at its new

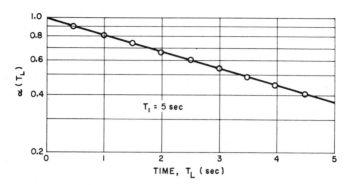

Fig. 9-4. Thermal relaxation curve for oxygen free distilled water. (After Brown and Gamson, courtesy of the AIME.)

equilibrium position is called relaxation. The rate of relaxation in many systems that are simple and homogeneous is exponential in character, i.e., the size of the vector component when plotted versus time on semi-logarithmic paper is a straight line. Figure 9-4 is an example of a simple exponential relaxation. The slope of the straight line is a characteristic of the particular system. It is customary to express the rate of relaxation of a system in terms of the slope of this straight line. The relaxation time T_1 is the time necessary for the thermal relaxation component of polarization to change by a factor of e, the natural logarithm base ($= 2.718$). The time T_2 is the time necessary for the transverse component to change by a factor of e. For low-viscosity homogeneous fluids, the two characteristic times for proton relaxation are approximately equal, although this is not necessarily so.

At the beginning of precession the fields from the precessing protons generally reinforce one another, and the signal received by the coil is the sum of all precessing protons. As time progresses, small inhomogeneities in the weak field cause the various precessions to fall out of phase gradually, and the signal from the transverse component falls rapidly to zero. Thus the observed T_2 component of polarization may be much smaller than the T_1 component.

Since the T_1 and T_2 components of relaxation do not bear any fixed relation to one another, and since the T_1 component cannot be measured directly (only the transverse component contributes to the observed signal), it is necessary to resort to an indirect method to determine the thermal relaxation time of a sample. Either of two procedures may be followed, depending on the method of application of the electromagnetic field. In either case the earth's field is used to cause precession.

In the high field strength method, the sample is placed in the field of the polarizing coil and the magnet is turned on. This causes a net orientation or polarization of the spins in the direction of the magnetic field. The thermal component of this orientation is shown as the dotted line in Fig. 9-5. After a period of time, T_{p1}, the magnetic field is cut off and the protons are allowed to precess about the earth's field. The signal received from this precession follows the curve of the dashed line. The strength of this signal at the instant precession starts is a measure of the orientation of the protons that was achieved by the electromagnet field operating for a period of time, T_{p1}. The experiment is then repeated with another period of polarization, T_{p2}. If it is known that relaxation of the thermal component is exponential, two measurements are sufficient to establish the characteristic thermal relaxation time, T_1. In the systems encountered in nuclear magnetic logging, this assumption is invalid, and a series of relaxation measurements must be made to establish a curve showing the change of the thermal component with time.

In the low field strength method, a high field strength is again used to cause polarization, but in this case it is left on long enough to permit the equilibrium condition to be reached, as shown in Fig. 9-6. At that time the strength of the field is greatly reduced, although still kept stronger than the earth's field so as to prevent precession. During the period of time, T_L, the orientation of the protons becomes more random and polarization decreases toward that which would be in equilibrium with the lower field strength. The field is then completely removed, and precession occurs about the earth's field. From the measured signal

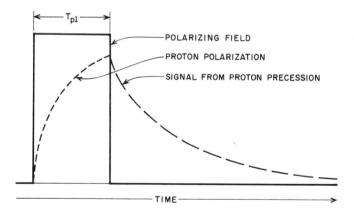

Fig. 9-5. Illustration of the high field strength relaxation method. (After Brown and Gamson, courtesy of the AIME.)

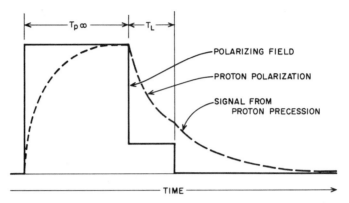

Fig. 9-6. Illustration of the low field strength relaxation method. (After Brown and Gamson, courtesy of the AIME.)

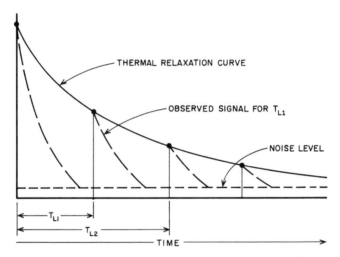

Fig. 9-7. Method of constructing a thermal relaxation curve from precession data. (After Hull and Coolidge, courtesy of the AIME.)

at the start of precession, the polarization at the end of period T_L can be determined. A series of measurements with different values of T_L defines the rate of thermal relaxation, in this case from the high to the low field strength condition. Figure 9-7 shows how the results of a series of such measurements would look.

Nuclear Magnetism Logging Methods

The sonde used in nuclear magnetism logging contains a suitable coil, switching circuits, and an amplifier. Power for energizing the coil to create a high magnetic field is supplied from the surface. After the switching circuits cut off the power to the magnet, this same coil may be used to record the flux changes caused by the precessing protons. In the period of time during which the switching operation takes place, it is impossible to record a signal from the coil. This results in an instrumentation delay as shown in the pictorial representation of Fig. 9-8. In order to get the strength of the signal at the instant precession begins, it is necessary to extrapolate the curve back to zero time. Fortunately, most of the signal curves are approximately exponential, and the extrapolation is easily made.

An important factor in nuclear magnetism logging is that the system is responsive only to the element hydrogen. The principal isotopes of many of the other elements encountered in subsurface formations, such as carbon, oxygen, magnesium, silicon, sulfur, and calcium, do not have magnetic moment or spin. Potassium and iron have very weak magnetic moments. Sodium and aluminum have somewhat higher magnetic moments, but the detection efficiency is low for these elements. In addition, the material containing the hydrogen must be in the fluid state. Very high-viscosity fluids (> 600 cp) and solids have very short transverse relaxation times. They therefore provide a signal that cannot be measured because it decays to zero during the instrumentation delay period. Fluids that are bound mechanically to shales or silts also do not have a measurable signal.

The presence of magnetite in the formations causes a marked decrease

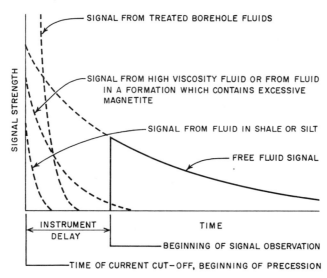

Fig. 9-8. Pictorial representation of fluid signals in nuclear magnetism logging. (After Hull and Coolidge, courtesy of the AIME.)

in the transverse relaxation time because of the inhomogeneities it creates in the magnetic field. If sufficient magnetite is present, it may kill the signal completely. This fact is not entirely detrimental, however, since magnetite can also be used to kill the otherwise large signal that would be received from the fluid in the borehole. It has been determined that 65 μg per cubic centimeter (25 lb per 1000 bbl) of powdered magnetite dispersed in the drilling fluid is sufficient to prevent observation of any signal from this source. This amount of magnetic material is usually present in most muds from the steel worn from the drill pipe and bits during normal use.

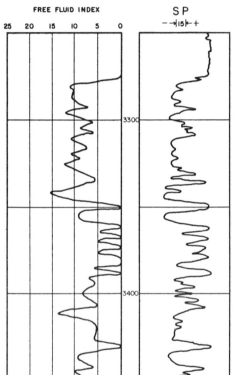

Fig. 9-9. Example of a free fluid log. (Brown and Gamson, courtesy of the AIME.)

Free Fluid Log. One of the two logs recorded in nuclear magnetic logging is a record of the high field strength relaxation time at each formation level for a single high field strength and a single time period. At present this log is recorded every 2 ft over the entire interval of interest. It is calibrated in such a way that the reading is equal to the porosity for clean formations. The immobile water contained in shales gives no measurable signal, so the log reading is zero for all shales. Shaly sandstones and carbonates represent an intermediate condition.

The circumstantial relation between the log reading and the mobility of the pore fluids is responsible for the name of the *free fluid log*.

The free fluid log is displayed as a free fluid index (FFI) versus depth curve. The free fluid index is calculated from the equation

$$\text{FFI} = \frac{V}{EG} \tag{9-6}$$

where V is the extrapolated value of the voltage induced in the sensing coil, G is a geometrical factor, and E is an environmental factor that allows for the magnetic susceptibility of the hydrogenous material, the angle between the earth's field and the borehole, and the Larmor precession frequency. An example of the FFI log is shown in Fig. 9-9. The SP curve is shown for comparison.

The FFI curve has been found to be an excellent lithology correlation curve. The effectiveness in this application is largely the result of the clear distinction that it makes between shales and porous non-shales.

Thermal Relaxation Measurements. On the basis of the data obtained from the FFI curve, and other logs, interesting zones are selected for more extensive investigation of the thermal relaxation characteristics of the contained fluids. The shape of the relaxation curve and the time necessary for relaxation depend on the nature of the fluid and the amount of solid surface that is exposed in the pores. High-gravity oils at high temperatures are likely to have long relaxation times. Heavy oils at low temperatures are likely to have very short relaxation times, possibly too short to be measured. The relaxation time T_1 for water is usually between 50 and 300 msec, depending on the amount of surface

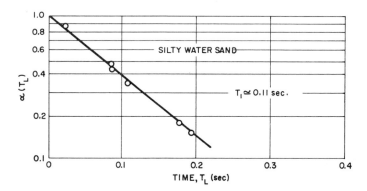

Fig. 9-10. Thermal relaxation curve for a silty water sand. (After Brown and Gamson, courtesy of the AIME.)

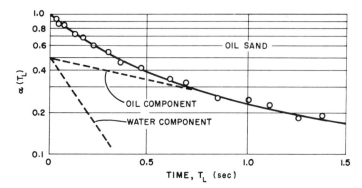

Fig. 9-11. Thermal relaxation curve for an oil sand. (After Brown and Gamson, courtesy of the AIME.)

area of the rock matrix. The interaction between the rock surface and the pore fluid accelerates the thermal relaxation. It is because of this interaction that no fluid signal is observed from the fluid in shales. It has been found that water is particularly sensitive in this respect. The effect of surface interaction is readily apparent when Fig. 9-10 and Fig. 9-4 are compared.

Water contained in water-saturated zones shows a greater surface interaction effect than water in oil sands, even if the oil-bearing rocks are water wet and most of the oil has been displaced by mud filtrate. Oil sands may be identified therefore by the unusually long relaxation times for the signal coming from water (usually longer than one-half second) as compared to the time that is found for water alone. Oil sands may also be identified by the distinctly nonexponential character of the relaxation curve. If both oil and water are present, they are likely to have different relaxation times, and the sum of the two signals is not a simple exponential function, i.e., a straight line on semilogarithmic paper. It has also been found that most crude oils, even in bulk, do not have a simple exponential relaxation curve. Identifying an oil zone by means of the nonexponential shape of the relaxation curve must be done with care, however, since similar shaped curves can be obtained when the tool spans zones with different amounts of surface area but which contain only water. The distinction between the two cases can be made by noting the difference in the relaxation times.

In some instances where "two-phase" curves are obtained, it can be established that the long relaxation component of the curve represents oil, and the short one represents water (or vice versa). In these cases the amounts of oil and water can be obtained separately, as illustrated in Fig. 9-11, if the relaxation times are sufficiently different. In the case illustrated there, the measured signal (solid curve) is split into its two components (dashed curves). This is easily done because at the higher values of T_L only the hydrocarbon signal is present, and the straight line extrapolation of this part of the curve provides the approximate contribution of the hydrocarbon component to the total signal. The water component is the difference. These curves cross the zero time line at approximately 0.5 and indicate an oil saturation of approximately 50 percent.

At the present time the art of interpretation of nuclear magnetism logs is not highly developed, and the eventual importance of this logging method is still uncertain.

THE DETERMINATION OF THE DIP OF SUBSURFACE FORMATIONS

Two points in space determine a straight line. Three points in space, not in a straight line, determine a plane. The problem of the determination of formation dip, therefore, evolves into one of locating three points within a depositional layer with reference to the horizontal plane. This can be accomplished by using the electric logs from three adjacent wells, and locating the boundary of a particular bed on each log. The corresponding depths, corrected to the proper datum, provide the three points necessary to define the plane of the bed (i.e., to determine the magnitude and the direction of the dip). This method assumes that there are no formation anomalies between the wells and that the formation is in fact a continuous flat plane over the distances involved. In many productive areas such an assumption cannot be tolerated. Even

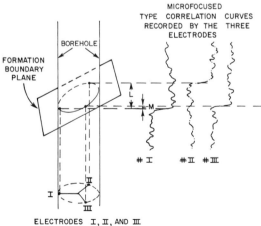

Fig. 9-12. Schematic drawing showing the principle of operation of the dipmeter. (Courtesy of Schlumberger Well Surveying Corporation.)

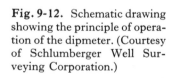

more important in the case of exploratory work is the fact that information from two other nearby wells is simply not available. A better method, then, is to use an instrument which can record three electric logs, properly spaced and oriented, in the same well. This principle, on which modern dipmeters operate, is illustrated by Fig. 9-12. Determining the dip by this method requires an accurate directional survey of the well, so the pertinent methods of directional surveying are also included here.

Dipmeters

Wireline dipmeters must make three basic measurements. The first is the measurement of the dip of the formation relative to the borehole. This is done with three identical sets of electrodes spaced at 120° and all on the same plane perpendicular to the axis of the tool. The second is the measurement of the direction and angle of inclination of the borehole. The third is the measurement of the orientation of the tool relative to magnetic north.

Early Dipmeters. The first practical dipmeter was introduced in 1942 (4). It recorded three SP curves to get the dip relative to the hole axis, and used the photoclinometer to determine the hole inclination and direction. It worked well in low-resistivity sand and shale sections where the SP deflections were large, and where there were sharp changes in the SP at the bed boundaries. In hard rock areas, the SP lacks the necessary character to serve as a dipmeter tool, and so in 1945 a dipmeter was introduced that used three lateral curves for the dip measurement. The AO spacing for these laterals was 3 ft. Again the photoclinometer was used for finding the hole inclination and direction.

The really serious limitation to these methods of measuring dip came from the use of the photoclinometer. This device is shown schematically in Fig. 9-13. Hole inclination is determined by allowing a small steel ball to roll freely on a spherical glass dish which is etched with circular graduation marks. The position of the ball relative to these graduations indicates the amount that the device is tilted from the vertical. Below the dish a compass needle indicates the direction of magnetic north. Above the dish a camera records the position of these two objects. A record like that shown on the right of Fig. 9-13 is made on frames of 35-mm film. On this particular record, the position of the ball indicates that the hole deviates 5° from the vertical and the direction of the drift is 157° from magnetic north (or 167° from true north in this location where the magnetic declination is 10°E). The small triangle shows the location of the No. 1 electrode of the dipmeter, and the arrow indicates the direction of advance of the film so that the individual shots may be identified from the sequence in which they appear. Exposure of the film for the individual records is accomplished by turning the light on and off from the surface.

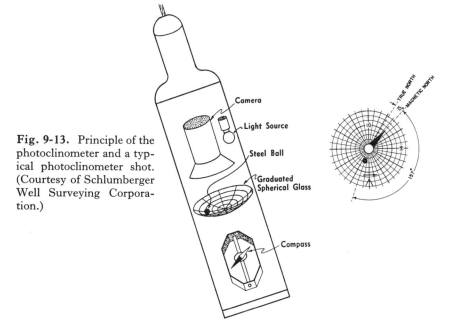

Fig. 9-13. Principle of the photoclinometer and a typical photoclinometer shot. (Courtesy of Schlumberger Well Surveying Corporation.)

Photoclinometer readings must be made as a series of separate measurements at different levels in the hole. When the device was used as part of the dipmeter, readings were usually made at the bottom, top, and middle of the section that was logged. The length of the section surveyed for dip generally could not exceed 40 or 50 ft; otherwise, the rotation of the instrument as it was pulled up through the hole would make the direction of dip relative to magnetic north too uncertain. Figure 9-14 is an example of the record made with this early type of dipmeter.

Continuous Dipmeters. In 1952 the continuous type of dipmeter was introduced (3). This tool employs three microlog devices to make the required electrical logs. The great detail afforded by these devices makes precise dip measurements possible. Since the microdevices are always pressed against the wall of the hole, the spacing between them is always changing, and it is therefore necessary to record the hole size as well. The major advance in this tool is in the use of the teleclinometer in place of the photoclinometer.

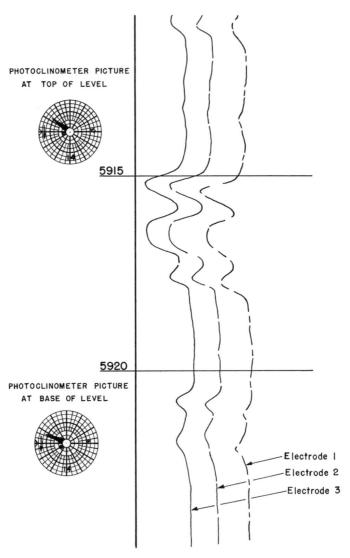

Fig. 9-14.   Typical SP dipmeter level. (Courtesy of Schlumberger Well Surveying Corporation.)

The teleclinometer is an electrical device which continuously records the direction and magnitude of the deviation of the borehole from the vertical. This is accomplished through the use of two pendulums which are free to swing only at right angles to each other; the movement of the pendulums changes the inductance of two coils, thereby providing an electric signal for transmission to the surface. The direction of the tool relative to magnetic north is also recorded electrically. The signals recorded at the surface can be resolved into a single resultant giving the magnitude and direction of the hole inclination. Since all the necessary information is recorded electrically and continuously, this type of dipmeter can be used over extended intervals. It is called the *continuous dipmeter-teleclinometer* or CDM-T by Schlumberger. A photograph of this type of device is shown in Fig. 9-15.

The teleclinometer dipmeter was superseded in 1956 by the poteclinometer dipmeter, which is similar in principle to the CDM-T. In order to improve the operation in harder formations, the microcurves of the CDM-T have been replaced by focused microcurves. The orientation and hole deviation signals are controlled by potentiometers from which the instrument takes its name (*continuous dipmeter-poteclinometer* or CDM-P). The electrical instrumentation of this tool is simpler and easier to maintain than its predecessor.

It is understood that still another improvement in dipmeter design will be made in the near future, although no details are available as yet on the new instrument.

Calculation of Formation Dip.   Figure 9-16 shows a section of a dipmeter log made by the CDM-T tool. The solid curve in the left-hand track is the magnetic orientation of the No. 1 electrode; each division on the log represents 36° with magnetic north (0°) plotted at the extreme left. In this case the orientation of the No. 1 electrode is 234°, clockwise from magnetic north. The other two curves in this track are the hole deviation curves. These may be plotted relative to magnetic north (resolver in), as was done in this case, or they may be plotted relative to the No. 1 electrode (resolver out). Hole drift is measured from the center line which represents 0°. In this case the hole is drifting 6°30′ north and 4°30′ east of the vertical. (The maximum values on these scales are not limited to the 10° shown here. Other ranges up to 90° are available.)

Fig. 9-15.   Photograph of the CDM-T dipmeter. (Courtesy of Schlumberger Well Surveying Corporation.)

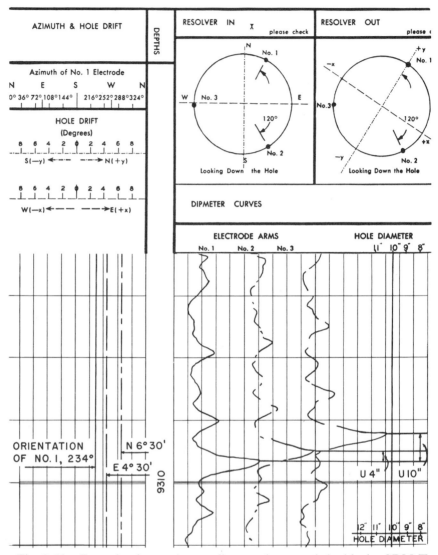

Fig. 9-16. Example of a continuous dipmeter log recorded with the CDM-T. (Courtesy of Schlumberger Well Surveying Corporation.)

To the right of the depth scale are the three microresistivity curves: the solid curve is the No. 1 trace, the dot-dash curve is the No. 2 trace, and the dash curve is the No. 3 trace. These curves do not have a fixed zero, nor any definite scale. They are located on the chart so that they do not overlap excessively, and the sensitivity of the log is such that a clear picture is obtained of changes in resistivity as recorded by each of the electrode systems. At the extreme right of the chart is a solid line representing the hole diameter. In this case, the hole diameter is 10 in. In order to get the necessary detail for dip measurements, the depth scale on the log is plotted as 60 in. for each 100 ft of hole; $\frac{1}{10}$ in. of log is equal to 2 in. of actual hole.

Precise computation of the amount and direction of dip of the formation should be done at a dip computation center; however, the following paper and pencil procedure may be used with fair accuracy in the field. First, a duplicate print or overlay is made of the resistivity curves. Then, by the use of the overlay, it can be determined how much curves 2 and 3 are displaced relative to curve 1. For the example of Fig. 9-16, No. 2 is up 4 in. and No. 3 is up 10 in. These values are then plotted on Fig. 9-17 with a suitable scale. If the displacement of the No. 2 electrode is down, the vector representing the displacement is plotted from the center towards II; if the displacement is up, the vector is plotted from the center away from II. A similar procedure holds for the No. 3 electrode. In this case, No. 2 is plotted 4 units in the direction of 300° and No. 3 is plotted 10 units in the direction of 60°. The resultant sum of these two vectors is a vector 8.8 units in length and in a direction

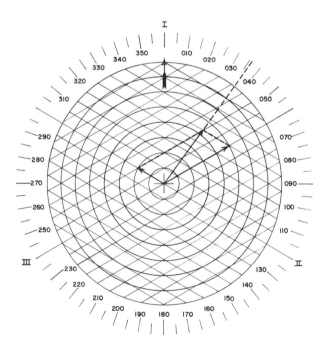

Fig. 9-17. Determination of the apparent dip direction for the sample problem. (Chart courtesy of Schlumberger Well Surveying Corporation.)

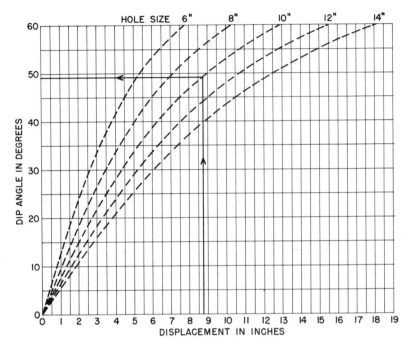

Fig. 9-18. Determination of the apparent dip angle for the sample problem. (Chart courtesy of Schlumberger Well Surveying Corporation.)

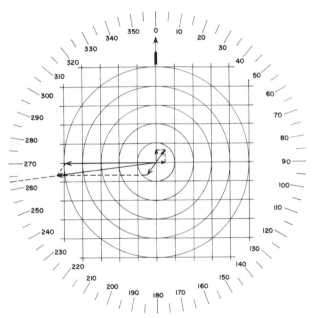

Fig. 9-19. Calculation of true dip angle and direction for the sample problem. (Chart courtesy of Schlumberger Well Surveying Corporation.)

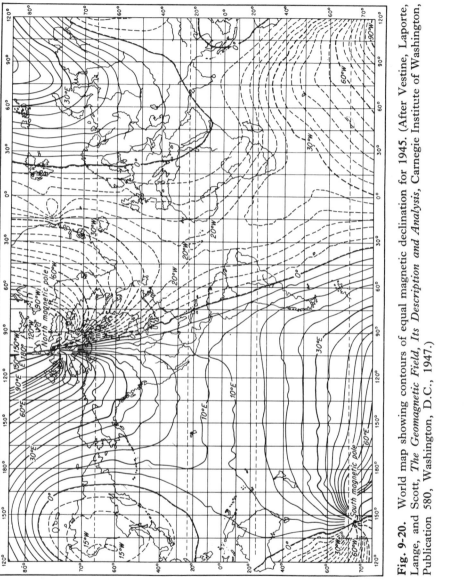

Fig. 9-20. World map showing contours of equal magnetic declination for 1945. (After Vestine, Laporte, Lange, and Scott, *The Geomagnetic Field, Its Description and Analysis*, Carnegie Institute of Washington, Publication 580, Washington, D.C., 1947.)

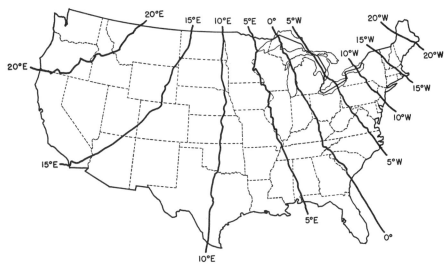

Fig. 9-21. Map of the United States showing contours of equal magnetic declination for 1945. (Data from U.S. Coast and Geodetic Survey.)

of 36° from the No. 1 electrode. Since No. 1 is at 234°, the direction of dip (uncorrected for hole deviation) is 270° from magnetic north. From Fig. 9-18, for a displacement of 8.8 in. and a hole size of 10 in., the dip angle (uncorrected for hole deviation) is 49°.

Now on Fig. 9-19 is plotted the hole drift data of 6°30' N and 4°30' E, with a suitable scale. It is determined by forming the resultant sum of these two vectors that the direction of the deviation is 35° E of magnetic north, and the angle of deviation is 8° from the vertical. The direction and amount of dip are now plotted on this same figure with the same scale as the hole deviation vector. A resultant of the two vectors is now formed by subtracting the hole deviation vector from the dip vector. The resultant is the true dip and dip direction (263° from magnetic north at an angle of 55° from the horizontal). If the direction relative to true north is desired, the magnetic declination correction can be determined from Fig. 9-20 or 9-21.

Figure 9-22 is a section of a dipmeter log made with a CDM-P tool. The right-hand side of this log contains the same information as the CDM-T log, except that the correlation curves have been made with focused electrodes. The orientation and hole deviation data in the left-hand track are quite different, however, being in polar coordinates rather than rectangular coordinates. The orientation of the No. 1 electrode is given as before by the solid line. In this example it is 172°

from magnetic north at a depth of 3032 ft. Relative bearing (dashed trace) gives the direction in which the hole is deviating relative to the position of the No. 1 electrode. At 3032 ft the relative bearing is 162°. Figure 9-23 shows how this is used with the No. 1 azimuth to get the direction of hole drift. For this example, the solid trace is 172-162 or 10° to the right of the dashed trace, so the hole deviates 10° from magnetic north. The amount of deviation is given by the dot-dash

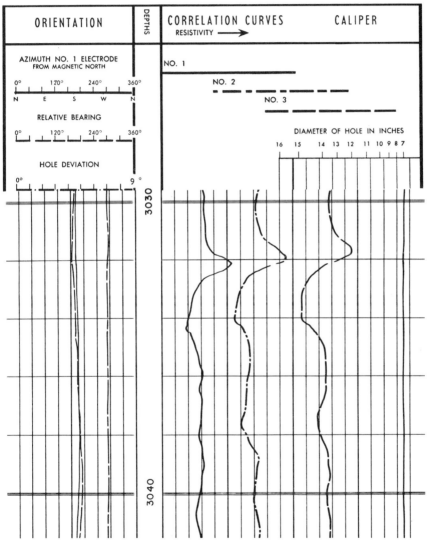

Fig. 9-22. Example of a CDM-P log. (Courtesy of Schlumberger Well Surveying Corporation.)

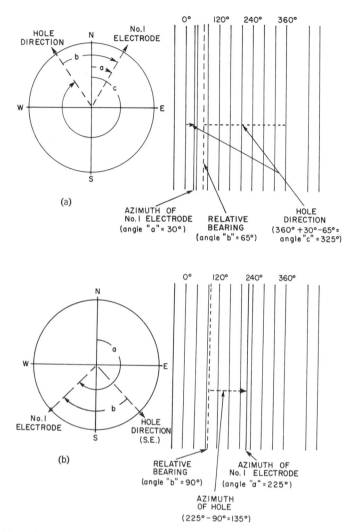

Fig. 9-23. Illustration of the use of CDM-P orientation curves: (a) angle between azimuths of hole and No. 1 electrode does include North and (b) angle between azimuths of hole and No. 1 electrode does not include North. (Courtesy of Schlumberger Well Surveying Corporation.)

trace as 6.8°. From here on, the method of solution for the dip angle and direction is identical to that of the illustrative problem for the CDM-T.

In selecting dipmeter levels for computation, marker beds should be chosen which are known to be fairly extensive in the area. Minor resistivity anomalies appearing in long sections of a uniform bed should be avoided, but rather the boundary between one bed and the next one of different lithology should be selected. Best dip determinations result from the use of thin beds having a high resistivity contrast with their surroundings. In general, for hole diameters of about 8 in., dips of greater than 10° can be determined with good accuracy; between 5° and 10°, reliable results may be obtained if there is a good correlation among the resistivity curves, and the correction for hole deviation is not too great; below 5°, only the general direction of the dip can be obtained.

REFERENCES

1. Brown, R. J. S., and Gamson, B. W., Nuclear magnetism logging: *Trans. AIME*, v. 219, 1960, p. 201.
2. Coolidge, J. E., and Gamson, B. W., Present status of nuclear magnetism logging: *Formation Evaluation Symposium*, AIME, Houston, Texas, 1960, p. III-9.
3. De Chambrier, Pierre, The microlog continuous dipmeter: *Geophysics*, v. XVIII, no. 4, 1953, p. 929.
4. Doll, H. G., The spontaneous potential dipmeter: *Trans. AIME*, v. 164, 1946, p. 278.
5. Hull, P., and Coolidge, J. E., Field Examples of nuclear magnetism logging: *Jour. Petroleum Technology*, August, 1960, p. 14.

10

Well Completion

Because of its close association with formation evaluation and its dependence on the use of formation evaluation tools, well completion is included here in abbreviated form. The actual mechanics of well completion depend largely on experience with the formations which are to be opened to production.

WELL COMPLETION METHODS

Figure 10-1, which is taken from the API Study Committee Report on Well Completions (2), illustrates the general methods of completion and the conditions under which each method would be used. A description of these methods follows here:

I. Competent formations

    A. *Open hole.* The simplest type of completion and the least expensive is to set casing to the top of the productive interval and leave the interval without any type of mechanical support whatever. This type of completion is most common in limestone formations where there is no danger of the formation sloughing into the hole, and where permeability may be discontinuous. A difficulty with this method is that it is impossible to control the entry into the well of unwanted gas or water.

    B. *Screen and liner.* In formations where there is a possibility of the formation sloughing into the hole during production, the necessary support can be obtained through the use of a section of perforated pipe (or liner) set through the interval. In a carbonate formation this might be allowed to rest free on the bottom.

354

COMPETENT FORMATIONS

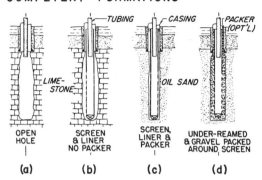

(a) (b) (c) (d)

Fig. 10-1. Well completion
methods. (Reproduced by
permission from API Bul-
letin D6: Well Completion
Methods.)

CAVING FORMATIONS

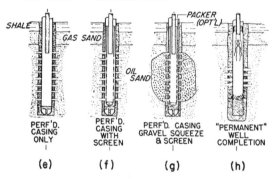

(e) (f) (g) (h)

C. *Screen and liner with packer.*   This is used under the same general
circumstances as *B*, but where there is a possibility of producing
sand into the well, it is necessary to close off the annulus between
the liner and the casing with a packer. If there were an excessive
amount of sand being produced, it would be necessary to go to
a more elaborate completion method.

D. *Underreamed and gravel packed around screen.*   When the liner
and screen are not able to control the production of sand into
the well, it is necessary to pack gravel around the screen. The
gravel is of such a size that it will bridge over the screen openings,
and will in turn provide a bridge for the sand. Gravel used for
packing is about 4 to 10 mesh (0.185 in. to 0.065 in.).

II. Caving formations, thin pay zones

E. *Perforated casing only.*   Where formations need substantial
support, or where thin pay zones are encountered, it is customary
to cement casing through the producing zone. When the cement

has set, the casing is perforated at the desired depth by means of gun or jet perforators. If a good cement bond has been obtained, this method allows opening of any formation or any portion of a formation to production. It is very useful where a well has penetrated the gas cap or the water table as well as the oil zone. The round holes in the casing may also be selectively plugged with balls for selective formation treatment.

F. *Perforated casing with screen.* Where a minor amount of sand is produced through the casing perforations, it may be controlled with a linear hung inside the casing through the interval.

G. *Perforated casing, gravel squeeze and screen.* Incompetent formations producing major amounts of sand require gravel packing. After the casing has been set, cemented, and perforated, the surrounding sand is washed out to form a cave into which gravel is introduced. The liner is then set through the interval by washing it into the gravel.

H. *Perforated casing and "permanent" type completion* (5). In a "permanent" type of completion the tubing is set in the well before perforating and is not removed during its usable life. Special tools for workover operations, logging, and perforating may be run and retrieved on a wireline. This arrangement gives quick and cheap completions in formations which normally have sand problems, and allows for low cost workovers. The tools are small and intricate, and their use may be limited if corrosive conditions are present.

Instead of the gravel packs shown in D and G, it is possible to use prepacked liners which have a sleeve containing carefully sized and packed gravel already on them. No additional packing is needed after the liner is set.

CASING PERFORATION

The completion methods E through H all require perforation of the casing after it has been set to the bottom of the hole and cemented in place. There are two methods of perforation which are in general use, guns and jets, and each has its advantages and disadvantages. The method that is selected must depend on the particular needs of the situation.

Bullet Perforating

A cross-sectional view of a bullet gun is shown in Fig. 10-2. The various components are: (*a*) the fluid seal disks which prevent the well fluids from entering the gun and impairing the firing of the powder, (*b*) the gun barrel, (*c*) the gun body into which the barrel is screwed, and which also holds the igniter and propellant powder charge, (*d*) the bullet with a shear disk at its base which holds the bullet in place until the maximum pressure is created by the burning powder, and (*e*) the wire which conveys electric current from the firing control mechanism to the powder charge. The gun body is a long cylindrical piece of steel and a number of guns are fitted into it at regular intervals. A control head is attached to the gun body, and it is lowered into the well on logging cable. Operation of the gun is controlled electrically from the surface. This gun may be fired selectively, in banks of a few shots each, or all of the guns at once. The gun barrels are spaced in the housing so a suitable pattern of holes will result in the casing.

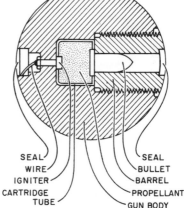

Fig. 10-2. Cross-sectional view of a perforating gun. (Bohn, courtesy of Lane-Wells Company.)

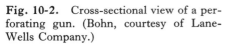

SEAL
WIRE
IGNITER
CARTRIDGE
TUBE

SEAL
BULLET
BARREL
PROPELLANT
GUN BODY

Other bullet guns are available of similar construction, but without the individual wiring from the control head to each of the firing chambers. In this type all the powder cartridges are connected by a primacord so that one signal from the surface fires all the guns simultaneously. This type of gun is comparable in performance to the electrically ignited gun if the flame passages are properly designed.

Jet Perforating

Jet perforating works on a different principle. Instead of the force of the powder being used to propel a bullet, it is directed, by shaping the

A CROSS SECTION OF
THE KONESHOT CHARGE

THE "WAVE FRONT" OF
DETONATING EXPLOSIVE

TRAVELS DOWN
THE CHARGE
AND STRIKES
THE APEX OF
THE CONE

WHEN THE "WAVE FRONT"
REACHES THE LINER
IT COLLAPSES IT !

THE LINER'S
INNER SURFACE
DISINTEGRATES
TO FORM PART OF
THE "FORCE STREAM"

AS THE "WAVE FRONT" ADVANCES
THE OUTER SURFACE OF THE CONE
FORMS A SLUG OR "CARROT" WHICH
FOLLOWS THE FORCE STREAM

THE FORCE STREAM

UNTIL ALL THE CHARGE
HAS BEEN DETONATED –
AND THE FORCE STREAM
LOOKS SOMETHING LIKE THIS

"CARROT"
OR SLUG
OF COARSE PARTICLES
FROM "APEX" OF THE LINER

powder charge, into a force stream which is capable of penetrating the casing. The process of detonation of a jet perforator is shown in Fig. 10-3. The powder charge is in the form of a double inverted cone. The cone is ignited at the apex, and as the detonating wave passes down the cone, the inner liner collapses and forms a series of fine particles which move in the force stream. In the older types of shaped charges, a part of the liner formed into a slug at the end of the force stream and followed it into the perforation. Sometimes this "carrot" would be large enough to plug the opening just made by the jet. This problem has been overcome by superior design of the charge and the proper selection of the liner material. Today's jet perforators are essentially carrot-free.

Shaped charges may be run in retrievable carriers similar to those used for simultaneously fired gun perforators, or they may be run in frangible carriers which are destroyed by detonation of the charges and remain in the well as small pieces of junk. A drawing of an expendable perforator is shown in Fig. 10-4. This particular variety of perforator (4) may be run through

Fig. 10-3. Sequence of events in the firing of a jet perforator. (Forsyth, reproduced by permission from API Drilling and Production Practice, 1950.)

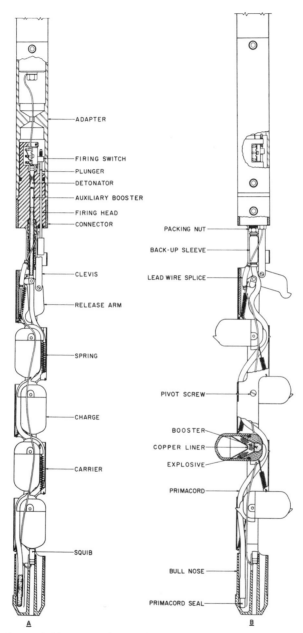

Fig. 10-4. Expendable jet perforator for perforating below tubing: (A) closed position for running-in and (B) open position for firing. (Caldwell and Owen, courtesy of the AIME.)

tubing and then swung into firing position at the bottom of the well. Such a device would be used for perforating with the permanent type of well completion.

Relative Advantages of Bullets and Jets

I. Bullets

A. *Advantages*

1. Bullets cost less than jets. Economies may be effected where bullets can be used.
2. Bullets cause formation fracturing. This may be an advantage or disadvantage, depending on the conditions. In thick sections of hard rocks, such as limestones, fracturing can improve the permeability around the well and improve the well performance. This is also important where fracturing or acidizing is to be performed subsequent to perforating.
3. It is possible to obtain a round burrless hole with bullets. This can be advantageous when it is desirable to treat a perforated section selectively by plugging some of the perforations temporarily with small balls.

B. *Disadvantages*

1. Bullets cause fracturing of cement and formations. This is disadvantageous when perforating thin zones near water or gas-bearing formations. Fracturing of the cement may cause channeling of unwanted fluids into the perforations.
2. Bullets may not be used in high-temperature wells. The pistol powder used in bullet perforators is limited to about 250°F.
3. Bullets usually do not attain as deep a penetration as shaped charges.

II. Shaped charges

A. *Advantages*

1. Shaped charges can be used at temperatures up to 350°F.
2. Shaped charges cause little fracturing of the cement so they may be used in shooting thin zones or in making water shut-off tests.
3. Many more shots can be fired in one trip in the hole. For perforating long sections this advantage may be sufficient to make jets cheaper than guns.
4. Shaped charges penetrate deeper than bullets.
5. In an operation where it is necessary to work through tubing, shaped charges must be used. Bullet guns of less than 3 in. diameter are not effective for perforating.

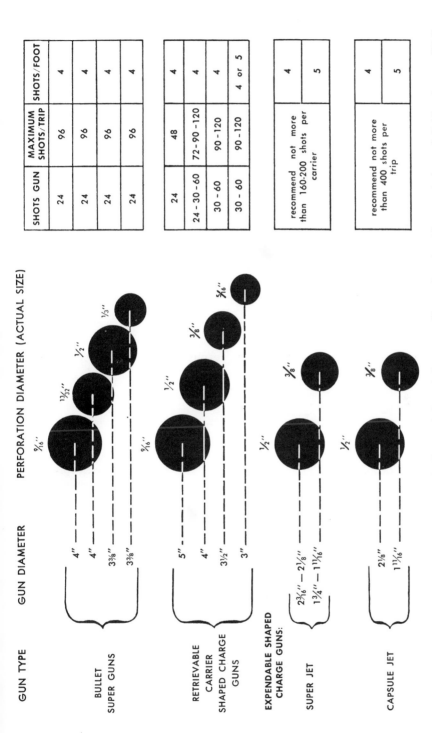

Fig. 10-5. Operating data on Schlumberger bullet and jet perforators. (Reproduced with permission of Schlumberger Well Surveying Corporation.)

B. *Disadvantages*

    1. Shaped charges do not cause as much fracturing as bullets and so do not improve the permeability of the formation around the hole as much.

    2. Shaped charges punch a hole in the casing which is not round and which has an internal burr. If packers are to be run through the interval, the burr must first be milled off. The lack of a round hole makes it difficult to perform selective treating through the perforations.

    3. Shaped charges are more expensive.

Figure 10-5 gives some of the operating data on bullet and shaped charge perforators which are used by the Schlumberger Well Surveying Corporation. Other companies provide a similar line of services.

Productivity Relations

Surprising as it may seem, the rate of production of well fluid into a few perforations may be as high or higher than production into the uncased well. Figure 10-6 shows the results of an electric model study

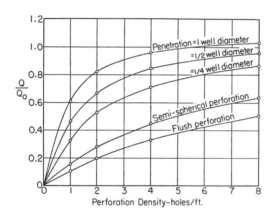

Fig. 10-6. Effect of perforating density and depth on relative well productivity for 6 inch casing. Perforation diameter $= \frac{1}{2}$ in. (McDowell and Muskat, courtesy of the AIME.)

made by McDowell and Muskat (6) on the effect of shot density and penetration depth on the productivity ratio. Since an electric analog was used to obtain these data, they may not conform to actual field conditions in all circumstances. The results do indicate that little improvement is likely to be obtained in the productivity ratio by shooting more than four holes per foot. Also, the placement of the holes around the periphery of the casing and the size of the holes (so long as they were larger than $\frac{1}{4}$ in.) had little influence on the productivity ratio.

Depth Control

In shooting thin sands, precision control of depth is necessary. Usually, the intervals to be perforated will be picked from the electric log. It is not judicious, however, simply to lower the gun to the same indicated depth to perforate. The uncertainty in the depth from a logging cable measurement is about 1 ft in every 1000 ft, even though the average measurement is not this poor.

In order to get accurate depth control, it is necessary to run a series of logs. If the formation is selected from an electric log, then the SP must be rerun with a γ-ray log in open hole. The hole is then cased and the γ ray log is rerun with a casing collar locator. (See Chapter 9.) Finally, the casing collar locator is run on the gun perforator. Since the series of logs has made it possible to correlate the electric log with the location of the casing collars, the only cable measurement that has to be made is from the nearest casing collar. This distance is no greater than 15 ft (except at the bottom of the hole), and so the gun may be positioned with great accuracy.

REFERENCES

1. Allen, T. O., and Atterbury, J. J., Jr., Effectiveness of gun perforating: *Trans. AIME*, v. 201, 1954, p. 8.
2. *API Bulletin D-6: Selection and Evaluation of Well Completion Methods:* American Petroleum Institute, Division of Production, Dallas, Texas, July, 1955.
3. Bohn, F. O., Perforating casing—A lecture for Petroleum Engineering 270, University of Texas: Lane Wells Company, December, 1959.
4. Caldwell, B. M., and Owen, H. D., A new tool for perforating casing below tubing: *Trans. AIME*, v. 201, 1954, p. 302.
5. Huber, T. A., and Tausch, G. H., Permanent-type well completion: *Trans. AIME*, v. 198, 1953, p. 11.
6. McDowell, J. M., and Muskat, M., The effect on well productivity of formation penetration beyond perforated casing: *Trans. AIME*, v. 189, 1950. p. 309.
7. Rodgers, C. J., Some practical aspects of gravel packing: *Trans. AIME*, v. 201, 1954, p. 15.

11

The Formation
Logging Program

The tools that have been discussed individually in the preceding chapters are portions of a large package that is available to the logging engineer, and from which he must select a particular set or group to be used for each well that is drilled. The purpose in planning a logging program before the well is drilled is to ensure that an adequate amount of information will be obtained about the nature of the subsurface formations and that it will be obtained as economically as possible. With this thought in mind, this chapter is divided into three parts: the sources of information, the cost of logging, and the formation logging program.

INFORMATION

There is a variety of information that should be obtained during an exploratory drilling operation. No one tool will provide all of it, and where several tools are available for the determination of one factor, they will not all function with the same diagnostic efficiency. This general subject of information, therefore, is considered under specific subheadings, with an indication of the tools which are available for for each one, and a brief description of the conditions under which they provide the most accurate answers.

Lithology of the Geologic Column

Ditch Samples. Whether these are obtained by a company-employed geologist or by a geologist on a mud logging unit, they are important to any evaluation program. A definite effort should be made to see that good samples of the drill cuttings are obtained at regular intervals, that they are carefully examined, and that they are properly described.

SP Curve of the Electric Log. With fresh muds in low- and medium-resistivity formations the SP provides an excellent method of locating porous and permeable beds. In high-resistivity formations it is still useful, but the bed boundaries cannot be picked with accuracy. With salt muds the SP usually has very little definition and can best be described as having a wandering appearance. It does not work at all in holes drilled with oil-base muds.

Short Normal Curve of the Electric Log. This curve can be used with fair accuracy to determine bed boundaries. Changes in lithology may be inferred with proper control based on ditch samples and the SP. The short normal works best in fresh muds, poorly in salt muds, and not at all in oil-base muds.

Microdevices. The wall resistivity log is the best device for the accurate location of bed boundaries and the definition of permeable zones. It is particularly good when run with a caliper log for supporting evidence of the presence of shales (washed-out zones) and mud cakes. With salty muds or in high-resistivity formations a focused device such as the microlaterolog is preferable. Wall resistivity devices do not function properly in oil-base muds.

Radiation Logs. The γ-ray log can be used to distinguish between shales and other formations and is used in place of the SP curve in salty muds and oil-base muds. The neutron log can be used to distinguish between porous and nonporous intervals when used in conjunction with the γ-ray log. These are the only effective logs where logging must be done inside of casing.

Acoustic Velocity Log. The acoustic velocity log is a very good device for distinguishing between porous and nonporous beds and between limestones or sandstones and shales. Shaly material has an effect which is qualitatively similar to porosity, so that some indication of the presence or absence of shale is needed. The SP and the γ-ray log are helpful in this respect. Sonic logs may be run in fresh, salty, or oil-base muds.

Drilling Time Logs. This log is recorded by mud logging units, but it may be run separately when mud logging is not used. With proper control of the drilling variables, the drilling time log will frequently reflect lithologic changes. In many cases it has an appearance like the SP curve.

Induction Log.   Because of the limitations put on conventional electrical logging devices by oil-base muds, the induction log may find use in this case as an aid in defining lithology.

Correlation of Formations Between Adjacent Wells

Correlation of logs between two or more wells is a process of comparing the logs for similarities in curve shapes which are characteristic of particular formations. (Usually there are natural marker beds such as chalk, anhydrite, or shale sections which help in orienting the logs from adjacent wells; such beds may have unusual resistivity or radioactivity characteristics.) Almost any lithology log or wireline log is suitable for this purpose. For long-range correlation, logs having a large radius of investigation are generally most suitable. Within a proven field, the microdevices are most useful in making a detailed correlation. The sonic log has been found to be a particularly good general correlation tool. When a correlation has been established, it is then possible to use the information in plotting subsurface contour maps and isopachous maps. These are useful as a control for development and exploratory drilling, and in the calculation of reserves and future performance by the methods of reservoir engineering.

Determination of Porosity

Core Analysis.   This is the primary method of porosity determination and the basis for calibration of all other porosity determining devices. While it is given great credence because of its basic nature, it does have one major weakness. Usually a 1-in. by 1-in. core plug is used to represent a section of formation 1 ft in thickness and at least 10 acres in areal extent. This represents an extrapolation of 75 million times. Most of the other formation evaluation tools, while less accurate in measuring porosity, do have a much better sampling volume (2) (see Fig. 11-1). Cores taken with percussion sidewall devices do not give accurate values of porosity.

Acoustic Velocity Log.   In well-consolidated formations containing little or no shaly material, the acoustic velocity log is probably the best wireline tool for porosity determination. In soft formations it is sensitive to the formation fluids and corrections must be made for the presence of oil or gas. In unconsolidated formations (nearby shale velocity less than 10,000 ft per second) and in formations containing shale, corrections of an uncertain magnitude must be made. This detracts from the use of the acoustic velocity log. The experiments of Wyllie also indicate that the tool may not respond too well to vuggy porosity, and the presence of fractures introduces operating difficulties. The porosity limits for the tool are from 5 to 30 percent.

Neutron Log. In well-consolidated sandstone and carbonate rock areas where the porosity is low, the neutron log finds an important place as a means of determining porosity. Where possible, it should be calibrated for the particular area and hole conditions under which it will be used. Where calibration is not possible, service company charts relating neutron count to porosity may be used. The neutron log has the advantage of a large sampling volume, a factor that can be of great importance when the porosity is very irregular. Corrections for the presence of shale are necessary. When the porosity is below 5 percent, the neutron log becomes sensitive to lithologic changes.

Density Log. Another radiation log which is very useful for porosity determination is the density log, provided that the borehole is uniform in size and contains a thin uniform mud cake. This device does not have the large sampling volume of the neutron log, but neither is it sensitive to physically bound water (as in shales) or chemically bound water (as in gypsum). Lithologic control from ditch cuttings is essential for accurate porosity estimation. It is most accurate for porosities greater than 8 percent.

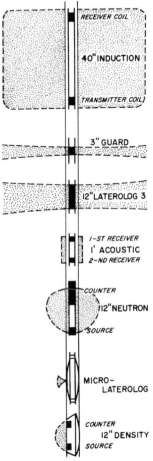

Fig. 11-1. Volumes investigated by various logging devices. (After Chombart, courtesy of *Geophysics*.)

Electric Logging Methods. *Clean formations.* Electric logging methods for determining porosity in clean formations are based on the three equations introduced by Archie (5-54, 5-53, 5-56):

$$F = \frac{1}{\phi^m} \qquad F = \frac{R_0}{R_w} \qquad S_w^n = \frac{R_0}{R_t}$$

In these equations m and n are usually taken as approximately 2 although a range of values is possible. Other empirical relations between porosity and formation factor have also been developed. Where it is possible, values of m and n should be determined by measurements in the laboratory on a suite of cores taken from the formation in question. Using equation 5-53 as it stands, evaluation becomes a problem of finding:

1. R_w. This may be determined from water recovered on formation tests either from this well, or from adjacent wells when it can be assumed that water salinity is areally constant. Sometimes water salinities from adjacent formations in the same well may be used. Under the proper conditions, R_w may be calculated from the SP curve.
2. R_0. If any of the sand in question may be assumed 100 percent saturated with formation water, R_0 may be determined from the appropriate deep investigation log. When this is not possible, R_0 may be used for the same formation in an adjacent well, or an adjacent formation in this well; this procedure assumes that the formation factor is constant either vertically or horizontally as the case may be.

Equation 5-53 may be rearranged and combined with equation 5-56 to give an equation suitable for use with the microdevices under most circumstances.

$$F = \frac{R_{xo}}{R_{mf}} S_{xo}^2 \qquad (5\text{-}57)$$

S_{xo} in this equation must generally be estimated. It depends on the viscosity of the crude oil and the permeability of the formation; 0.8 is a good average value. R_{mf} can be measured at the surface and corrected to formation temperature, or it may be obtained from R_m by means of empirical curves. R_m can usually be obtained from the mud survey run with the microdevices. R_{xo} can be obtained from the microlog if the porosity is greater than 20 percent or it may be obtained from the microlaterolog if the porosity is greater than 8 percent. In either case a thin mud cake is a prerequisite. Equation 5-57 is the most common method of determining porosity by electrical logging methods. In rocks where the invasion is sufficiently deep, either the limestone lateral or the short normal may be used with an empirical chart based on equation 5-57 to give the porosity.

Shaly formations. The presence of interspersed clays in reservoir rocks introduces extreme difficulties in the interpretation of electric logs. Not only may the clay be mixed in all possible proportions with the sandstone, but each type of clay has a different effect on the electrical properties of the composite rock. The formation factor is then a function of the resistivity of the interstitial water so that equation 5-53 of Archie must be rewritten

$$F_a = \frac{R_0}{R_w} \tag{5-65}$$

R_0 and R_w are defined and determined as before. Because of the variable nature of F_a, it cannot be related directly to the porosity. Hill and Milburn have determined an empirical relation which offers the most fundamental approach to this problem that is currently available. They have defined

$$F_{.01} = \frac{1}{\phi^m} \tag{11-1}$$

and

$$F_a = F_{.01}(100R_w)^{b\log(100R_w)} \tag{5-70}$$

The factor b in equation 5-70 is related to the chemical exchange capacity of the clay per unit pore volume. To date, this approach has been developed only for the condition where the formation is water saturated, and this is a rather severe limitation in many cases. Less fundamental but more useful than the Hill and Milburn approach is the method developed by Poupon, Loy, and Tixier. They have combined the apparent formation factor, F_a, with the SP reduction factor, α, and the resistivities R_{xo} and R_t, in a semi-empirical solution which is presented in the Schlumberger Chart D-6.

The use of electrical methods for the determination of porosity in shaly sands is not generally recommended unless it is based on reasonable experience in the area and is supported by other information.

Determination of Permeability

Core Analysis. This is the primary method for the determination of permeability and it has the same general advantages and disadvantages that were mentioned under porosity.

Drill Stem Tests. Analysis of the pressure build-up curve obtained during the shut-in part of a drill stem test provides an excellent method of determining permeability if the conditions of the test approach the conditions assumed in the mathematical model. An important advantage of permeability determined by this method is that it represents the effective permeability of a large volume of reservoir rock under reservoir conditions.

Electric Logs. Schlumberger has presented two semi-empirical methods in their Charts E-2 and E-4 which may be used with discretion to determine the general range of permeability of the formation. Errors of the order of 100 percent are easily possible with these methods.

Determination of Water Saturation and the Nature of the Reservoir Fluids

Drill Stem Test. The most important method for determining the fluid content of a reservoir is the drill stem test. While this does not give an exact value for water saturation, it is possible to estimate saturation from the fluid recovery and a knowledge of other factors, such as permeability and viscosity, which influence production.

Mud Logging. In its present state of development, mud logging is incapable of giving quantitative estimates of fluid content. It is nevertheless one of the most important logging methods on exploratory wells because it looks directly for the presence of oil.

Core Analysis. Core analysis cannot give quantitative estimates of fluid saturation in the reservoir because every core that is taken is flushed with mud filtrate. Core analysis supported by experience, however, can provide an estimate of the probable saturation and probable production. When an interval is known to contain hydrocarbon, it can be cored with an oil-base mud; this provides a very good value of the irreducible water saturation. Cores obtained with a percussion sidewall sampler are very useful for qualitative substantiation of the conclusions drawn from interpretation of the electric log.

Electric Logging. *Clean formations.* The interpretation of electric logs in clean formations is based on equation 5-56. The use of this equation gives the greatest certainty when R_0 and R_t can be obtained from the same log, as for example when a well penetrates the water table, provided that F does not change throughout the formation. In this case, the only uncertainty is in the value of n, unless bedding problems or invasion make the measurement of R_t unusually difficult. More often, R_0 must be resolved from F and R_w, and so contains the errors involved in obtaining these two additional pieces of information. If possible, n should be obtained from laboratory analysis. More often a value of $n = 2$ is assumed.

Depending on the bed thickness and the resistivity of the mud and the formations, R_t may be obtained from the 64-in. normal curve, the 18 ft 8-in. lateral curve, the induction log, or the laterolog or guard log. Originally the long normal was used for beds of low to medium resistivity, and the long lateral was used for beds of medium and high resistivity. These logs had to be corrected for invasion and bed thickness effects, and in difficult cases only a general idea of the actual resistivity could be obtained. With the recent technological improvements, the induction log and laterolog have almost entirely superseded the standard type of resistivity logs. Except for very thin beds, (less than 5 or 6 ft), these logs have no bed thickness correction, and in many cases there is little or no correction necessary for invasion. The induction log is most useful when high-resistivity muds are used in high-porosity formations. The laterolog acts as a complement to this, functioning best when the mud is salty. In cases where it is possible to control the mud resistivity, the combination of the microlaterolog and laterolog can be used very effectively. If the mud resistivity is set so that $R_{mf} = R_w$, then any interval where the laterolog reads higher than the microlaterolog is oil bearing, and where they read the same, the interval is wet. No assumptions are necessary except that invasion is not too deep. When an interval is known to contain oil, the best value of saturation, S_w, can be obtained by setting the mud resistivity so that

$$R_{mf} = R_w \frac{S_{xo}^2}{S_w^2}$$

Under these circumstances good log values of R_t can be obtained because the uninvaded and invaded zones have the same resistivity.

Shaly formations. The only satisfactory method of handling shaly formations at the present time is based on the equation of Poupon, Loy, and Tixier,

$$PE'_c = -K \log \frac{R_{xo}}{R_t} - 2\alpha K \log \frac{S_{xo}}{S_w} \tag{5-74}$$

PE'_c and α in this equation are derived from the SP curve; R_{xo} is obtained from the microlog or microlaterolog; R_t is obtained from one of the logs mentioned above; and S_{xo} is estimated. Five pieces of information are needed which are obtained from four different sources. In addition, a reference bed is needed which should be clean and water saturated, and which contains the same type of water as the unknown bed. The value of S_w calculated by this method must be considered accordingly.

Radiation Logging Methods. The comparison of porosity determined from the neutron log with porosity determined by some other method can be used to predict the presence of gas. Also, multispaced neutron curves can be used for this purpose. The recent development of the

TABLE 11-1. COST OF VARIOUS WIRELINE·SERVICES
(Land operations in California and the Mid-Continent)

Service	Depth Charge,[a] cost/ft	Operation Charge,[b] cost/ft Logged
Electric log	$0.05	$0.06
Induction-laterolog	0.08	0.08
Induction-electric log	0.06	0.08
Laterolog	0.05	0.06
Laterolog-gamma-ray log	0.06	0.09
Microlog-caliper	0.05	0.06 ($75 min)
Microlaterolog-caliper	0.06	0.07 ($75 min)
Gamma ray	0.05	0.05
Neutron log	0.05	0.05 ($75 min)
Gamma ray-neutron	0.06	0.08 ($80 min)
Sonic log	0.06	0.07 ($70 min)
Sidewall core	0.06	22.00 per core
Continuous dipmeter	0.07	0.10 plus $200
Temperature survey	0.05	0.03
Formation tester	0.05	0-4000 ft: $265 $30 for each additional 1000 ft up to 20,000 ft

In addition to these logging charges, there are other charges:

Mileage charge	$0.50 per mile for all mileage in excess of 150 miles round trip from the nearest service location.
Service charge	$150.00, field units operating on land. Only one service charge is made for multiple operations on one trip to the well.
Standby time	$150.00 per hour. This is all time spent at the well, exclusive of operating time. An allowance of 10 free hours is made prior to completion of the first operation. An allowance of 5 free hours is made for each additional service performed under the same service charge.
Special pressure charge	A charge applied only once for a series of operations for going into the well under pressure: $100 for pressures from 100 to 1000 psi $150 for pressures from 1000 to 2000 psi $200 for pressures from 2000 to 3000 psi $100 for each additional 1000 psi.

[a] There is a minimum on all depth charges equivalent to 2000 ft, (e.g., the minimum depth charge on the electric log service is 0.05 × 2000 = $100). Depth charge applied from surface to deepest reading.

[b] Operation charges have the following stipulations:
1. First runs in new wells—from the surface to the deepest reading, if the basic Resistivity log (electric log, laterolog, laterolog-gamma ray, induction log, or the induction-electric log) has not been run; otherwise, actual section logged with the minimum as shown.
2. First runs in workover, secondary recovery, or cable tool wells—from casing shoe or top of fluid level, whichever is deeper, to the deepest reading.
3. Subsequent runs—from depth of previous basic resistivity log, casing shoe, top of sidetrack, or fluid level, whichever is deepest, to deepest reading.

SOURCE: Courtesy of Schlumberger Well Surveying Corporation.

chlorine log also promises to make the neutron curve more useful in the determination of fluid content.

COST OF EVALUATION SERVICES

Representative cost figures are given here which were in effect at the time of writing. Cost figures for the wireline services are taken from the price schedule for the Schlumberger Well Surveying Corporation. These are shown in Table 11-1 and Table 11-2. Core analysis costs are shown in Table 11-3. These are taken from the price schedule of Core Laboratories, Inc. Cost figures for drill stem testing are from Halliburton Company and are given in Table 11-4. Cost figures for mud logging are from the Baroid Division, National Lead Company and are shown in Table 11-5.

TABLE 11-2.   COST OF PERFORATING WITH THE SCHLUMBERGER NO PLUG SHAPED CHARGE OR SUPER BULLET GUN

Depth	20 Shots or Less	Per Shot 21 to 100	Per Shot 101 to 500	Per Shot 501 to 1000	Per Shot Over 1000
0'- 2000'	$ 165	$ 5.60	$ 4.10	$ 3.70	$ 3.20
2001'- 3000'	180	5.80	4.20	3.80	3.30
3001'- 4000'	195	6.00	4.40	3.90	3.40
4001'- 5000'	210	6.20	4.60	4.10	3.60
5001'- 6000'	230	6.40	4.80	4.30	3.80
6001'- 7000'	260	6.60	5.00	4.50	4.00
7001'- 8000'	290	6.90	5.20	4.70	4.20
8001'- 9000'	330	7.30	5.50	5.00	4.50
9001'-10000'	370	7.80	5.80	5.30	4.80
10001'-11000'	410	8.30	6.20	5.70	5.10
11001'-12000'	450	8.80	6.60	6.10	5.40
12001'-13000'	495	9.30	7.00	6.50	5.80
13001'-14000'	540	9.90	7.40	6.90	6.20
14001'-15000'	585	10.50	7.80	7.30	6.60
15001'-16000'	635	11.10	8.30	7.70	7.00
16001'-17000'	685	11.70	8.80	8.10	7.40
17001'-18000'	735	12.30	9.30	8.50	7.80
18001'-19000'	785	12.90	9.80	9.00	8.20
19001'-20000'	835	13.50	10.30	9.50	8.60
20001'-21000'	885	14.10	10.80	10.00	9.00
21001'-22000'	945	14.80	11.30	10.50	9.40
22001'-23000'	1,015	15.60	12.00	11.10	9.90
23001'-24000'	1,105	16.60	12.80	11.90	10.70
24001'-25000'	1,215	17.80	13.90	12.90	11.70
Below 25000'	1,345	19.20	15.20	14.00	12.80

Minimum, 10 shots per trip in hole.

SOURCE: Schlumberger Well Surveying Corporation.

TABLE 11-3. COST OF CONVENTIONAL CORE ANALYSIS SERVICE
ON CORE PLUGS 1½ IN. DIAMETER OR SMALLER

Number of Samples	Cost per Sample
1 to 20	$11.50
21 to 40	10.00
41 to 60	9.00
61 to 80	8.00
81 and over	7.00

This includes measurement of porosity, permeability, and oil, water, and gas saturation. If it is necessary to go to the rig to pick up samples or to analyze samples, additional charges are made for mileage, personnel transportation time, and equipment transportation time.

Special Core Analysis

Service	*Cost per Sample*
Capillary pressure	$ 15.00 for one point
	$ 24.00 for two points
	$ 40.00 for complete curve
Formation resistivity factor	$ 3.00
Resistivity ratio (in conjunction with capillary pressure measurement)	$ 3.00 per test
Water/oil relative permeability	$150.00
Gas/oil relative permeability	$165.00

SOURCE: Courtesy of Core Laboratories, Inc.

TABLE 11-4. COST OF FORMATION DRILL-STEM TESTING (Open Hole)

Depth of Test, ft	Price	Depth of Test, ft	Price
0 to 4,000	$220	10,001 to 11,000	$321
4,001 to 5,000	242	11,001 to 12,000	334
5,001 to 6,000	260	12,001 to 13,000	346
6,001 to 7,000	272	13,001 to 14,000	358
7,001 to 8,000	285	14,001 to 15,000	371
8,001 to 9,000	296	Each 1000 ft below	
9,001 to 10,000	309	15,000	13

Price is determined by the total depth of the hole. When a straddle test is run, the price is determined by the depth of the lower packer.

There is an additional charge for rental of certain specialized tools.

Tests run inside casing are about $30.00 cheaper than tests in open hole.

A mileage charge of $0.25 per mile, one way, is made for each additional mile over 35 miles from the nearest service location.

SOURCE: Courtesy of Halliburton Company.

TABLE 11-5.   COST OF DRILLING FLUID AND CUTTINGS ANALYSIS LOGGING

	Complete Well Logging Service	Special Service with 1-Man Crew	Automatic Recording Gas Detector Unit
First 60 days	$160 per day	$80 per day	$22 per day
Next 120 days	$145 ” ”	$75 ” ”	$19 ” ”
After 180 days	$135 ” ”	$70 ” ”	$17 ” ”
If contracted for in advance:			
60 days	$145 ” ”	$75 ” ”	$19 ” ”
180 days	$135 ” ”	$70 ” ”	$17 ” ”
Stand by	$90 ” ”	$60 ” ”	
Minimum charge per job	$960	$480	$220

SOURCE: Courtesy of Baroid Division, National Lead Company.

The costs given in these tables are only those for the service. The wireline services and drill stem testing require rig time in addition, and this will often turn out to be the larger part of the cost of evaluation. Rig time costs average about $50 per hour for small rigs (less than 10,000 ft) and $60 per hour for large rigs in the United States. (Offshore and foreign work may run more than ten times this high.) If it is necessary to make a round trip or condition the hole in order to use the particular tool, then this time must also be considered as part of the cost. Consider, for example, a decision to drill stem test at a depth of 8000 ft in the middle of a bit run. Time necessary to condition the hole might be of the order of 2 hours. If pipe can be pulled or run at an average speed of 2500 ft per hour, then for the two round trips required to test and resume drilling it would take 12.8 hours. If the flow period of the test were 1 hour and the shut-in period were 1 hour, then a total of 16.8 hours would have to be assigned to formation evaluation; this is $840 worth of rig time. The service company charge for testing would be only about $350, a small figure by comparison.

For a deep exploratory well, i.e., greater than 10,000 ft, it might be expected that costs assigned to formation evaluation will run about 20 percent of the total drilling cost. This can be broken down into: (a) electric logging and related wireline services, 5 percent; (b) mud logging, 5 percent; (c) coring, 5 percent; and (d) drill stem testing, 5 percent. Where any of these items can be safely omitted, corresponding savings in evaluation cost may be expected. The cost limits for evaluation on exploratory wells are between 8 and 25 percent of the drilling cost.

The 25 percent figure would apply where it was necessary to set casing in order to test. The evaluation cost of development wells is between 3 and 10 percent of the drilling cost. The higher figure might apply where there was a long section of interbedded wet and productive sands.

The costs of formation evaluation are admittedly large. It should be remembered, however, that the purpose of drilling an exploratory well is not to make a hole in the ground, but to find oil. To drill and abandon a well, and leave doubt about the area through the inadequate use of formation evaluation methods is indefensible. On the other hand, some discretion must be shown if costs are to be kept within reason. With these thoughts in mind we enter into the final phase of the study of formation evaluation, that of writing a program which will provide the needed information as economically as possible.

FORMATION LOGGING PROGRAMS IN EXPLORATORY DRILLING

Almost all formation evaluation programs for exploratory drilling utilize mud logging, coring, wireline logging, sidewall sampling, and drill stem testing in some combination, but the relative importance of each varies with the particular case. In some areas wireline logging is very diagnostic and in others it is not. In some special instances coring is impractical; in others it can be replaced largely by sidewall sampling; in still others, sidewall sampling is impossible, and cores must generally be taken with a diamond coring bit.

The most effective combination of tools to use and the manner in which they are employed depend on a number of factors that must be taken into consideration before a program is written. In an excellent paper on this subject, Walstrom (3) has listed these as:

I. Characteristics of the objective zone
   A. Nature of the zone: stratigraphic trap, fault accumulation or anticlinal structure.
   B. Number, estimated depth, thickness, and distribution of the possibly productive intervals that may be penetrated.
   C. Physical nature of the objective zone: unconsolidated sand, hard sandstone, fractured chert or shale, porous limestone, or fractured limestone; heavy oil, light oil, or gas; high pressure zones or low pressure zones.
   D. Chemical nature of the formations: salt, anhydrite, or sulfur.

II. General subsurface considerations
   A. Number of available well logs and histories in the area.
   B. Probable accuracy of electric log correlations.
   C. Degree of known faulting.

III. Drilling technique
   A. Presence of high head waters.
   B. Possibility of encountering zones of lost circulation.
   C. Possibility of encountering zones of caving shale.
   D. Presence of known gas zones overlying the objectives.
   E. Presence of known productive oil zones overlying the objectives.
IV. Effect of type of drilling fluid used on the formation evaluation methods.

The application of these factors will become evident in the following sections.

The sequence of use of the various evaluation tools is fairly well dictated by circumstances. Mud logging and coring must necessarily be done while drilling is in progress. Wireline logging is used at predetermined intervals after a certain footage has been drilled or a maximum period of time has elapsed. Sidewall sampling usually follows and is guided by the results of the wireline log survey. For drill stem testing, however, two alternatives are open. Testing may be done in open hole on the way in; that is, when a show is obtained in the mud or cuttings, or on the basis of the electric log, drilling is suspended temporarily and a test is run. Alternatively, drilling may be done continuously until the bottom of the hole is reached. Casing is then set, and on the basis of shows and electric log data the various intervals are perforated one at a time and tested. It is possible to either straddle test, or plug back and set the tail pipe on the bridge plug.

Usually, testing is done on the way in and for the following reasons. First, testing on bottom in open hole is much less expensive; there is no cost for casing and cementing the hole, and there is no problem with running water shut-off tests above and below the interval, or of squeeze cementing in case of a failure of the cement bond behind the casing. Second, there is less danger of contamination of the fluid recovery with water leaking behind the casing from another formation. Third, there is less danger of formation damage from mud filtrate penetrating the formation, because it is not exposed as long before testing. Fourth, there is more assurance that a shallow formation will be tested; there is always the very real possibility that if a hole is cased and the deepest formation proves to be commercial, the well will be completed in the deep zone and the shallower zones will never be tested.

On the other hand there are times when testing inside casing is absolutely necessary, and times when it may prove more desirable in spite of the cost. When testing inside casing there is little danger of sticking the packer; it is therefore possible to make the test as long as desired so that the well can be swabbed or bailed to promote flow.

Long flow and shut-in periods are more amenable to quantitative test analysis. There is also less danger in losing the hole because of a fishing operation; the deeper zones are usually tested first, and if tools are lost in the hole, it can be plugged back and testing continued above. Long sections of hole may be tested at one time, and straddle testing is easily done. The danger of blowout due to swabbing or lost circulation caused by running the testing tools is completely eliminated.

On the basis of this choice, two general logging programs can be written, and a consideration of the above factors will determine which one will be chosen. The first program is:

1. Install a mud logging service. This service will collect ditch samples and examine the mud and cuttings for evidence of hydrocarbons.
2. Drill ahead; core if there are significant oil shows, or if there are drilling breaks near the objective interval.
3. If the core shows evidence of hydrocarbon, run a drill stem test. If the test is positive, consider completing the well in this interval. If the test is negative, ream out the interval (if core was taken in reduced hole), and drill ahead in full hole.
4. Run the electric log at preset depths or times (other wireline logs may be run in addition to or instead of the electric log).
5. On the basis of the electric log and ditch samples, sidewall sample all zones of interest.
6. On the basis of the sidewall samples, test zones which appear promising. This may be done by straddle testing in open hole, by plugging back, or by testing on the way out inside pipe. The method of testing depends on the formations.

The second general program is:

1. Install a mud logging service.
2. Drill ahead; core if there are significant oil shows, or if there are drilling breaks near the objective interval.
3. Run the electric log at preset depths or times.
4. On the basis of the electric log and ditch samples, sidewall sample all zones of interest.
5. When total depth has been reached, run and cement casing. Test inside casing through perforations starting with the most promising interval. If all zones appear to be of about equal promise, test from the bottom up.

In a paper on this subject, Walstrom and Wells (4) outlined the considerations and the programs that would be used in five typical areas.

These are reproduced here with minor variations (changes resulting from the introduction of new tools).

Accepted Evaluation Practices in Various Areas

California Tertiary

Although many complex and diversified problems are encountered in California, it is possible to make some generalizations which might be summarized as follows:

1. Formation waters encountered in possible productive horizons range from fresh (50 G/G) to moderately salty (2500 G/G), but most commonly fall in the range of 500-1500 G/G (one grain/gallon $\simeq$ 17 parts/million).
2. Productive sands are unconsolidated to partially cemented and commonly show poor sorting. Grain size may vary from silt to boulder conglomerate and clay is present to some degree in nearly all California sands.
3. Fractured rock production is limited to cherty shales and basement rocks (usually schist).
4. Carbonate rocks are absent in the Tertiary section except for a few thin limestone beds which have no effect on the evaluation program.
5. Heavy mud is required in many areas to combat high pressure water and gas zones.
6. Regional correlation is difficult because of rapid facies changes and complex structures.

Generally accepted evaluation practices are as follows:

1. Mud logging units are now used on most exploratory wells and coring and testing programs are usually dependent upon shows obtained.
2. Coring is usually held to the minimum required for evaluating shows, checking lithology and obtaining dip and faunal information. In some deep tests, however, particularly in Eocene rocks, where oil-base mud is used to combat bad hole conditions, continuous diamond coring has proven to be almost as economical as drilling.
3. The induction-electric log is now run in most wells in place of the conventional electric log, and the Microlog is run in nearly all exploratory wells. Current focusing logs are rarely used because the resistivity contrast between the drilling fluid and formation water is usually too high. Because of poor radioactivity contrast, radioactivity logs are rarely used in exploratory drilling except for accurate depth measurement when perforating for completion, and to check for dry gas.
4. Quantitative calculations for water saturation utilizing the electric log and Microlog can usually be made with sufficient accuracy to guide the testing program except where extreme thin bed conditions are encountered. The clayey sand nomograms developed by Schlumberger are very helpful where formation waters are sufficiently salty to give a good SP curve. The sonic log is frequently used with, or in place of, the Microlog.
5. Preferred practice with most operators is to test on the way down, and hole conditions are usually such that open hole formation tests can be made

safely. Sidewall packer tests with the tail pipe resting on the bottom are the usual procedure, and deep tests are usually made in reduced hole. Straddle packer tests and selective zone tests have met with some success, but are often hazardous because caving formations within the test interval stick the bottom packer. The Schlumberger wire line tester can sometimes be substituted.

Gulf Coast Tertiary

Evaluation problems, though serious in this region, are not as diversified as in the California Tertiary. Consequently, the accepted practices are more standardized. Conditions affecting the program might be summarized as follows:

1. Formation waters in possible productive horizons are very salty.
2. Productive sands are unconsolidated and usually well sorted. Clayey sands are common but massive boulder conglomerates are absent. Both sands and shales cave and slough badly.
3. There is no fractured rock production and carbonates are absent.
4. Heavy mud is required to combat high pressures in deep wells.
5. Prominent sands are more continuous than in California and can be correlated over large areas.

Generally accepted evaluation practices are as follows:

1. Mud logging units are now used on all exploratory wells from surface pipe to total depth and on many wells from conductor pipe to total depth.
2. Coring has been largely replaced by sidewall sampling for evaluating shows. Percussion type samples can be obtained quickly at any point in the bore hole and conditions are ideal for good recovery.
3. The induction-electric log and Microlog are run in all exploratory holes. Focused current logs are sometimes used where prospective sands are thin and where lignites and mineralized zones affect resistivity interpretations.
4. Mud resistivities are usually less than 0.5 ohm-meters at the surface and lime treatment is commonly used to reduce water loss. The SP curve is not seriously affected by the lime mud because of the very salty formation waters.
5. Quantitative calculations for water saturation utilizing the electric log and Microlog can usually be made with sufficient accuracy to guide the testing program. Clayey sand techniques work very well because of the very salty formation waters and relatively low mud resistivities. The sonic log is frequently used with, or in place of, the Microlog.
6. Open hole formation tests are seldom run, especially in deep holes, because of the soft formations which tend to cave and slough. Testing is normally done on the way out by running casing and selectively perforating the best looking intervals on the basis of mud logging shows, sidewall samples, and electric log interpretation. Wireline testing is now used extensively.

Rocky Mountains

This is hard rock country. Production is obtained from both intergranular and fracture porosity in sandstones and carbonates and from fractured shale. Formation waters range from very fresh (20 G/G) to moderately salty (1800 G/G). Salt beds present no serious problem, but anhydrite is abundant in many of the formations penetrated and gyp-base muds are used to prevent hydration and caving. Regional correlation of formational units is good and many individual beds can be traced over large areas. Although evaluation practices vary somewhat with different operators, the general procedure is as follows:

1. Mud logging units with core analysis equipment are now used on nearly all exploratory wells from surface pipe to total depth. Oil shows in cuttings are usually very diagnostic and are closely watched.

2. Coring is used extensively but less than formerly. Normal procedure is to diamond core and core analyze the major objective intervals in sandstones and check all mud logging shows and lost circulation intervals with cores. Diamond coring in hard sandstones and carbonates is as economical as drilling in some areas. Sidewall sampling is ineffective except in shallow horizons.

3. Although the conventional electric log or induction-electric log is run in all exploratory wells, it is often not very diagnostic because of the extreme resistivity contrast, thin beds, and deep invasion. The SP curve is usually dampened and rounded out because of the high resistivities, particularly in carbonate sections. Wall resistivity logs lose much of their quantitative value for determining porosity when the mud cake is thick but even under these conditions they can still be used very effectively for qualitatively defining permeable intervals and are usually run through all possible objectives. The Microlaterolog has been used effectively for obtaining porosity in some cases where mud cakes were less than 1/4" in thickness. Focused current logs are used to some extent in thinly bedded sections and could be used very effectively if less resistive muds were adopted.

4. Gamma and neutron logs are run in nearly all exploratory wells. Natural radioactivity contrast is good, thus making the gamma log very effective for correlation purposes, and the neutron log is useful for locating porous intervals in carbonates. The sonic or density log is now preferred for porosity determination.

5. The open hole formation test is generally considered to be the best evaluation method in the Rocky Mountain region and is used freely. Hole conditions are normally good in hard rocks; thus, the hazards of packer failures and stuck tools are largely eliminated. Tests are usually made with sidewall packers above the test intervals and tail pipe resting on bottom, but straddle packer and selective zone testers are also used with a high degree of success. Most operators prefer to test on the way down, and tests of several hours' duration are common practice because of slow fluid entry and deep invasion.

West Texas

The problems here are somewhat similar to those in the Rocky Mountains, in that production is obtained from both intergranular and fracture porosity in sandstones and carbonates, but a great deal is also obtained from vuggy carbonate reefs. The formation waters are generally saltier than in the Rocky Mountain region and thick salt beds are common, thus necessitating the use of salt muds in some areas. Accepted evaluation practices are as follows:

1. Mud logging units with core analysis equipment are now used on all exploratory wells from surface pipe to total depth. Oil showings in cuttings are very

closely watched as they may be the only clue to possible production from carbonate reefs, and returns are often poor because of lost circulation.

2. Coring is used extensively for evaluating shows and full core analysis is favored for porosity and permeability determinations.

3. The conventional electric log is not very diagnostic, particularly in the carbonate sections and where salt mud is used. The gamma ray log is used extensively as a substitute for the SP curve, and current focusing systems have been proven to be very useful for obtaining true resistivity in thin porous intervals. The acoustic velocity log is the prime porosity measuring tool, and the Microlog is used for qualitative definition of porous and permeable intervals where the porosity approximates the intergranular condition. The limestone device is preferred by some operators over the short spacing two electrode device for a shallow penetration curve, and is used in some areas for porosity studies.

4. Open hole formation tests are run freely to check shows in cuttings and cores, and lost circulation intervals are usually tested regardless of shows, particularly in areas where reefs may be present. Hole conditions are generally good for running all types of packer assemblies and most operators prefer to test on the way down.

Williston Basin

This is carbonate country and production is obtained from both intergranular and fracture porosity. Formation waters are very salty, and thick salt beds in the section necessitate the use of salt muds. Generally accepted evaluation practice which has become known as the salt mud technique is as follows:

1. Mud logging units are used on all exploratory wells to guide coring, logging, and testing.

2. Coring is used to evaluate persistent shows, but many productive porous intervals are so thin that they may be completely penetrated before a core can be taken.

3. The conventional electric logs are practically worthless for evaluation because of the salt mud and thin porous intervals. A new method for obtaining water saturation in porous intervals has therefore been developed by Schlumberger and major operators, which utilizes current focusing systems. The primary relationship is:

$$\frac{R_{LL}}{R_{MLL}} = A\,\frac{S_{xo}^2}{S_w^2} \tag{11-2}$$

where R_{LL} is the resistivity obtained from the laterolog, R_{MLL} is the resistivity obtained from the microlaterolog, and $A = R_w/R_{mf}$. This relationship assumes that $R_{LL} = R_t = FR_w/S_w^2$, $R_{MLL} = R_{xo} = FR_{mf}/S_{xo}^2$, that R_w is known from direct measurement of water samples from nearly wells, and that formation waters are fairly uniform. These assumptions have now been proven valid in a great many cases. Porosity is obtained from the sonic log, and the gamma ray curve is a good substitute for the SP curve for lithology determination and correlation.

4. Open hole formation tests are used freely as in West Texas and most operators prefer to test on the way down if possible.

LOGGING PROGRAMS IN DEVELOPMENT DRILLING

In development drilling operations the logging program is much abbreviated except in those cases where there are multiple objectives. The program is designed to determine, as accurately as possible, information which will be of interest primarily to reservoir engineers. Little mud logging or sidewall sampling is used since these are tools designed to find oil rather than to evaluate it quantitatively. During the early life of the field several wells should be cored and logged thoroughly to determine which of the wireline services is most accurate for determining porosity and water saturation. Correlations should be established for cementation factor, the exponent n in Archie's equation, for neutron logs, and other tools which might be used. Thereafter, coring should be limited to spot checks throughout the field which act as a control on wireline logging. Testing should also be limited to wells which penetrate the water table to define the oil-water contact. In this manner a cheap and effective evaluation program can be developed.

REFERENCES

1. Ball, C. R., and Fine, S. F., Information vs. cost in exploratory drilling: *API Drilling and Production Practice*, 1955, p. 469.
2. Chombart, L. G., Well logs in carbonate reservoirs: *Geophysics*, v. XXV, no. 4, 1960, p. 779.
3. Walstrom, J. E., Optimum use of various testing methods in exploratory wells: *API Drilling and Production Practice*, 1950, p. 79.
4. Walstrom, J. E., and Wells, J. C., Formation evaluation in exploratory drilling: *API Drilling and Production Practice*, 1955, p. 468.

APPENDIXES

Appendix A
Log Quality Control Checks

Precise and dependable quantitative log analysis requires logs of the best possible quality. The following check lists have been prepared for that purpose.

Geologists and engineers using these check lists will encounter logs that are poor because of equipment failure or operational difficulties. If a log is found to be of poor quality, and it can be corrected, always consider rerunning the log. After casing is run, or a well is abandoned, it is no longer possible to obtain logs which may be vital to full evaluation of the well or as a guide to future exploration. If a log were not necessary, it would not be included in the formation logging program. A log that is worth running is generally worth running properly.

Some of the checks refer to the logging equipment rather than to the logs. These should be used with discretion to avoid the suggestion that you are trying to tell the logging engineer how to run his job. The engineer will do his best to give you a proper log, however, if he knows that you are interested in these details.

PREPARATION FOR A LOGGING RUN

Ordering the Logging Truck

1. Notify the service company of logs you plan to run and additional equipment you may need, e.g., a sidewall sample gun, after you have reviewed the logs. A choice of log spacings is sometimes available with electric logs if the company is notified in advance.
2. If special logs are to be run, such as the continuous dipmeter, check with the service company district manager to be sure he is sending an experienced logging engineer. If an inexperienced engineer is doing the logging, ask that someone, such as the district manager, come out to check his work.
3. If the hole is apt to have unusually high temperatures or pressures, advise the service company in order that they may take special precautions to have suitable equipment.

Preparations at the Well

1. Have a copy of the check list plus any charts or nomograms necessary to interpret the logs.
2. Have logs of nearby wells for correlation and comparison, plus copies of all logs previously run in the well.
3. Check to see that mud samples are collected. Three one-quart mud samples, collected from the flow line at 15-minute intervals while circulating, are necessary for R_{mf} and R_{mc} measurements. On wildcat wells a 1-gallon sample of mud should be collected from the flow line for chemical analysis of the mud filtrate.
4. Check with the driller about hole size, total depth, casing size and depth, mud weight and viscosity, approximate bottom hole temperature, and hole conditions. This information is useful in discussing the logging program with the service company engineer.
5. Be prepared to give the logging engineer all the information necessary for filling out the log heading—correct elevations (ground, DF, and KB), well location, correct and full well name, field name, etc. For directionally drilled wells, the well location is that of the bottom of the well. The surface location can be shown under "remarks."
6. Check with the logging engineer to see that he is ready to log as soon as the pipe is out of the hole. Some causes for delay are: failure to have proper subs and connections, dead battery in the truck, wrong logging tools, not enough sidewall cores, and instrument troubles which were not found at the shop because of failure to check insulation and continuity of conductors.
7. Find out if the logging engineer knows of the check list. If necessary, review with him the requirements for the logs to be run.

GENERAL CHECKS FOR ALL TYPES OF LOGS

Before and During Logging

Always:

1. Ask for field prints of everything that happens. Impress on the logging engineer that no part of any log run in the well is to be destroyed. This includes calibration steps. It is not necessary to include everything on the final prints, but it should be on the film. You are entitled to a copy of everything that comes out of the well, even if it is an unsatisfactory log.
2. When you do not specify the horizontal scale, ask the logging engineer to select a scale which will give detail in the low-amplitude readings. Shales or water-saturated sands should normally read at least half of one division. All high amplitudes must be shown on some multiple scale. The tendency of logging engineers is to select a scale which is too insensitive, e.g., logs may be run on a 50 ohm-meter scale when a 20 ohm-meter scale would be more suitable.
3. Get detail (5 in. = 100 ft) over all intervals that include potential reservoirs. If an interval is detailed on one log, it should be detailed on all other logs run across that interval. Detail does not cost extra.

4. On second and subsequent runs *always* overlap all logs at least 200 ft. More overlap may be desirable for interpretation purposes.
5. Ask that a maximum recording thermometer be used on all logging runs.
6. Ask the engineer to put anything of interest in the "remarks" heading.

Occasionally:
1. Check with the logging engineer:
   a. Did he bring copies of logs of nearby wells for comparison? (This is not necessary in a field where he has run many logs.)
   b. Did he bring copies of previous runs on this hole?
   c. Has he checked mud and hole conditions?
   d. When was his cable last checked for length accuracy?
2. Ask the engineer if he has checked his cable insulation and conductor continuity before the survey.
3. Look at the sonde or electrode and see if it appears to be in good condition.
4. Check to see that the resistivities of the mud, mud filtrate, and mud cake were measured and that the temperature of measurement was taken at the same time.
5. Have 200-ft repeats run at half speed and check log quality against the full speed run.
6. Have 200-ft repeats run at half or twice scale and check values against conventional scales.
7. Ask the engineer to check for kicks on the log caused by something extraneous to the hole, such as slamming doors, starting engines, and switching off and on the circuits in the truck.

Additional Checks for New and Experimental Tools
   Always:
1. Check dimensions of tool and compare with hole size as a precaution against getting stuck.
2. Repeat a minimum of 200 ft of the log to check reproducibility.
3. Always get field prints of anything logged, even if the run is not successful. If you give rig time for an experimental log, you are entitled to copies.

LOG PRINTS

Field Prints (Any Log)
   Always:
1. Check to see that log headings are completed properly. Field prints should include all information which will be on the finished prints. Scales, location, elevation, complete mud data, casing particulars, etc., may all be necessary for interpretation of the log. Any pertinent information not normally included in the heading should be placed under "remarks."
2. Be sure that field prints are clear and completely legible.
3. Check that data, such as temperature or resistivity, which are calculated from charts or estimated are distinguished from measured values.
4. Ask that scales be printed at top and bottom of logs and at every scale change.
5. See that delivery of field prints is completed immediately after logging.

Finished Prints (Any Log)

Always:

1. Check to see that headings are completely filled out, with all information necessary for full use of the log. Any pertinent remarks for which there is no place on the log heading should be included under "remarks."
2. See that composite prints contain all information from every run. This includes overlaps, zero checks, calibration checks, remarks, and all other data.
3. Check that scales are printed at both the top and bottom of the log and at every scale change.
4. Look carefully for "tracing" and "touching up." Criticism is justified for much of this.
5. See that there is one composite log on the correlation scale (usually 1 in. = 50 ft) for the entire hole. This may, for example, require splicing an electric log to a radioactivity log. Check composites to see that the splices were correctly made.
6. Check depth lines to see that 2-ft, 10-ft, and 50-ft lines can be distinguished easily from each other.
7. Ask that measured values of mud resistivity, temperature, etc., be distinguished in the heading from calculated or estimated values.
8. Check that the heading includes a note of all services performed by that company in that hole.

DEPTH CONTROL (ANY LOG)

Two Types of Depth Control Must Be Considered

1. Total depth from surface of any correlative points on the log in order to know degree of accuracy of structural studies. In general this should be 1 ft per 1000 ft of depth.
2. Depth from a located datum (such as a collar) for use in working in the well (such as perforating). In general this should be ±1 ft at any depth.

Before Logging and in Hole

Always:

1. Find out driller's TD and casing shoe depths and compare with logging TD and casing shoe depths.
2. Ask that depths be measured with the cable under tension (coming out). This is standard practice.
3. Ask for check of casing shoe going in and check of TD on bottom.

Occasionally:

1. Where magnetic markers are used, ask logging engineer when his cable was last checked.
2. When a calibrated sheave is used, ask when it was last calibrated.
3. Ask to see latest "stretch curves" on cable and note date when cable was checked.
4. Watch to see how much cranking is done. Correction should be no more than 1 ft at a time and no more than 1 ft per 100 ft.

After the Log Is Run

Always:

1. Check TD and casing shoe against driller's depths.
2. Check TD, casing, and correlative markers against other logs in the same hole.
3. Check overlaps and repeats superimposed directly over the log.

Occasionally:

1. Relog after perforating with a magnetic collar locator to find perforations, as a check on the accuracy of perforating depths.

SELF POTENTIAL LOG

Before and During Logging

Always:

1. Check with the logging engineer to be sure the ground electrode is in a stable position, far removed from pipe connections and points in the mud pit of make-up water inlet or chemical addition. There should be no movement of water or mud where the ground electrode is located. The usual best place is a hole filled with mud about 150 ft in front of the truck.
2. Select an SP scale which will give about five divisions kick from the shale line in clean sands or limestones.
3. Ask the engineer to check for extraneous noise from such things as welders, generators, radio transmitters, high power lines, and pumps, and shut these down during the logging job, if possible. Where stray earth current cannot be stopped, techniques should be tried to get usable logs, for example, repeating the log many times or changing the ground electrode location.
4. Ask the engineer to record the SP on the bottom of hole before logging, with the current on and off.
5. Ask the engineer to record an SP calibration signal on the bottom of the log just before he starts logging. This could be 20, 50, or 100 mv, depending upon the scale being used.
6. Logging speed normally should not exceed 6000 ft per hour.

Occasionally:

1. While going in the hole, ask the engineer to stop opposite a dense, high-resistivity zone (or in casing as a second choice) and watch the SP galvanometer spot. Does it drift, agitate, or occasionally jump? Have the engineer switch all circuits off and on to see if they affect the spot. Any significant movement should be corrected before logging.
2. Have a 200-ft repeat run at about 3000 ft per hour to check for galvanometer response over thin beds.
3. Have a 200-ft repeat run at an amplified millivolt scale to check the calibration.
4. Ask the engineer if he notes any noise which may be due to dirty slip rings.

After Log Is Run

Always:

1. Check film or field prints for:
   a. Evidence of magnetism (sine waves of constant frequency superimposed on SP).
   b. Unwinding oscillations on the bottom of the log (sine waves of decreasing frequency).
   c. Evidence of bimetalism caused by freshly exposed metal on the sonde (usually spotted as sharp reversals opposite high resistivity zones).
   d. Evidence of drift. (This is more easily seen on the 1-in. or 2-in. depth scales. Sometimes this drift is accompanied by abrupt shifts.)
   e. Base line shifts which have not appeared in other wells; legitimate base line shifts may occur due to changes in shale mineralogy.
   f. Evidence of salt-water flows (generally decreased amplitude and drift toward the positive coming up).
   g. Noisiness, shown by irregular deflections not related to lithology.
2. If repeats were run, check exact reproducibility with conventional log.
3. Check millivolts deflection with millivolts in correlative zones of nearby wells. If there is a gross difference and the muds in the two holes were about the same, go back for a short repeat with a new calibration.

Occasionally:

1. Have the SP log repeated because of defects noted above.

RESISTIVITY LOGS (NORMALS AND LATERALS)

NOTE: Except under very unusual circumstances either the induction log or the laterolog or both should be substituted for the conventional electrical survey.

Before and During Logging

Always:

1. Select scales which will give at least one half division and preferably a full division on the long normal or lateral in water zones. If this requires a scale different from the usual correlation scale, it may be done by a repeat over the zone of interest. (Example: If R_0 is 2 ohm-meters, run a 20 ohm-meter log; if R_0 is 0.3 ohm-meter, run a 5 ohm-meter log.) Be sure high resistivities are recorded even if this means a repeat run.
2. Ask the engineer to record on the log:
   a. Galvanometer zero on bottom.
   b. Galvanometer zero at the top of the logged interval.
   c. About 25 ft of electrical zero into the casing even if the casing is above the top of the logged interval.
3. In low-resistivity areas (5 and 10 ohm-meter logs) each log should be run zeroed at the electrical zero rather than the galvanometer zero.
4. Have the SP run simultaneously on repeats and down logs for correlation with the conventional log.
5. Logging speed normally should not exceed 6000 ft per hour.

Occasionally:
1. Ask the engineer the exact spacings being used including the pickup span of the lateral and location of the current return electrodes.
2. Ask the logging engineer to show you that all galvanometer spots read zero in the pipe with the current on and off.
3. Run a 150-ft repeat at an amplified scale to check the calibration.

After Log Is Run
   Always:
1. Look at zeros to see how far off any curve may be from other curves.
2. See that all curves read the same in low-resistivity shales. Some difference may be explained due to enlarged hole.
3. Look for absent curves, discontinuous breaks, and any other "funny looking" kicks which will cause difficulty in interpretation later.

   Occasionally:
1. Check overlaps with previous runs.
2. Check repeats, if any.
3. Look for "noise."
4. Check normals to see that they reverse in thin hard streaks as they should.
5. Check laterals to see that blind zones and reflection peaks fall below hard streaks as they should.
6. Compare with the log of a nearby well for resistivities in the shales and water sands.
7. Compare values recorded in thick dense, high-resistivity zones on departure curves to see that all record the same true resistivity.
8. Look near the top of the log for evidence that No. 6 electrode came out of the mud column before the log was completed. The No. 6 electrode is the potential return electrode for the 64-in. normal and the 19-ft lateral and is placed 70 ft above the depth reference point of the electrode system.

LATEROLOG

Before and During Logging
   Always:
1. Use the same scale for the laterolog as for the electric log. The lowest resistivities encountered should read at least half of one division. Use enough multiple scales that the highest resistivities are recorded.
2. When the laterolog is run with $R_m \leq 5R_w$, use the same scales for the laterolog and microlaterolog.
3. Record the laterolog across two tracks, for all scales.
4. Have the SP recorded simultaneously if possible, even though the mud is salty, and even though the SP has been recorded on other logs.
5. Ask that the monitoring curve be recorded.
6. Have the galvanometer zero recorded at the top and bottom of the logged interval, and the electrical zero recorded in the casing.
7. Detail sections of interest on 25 in. = 100 ft scale, to simplify comparison with the microlaterolog.

8. Specify that the logging speed not exceed 3000 ft per hour.
9. Consider using the laterolog 3, rather than the laterolog 7, in thin bedded rocks where utmost detail is required.

Occasionally:

1. Ask to see the monitoring circuit checked while stopped in the casing. This is done by switching the logging current on and off. There should be no deflection on the galvanometer.

After Log Is Run

Always:

1. Check shale resistivities against other resistivity logs.
2. Be sure the sonde type (LL3, LL7, or any other identification of newer models) is indicated on the heading.
3. Look at monitor curve to see if it is reasonably straight. Sharp kicks will occur opposite high-resistivity beds, but the curve should return promptly to a base line. If the monitor curve is a mirror image of the laterolog, the log is no good.
4. See if 3-ft beds are sharply defined by the LL7, and 1-ft beds by the LL3 and guard log.
5. Check recorded zeros.
6. Check for "flat-topping"—evidence of a maximum resistivity beyond which the log will not read. The laterolog 7 should not flat-top in beds below 10,000 ohm-meters. The laterolog 3 may flat-top at much lower resistivities, particularly with very saline muds.

GUARD LOG

The Halliburton guard log is similar in performance to the Schlumberger laterolog 3. Use the same checks as for the laterolog.

INDUCTION LOG

Before and During Logging

Always:

1. The induction log resistivity scale should ordinarily be the same as the short normal. Select the conductivity scale in millimhos by dividing the resistivity scale in ohms into 10,000. The conductivity scale thus obtained will be equal to one track or ten divisions of the Schlumberger log. Conductivity is, of course, recorded from right to left, conductivity zero should be the tenth division of the third track, and the scale can be recorded in either the third track alone (particularly desirable if an amplified normal is to be recorded) or can be extended across the second track as well. All the higher conductivity readings should be recorded by using several off scales, if necessary, even if this means making an additional run through the extremely high-conductivity zones.

2. Ask the engineer to record calibration and zero checks on the wooden horses, in hole at the bottom and again at the top of the survey. These are known to Schlumberger as the "Houston checks." Ask that these be printed on the field and finished prints.
3. The wooden horses in above checks should be at least 20 ft from any large metal object.
4. Have mechanical zeros recorded on the log at the bottom and top of the survey and the electrical zero recorded in the pipe.
5. It is understood that results are best if the tool is allowed to warm up about 15 minutes before checks are started on the wooden horses. This is the logging engineer's responsibility, however.
6. Logging speed normally should not exceed 6000 ft per hour.

   Occasionally:
1. Repeat about 150 ft for reproducibility.

After Log Is Run

   Always:
1. Check values recorded in shales against other logs, if available.
2. Compare the values recorded by the conductivity scale against the reciprocated resistivity scale. If they disagree, use only the conductivity scale.
3. Check the zero conductivity recording in a zone of very high resistivity, such as a dense limestone.
4. Look for drift of the zero conductivity line in a series of high-resistivity beds.
5. Check zeros.
6. Look for abrupt sharp peaks characteristic of instrument troubles.

   Occasionally:
1. Compare the various values recorded on the "Houston checks" with each other. This will require prior instruction on what to check and how much drift may be tolerated.
2. Compare repeat log if run.

MICROLOG, MICROLATEROLOG, AND CONTACT LOG

Before and During Logging

   Always:
1. Be sure a good sample of mud was collected and ask that R_{mf} and R_{mc} be determined.
2. Discuss scales with logging engineer, using as a guide another log which gives you what you want. *The curves should extend over two full tracks.* In case of doubt as to scales, use:
   Microlog, fresh mud: 20 R_m, 2 tracks; 10 R_m, 1 track
   Microlog, salt mud: 50 R_m, 2 tracks; 25 R_m, 1 track
   Microlaterolog, salt mud: same scale as electrical log
   Microlaterolog, fresh mud: 50 R_m, 2 tracks; 25 R_m, 1 track

3. Always request that a microcaliper curve be recorded with all micro type logs. (In some areas it may be desirable to log considerable extra hole in order to obtain a caliper survey which can be used in the interpretation of various other logs as well as for the calculation of cement requirements.)
4. Ask for an R_m check which is recorded running in the hole with the microsonde collapsed.
5. Ask the engineer to record the galvanometer zeros at the bottom and top of the logged interval and the electrical zeros in the pipe as for electrical logs.
6. Ask the engineer to make notes of any places where the tool was sticking.
7. Ask that the monitoring curve be recorded on microlaterolog, if possible.
8. Logging speed generally should not exceed 1500-2000 ft per hour.

Occasionally:

1. Look at pad to see that it is in good shape, free of cracks and cuts and that the electrodes are properly recessed.
2. Run repeats over zones of interest to check reproducibility.
3. Ask if the special kit for calibration was used with the microlaterolog.
4. Check to be sure that all information regarding the type of tool is recorded in headings.
5. Run expanded depth scale for detail in very thinly interbedded zones.

After Log Is Run

Always:

1. Check zeros.
2. Check that information as to type of tool is recorded on the log heading.
3. Check repeats and overlaps, if any.
4. Check that one microlog curve can be distinguished readily from the other.
5. Compare resistivity of shales in uncaved sections (as indicated by microcaliper log) with values recorded by other resistivity logs.
6. Look at the general character of the log to see if it has intervals that you cannot interpret. Resurvey "peculiar" intervals, if possible.
7. Check the value of mud resistivity recorded by the collapsed microsonde with the value recorded on the log heading.
8. If significant negative separation occurs opposite many or most shale intervals, inquire into the condition of the tool pad.
9. Look for intervals with abnormally smooth curves where the hole is enlarged beyond the limit of the springs, or where the tool stuck but the cable was moving because of stretch.

RADIOACTIVITY LOGS OF ALL TYPES

Before and During Logging

Always:

1. Ask the engineer to put on the log heading all information required to identify the type tool used and its characteristics.

These are:
   a. Type detector: Geiger counter, scintillation counter, or ionization chamber.
   b. Length of detector.
   c. Type of neutron source.
   d. Type neutron log: neutron-gamma, neutron-slow neutron, neutron-fast neutron.
   e. Neutron source to detector spacing.
   f. Any serial or code numbers which may be used by instructed personnel to further identify the tools.
2. Ask the logging engineer to record calibrations and zeros before going in hole, at bottom and at top of survey. Nearly every company has a different method of calibrating its logging tools; therefore, it is important that the logging engineer be asked to give all the information needed to check his calibration.
3. Ask for a 2- or 3-minute statistical check, preferably in dense zones for the neutron, and shale for the gamma ray.
4. Ask for 150-ft repeat, preferably over the zone of interest.
5. Note that recording of these checks on the log applies to all radioactivity logs including the gamma ray run just for correlation.
6. Where thin beds are of interest, use short detectors (counters or chambers).
7. Ask for the SP (if possible) when logging in open hole for accurate correlation purposes.
8. Ask that collars be logged in cased hole logging even though they are of no interest at present. This may save another run in subsequent work on the well.
9. Consider the need for a caliper with the neutron is used as a porosity log.
10. Find out what system is being used to correct for the time lag between tool and recorder. Have this noted in the remarks of the log heading. In connection with correcting for time lag, it is necessary to know where to pick bed boundaries on the particular log being run.
11. Run two sets of statistical checks and repeats in high-activity and low-activity zones. Normally this would be one set in a clean dense limestone and another set in shale.
12. Where the background statistics are of the same order as the meaningful variations, and nothing can be done about it in terms of logging speed, time constant, and sensitivity, log the interval of interest four times and draw an average curve from these four runs.

Occasionally:

1. Investigate the sensitivity, time constant, and logging speed being used; and by repeats, changing these variables and comparing with other nearby logs, be sure you are getting the best log possible.

After Log Is Run

Always:

1. Superimpose repeat over log. If the reproducibility is so poor that it would change interpretation, have the log rerun.

2. Check zeros and calibration. These should not vary by more than half a division. If worse than this, consider rerunning log.

3. Compare core analyses with neutron porosity using the approved technique for the log under study. If there is gross disagreement, look for trouble in zeros and calibration.

SONIC LOG

Before and During Logging

Always:

1. Have the engineer select a logging scale which will give a range of deflection of at least ten divisions.

2. Have the sonic log recorded across two tracks.

3. If no radioactivity log has been run in the well use the gamma log-sonic log combination. If another gamma log will be run, use the sonic log-SP combination log (unless the coring and testing program specifies otherwise).

4. To ensure that all intervals are logged with a sufficiently sensitive scale, request a change of scale at each major change of lithology and matrix velocity. In almost all cases, carbonate sections should be logged with the most sensitive scale, 40-80 μsec. It is difficult to check the calibration of the 40-100 μsec scale, and this scale should usually be avoided.

5. Ask the engineer to record the bias voltage settings on the log heading. All changes of the bias control should be recorded on the film at the depth where the change was made.

6. Check that maximum logging speed is not greater than 5000 ft per hour. If the 1-ft detector spacing is used, a slower logging speed may be necessary. (This depends on the speed of galvanometer response; the engineer should know.)

7. Request that the complete calibration procedure be recorded on both field and final prints. Have the galvanometer mechanical zero recorded at top and bottom of the log.

8. The coring and testing program for the logged well will normally specify whether the 1-ft or 3-ft detector spacing should be used. If spacing is not specified, use the 1-ft detector spacing at least through all potential reservoir horizons.

9. The sonic log can be run with or without centralizers. This appears to make little difference for formation evaluation, but for seismic velocity information use of centralizers is preferable. Therefore, use them unless difficulty is expected because the hole or mud are not in good condition. Have the engineer record on the log heading whether or not centralizers were used, and how many.

10. Obtain 5 in.-100 ft detail over all potential reservoir zones and 10 in.-100 ft or 25 in.-100 ft detail over all intervals recorded on these vertical scales on other logs.

11. Ask the operator to record under "Remarks" on the log heading any unusual log response he notices while running the log.

12. Have 50 ft of log run in casing, even if the sonic log is not run to the top of the hole. This gives a useful velocity scale check point.

Occasionally:

1. Relog 200 ft of hole at half logging speed, to check galvanometer response. If the half-speed log has any additional detail, the logging speed is too high.
2. Relog a reservoir interval with several different bias control settings to observe if any improvement in log quality results.
3. Relog an interval with a different horizontal scale, as a check on the log calibration.

After Log Is Run

Always:

1. Check that all information needed to interpret the log is on all prints. Horizontal scales should be recorded at the top and bottom of each change of horizontal or vertical scale. The heading should be complete. Details of all bias settings should be recorded under remarks. The detector spacing should be given for all log sections. The presence or absence of centralizers should be shown.
2. Check the log calibration against another sonic log run in the same area, if one is available. The two logs should read very nearly the same in thick shale sections, opposite anhydrite or salt beds, and in tight dolomite and limestone sections.
3. If another log is not available for a time scale check, see if the transit time recorded is reasonable opposite beds of known lithology. Low-porosity carbonates should read in the range of 44-50 μsec. Anhydrite should have a transit time of about 50 μsec, salt of about 67 μsec. Deeply caved intervals may read the mud velocity, if the sonde is centralized; this should be of the order of 200 μsec.
4. Check log for excessive cycle skipping, or triggering due to "noise" (indicated by sharp deflections to the right). These may be due to incorrect bias control setting. If they will interfere with the log interpretation, consider rerunning the intervals with a different bias setting.
5. Check the bed definition of the log to see if it is adequate for the spacing used. The sonic log has no adjacent bed effect. Therefore, the 1-ft spacing should show 1-ft beds and the 3-ft spacing should show 3-ft beds.
6. Compare all overlaps and repeat runs. If any discrepancies are noted in the recorded interval velocities, ask the operator to explain them.

TEMPERATURE SURVEYS

Before and During Logging

Always:

1. Consider getting collars recorded and using as a depth measurement log.
2. When using the log to locate a cement top, record at least 1500 ft above expected top at the same constant speed.
3. Generally it is desirable that a weight be used to get uniform descent of the tool.
4. Ask that the second galvanometer spot come on the log several hundred feet before the first goes off to facilitate measurement of temperature gradients.

Occasionally:
1. Check the temperature in the air and in the mud pit against a good thermometer.
2. Use the heat of the hand and cold water to see if the instrument is working.
3. Check with logging company office as to optimum speed of recording and
   see if engineer records at this speed. Different thermometers have different
   optimum recording speeds.
4. Look at survey current to be sure that it is kept constant during survey.
5. Consider repeat log coming out to check something unusual, such as an
   unexpected cement top depth.

CALIPER OR SECTION GAGE

Before and During Logging
   Always:
1. Ask that a recording be made in the pipe as a check of calibration.
2. When possible, get the SP even though displaced.
3. Check the scale to be used. For log interpretation you should be able to
   distinguish changes of $\frac{1}{8}$ in.

   Occasionally:
1. Ask to see the calibration checked with rings and gages which should be on
   the truck for that purpose. Do this before and again after survey.
2. Have repeats run, preferably on bottom.

After Log Is Run
   Always:
1. Check recording in pipe against inside diameter of pipe.
2. Check hole size in dense zones near bottom against bit size.

   NOTE: Sometimes it may be more desirable to run a combination microdevice—microcaliper log over extremely long intervals rather than to run the
caliper log alone. The cost is only slightly more in most cases and would provide
the extra information of the microdevice.

PHOTOCLINOMETER

Before Going in Hole
   Always:
1. Tell the logging engineer at what interval to run stations (400 ft, 300 ft,
   200 ft). If available, driller's drift measurements should be reviewed.
2. If the hole is apt to be off more than 7°, tell the engineer so he can use
   10° or 20° glass.

   Occasionally:
1. Check the compass needle away from the rig; white end points south.
2. See that the pendulum swings freely.
3. See if the ball rolls freely.

4. See that the brass weight is run on the end of the tool.
5. Run the photoclinometer in the casing every 400 ft to get deviation although no direction.

COLLAR LOG

Before Log Is Run

Always:

1. Ask for the magnetic collar locator.
2. Ask for a field print of the collar log simultaneous with the correlation log (gamma ray, neutron, or temperature).
3. Find out time and depth lag between the collar log and the correlation log and ask that this be put in the remarks.

After Log Is Run

Always:

1. Check the logging engineer's pick of collars on the field print, original, or film. If there is any doubt of the accuracy of a collar location, it should not be recorded.

CONTINUOUS DIPMETERS

Before and During Logging

Always:

1. Ask that the caliper curve scale be shifted to place the bit size within one and a half divisions of the edge of the film so that interference between the caliper curve and the correlation curves will be minimized. Caliper should be capable of recording a 16-in. hole size.
2. Request the correlation curves to be recorded with zeros 5.0 divisions apart and with maximum deflections of between 5.5 and 6.5 divisions. Sensitivity should be chosen so that minimum deflections are at least 0.5 division.
3. Ask for headings complete with scales and types of instrument to be included on all rolls.
4. Ask for a minimum of 100 ft of repeated log on the bottom of the run and a maximum of 100 ft of overlap between rolls. (A roll of paper covers about 2000 ft of hole.)
5. Ask for a logging speed of not over 40 ft per minute.
6. Have a 2-in. or 5-in. scale dipmeter log recorded and delivered along with the regular 60-in. scale.
7. Ask for all calibration steps to be recorded on the bottom and/or top of the survey.
8. Check log as it is run to note zones which should be repeated.
9. Run repeats over important zones.

After Log Is Run

Always:

1. With the logging engineer check the survey for excessive sonde rotation. (This and most other checks are more easily made on the 2-in. or 5-in. scale.)

The dipmeter is inaccurate because of lag if rotating more than 2 rpm. At a logging speed of 40 ft per minute this would be one revolution each 20 ft. If rotation exceeds this, the section must be resurveyed. (Minute markers appear on all Schlumberger logs as short skips in the first vertical line on the left edge of the log.)

2. Check for poor contact or a floating pad. This is evidenced by low resistivity and lack of detail on one curve when present on the others and will, of course, occur where the hole is excessively enlarged. Often it is the result of insufficient spring pressure and can be corrected with relative ease.

3. Check the orientation curves. One of these records the azimuth of the No. 1 electrode, and the second records the relative bearing of the downside of the borehole with respect to the No. 1 electrode. In checking these curves be sure that both completely traverse the 360° of the scale and remain essentially parallel except where the hole drift changes direction. The third curve records the inclination of the borehole *without* regard to direction and must not reflect the rotation of the sonde. The orientation curves should be relatively smooth with no "stairstepping" except when the hole is very nearly vertical, where the inclination curve may bounce a little in rough holes and where the relative bearing curve may wander.

4. Ask the logging engineer to have both the fixing and washing of the log checked with the chemicals available for this purpose.

SIDEWALL SAMPLING

Before Going in Hole and While in Hole

Always:

1. Discuss in advance with engineer loading of bullets for hard or soft rock sampling.
2. In hard rocks pick sampling points off the microlog, find the same point by correlation on the SP.
3. Ask that shooting be done by observing the SP rather than line depths alone.
4. Consider repeats in very important zones on the same run to avoid a possible rerun for only one or two samples.

Occasionally:

1. Pick a very thin sand break in shale (about 12 in.), and sample to check depth measurement.
2. Repeat samples on different runs to check depth accuracy.

After Sampling

Always:

1. If samples are not removed from bullets by you, be on hand to observe removal of every one and carefully check the labeling of the samples.
2. When cores are to be analyzed for porosity, leave the samples in the bullets if possible.

Appendix B

Pressure-Temperature Ratings of Downhole Tools and Hole Size Limitations*

The recommended minimum hole sizes are for open-hole sections longer than 5000 ft in unconsolidated formation. For other hole conditions the minimum may be decreased, using the following correction table.

Length of Open Hole, ft	Correction, in.	
	Consolidated Formations	Unconsolidated Formations
Less than 500	-1	$-\frac{1}{2}$ to -1
Between 500 and 2500	$-\frac{1}{2}$ to -1	$-\frac{1}{2}$
Between 2500 and 5000	$-\frac{1}{2}$	0
Greater than 5000	0 to $-\frac{1}{2}$	0

The recommended maximum hole sizes are determined by the following considerations:

1. For noncentered tools, the hole limitations for quantitative use of the log.
2. For centered and wall contact tools, the maximum spring expansion.

In regard to the rated maximum temperature it must be kept in mind that the length of time that a tool with complex electric circuits is exposed to the maximum temperature is very important. The ratings given here are for exposures for 3 hours of tools in excellent condition. Repeated exposure to high temperature will eventually cause a tool to fail.

Heads and torpedoes can be used at temperatures considerably over their rated maximum temperatures, but if this is done, the "O" rings or gaskets should be replaced after each job.

* Courtesy of Schlumberger Well Surveying Corporation.

Service	Tool O.D., in.	Hole Size, in. Min.	Max.	Max. psi	Max. Temp.°F
Electrical logging					
Chronological sonde S-21	$3\frac{3}{8}$	$5\frac{1}{2}$	12	15,000	300°
Chronological sonde S-54 and 55	$3\frac{5}{8}$	$5\frac{1}{2}$	12	20,000	350°
Drill stem sonde S-22	2	a	8	20,000	350°
Drill stem bridle and weight S-56	$1\frac{1}{2}$	a	6	20,000	350°
Induction logging					
Induction-resistivity	$3\frac{7}{8}$	$6\frac{1}{2}$	12	15,000	300°
Induction-resistivity type E	$3\frac{7}{8}$	$6\frac{1}{2}$	12	20,000	400°
Laterolog					
Laterolog 7-LLS-G, H	$3\frac{5}{8}$	6	18	20,000	350°
Conductivity LL	$3\frac{7}{8}$	$6\frac{1}{2}$	12	20,000	300°
Microlog					
Microsonde, WRS-S	$5\frac{5}{8}$	6	9	15,000	300°
Microsonde, WRS-T	$6\frac{1}{8}$	7	16	15,000	300°
Powered microsonde PMS-A, Type IX pad	$4\frac{9}{16}$	$4\frac{3}{4}$ b	9	20,000	350°
Powered microsonde PMS-A, Type I pad	$5\frac{1}{16}$	$6\frac{1}{2}$	16	20,000	350°
Powered microsonde PMS-B	$5\frac{1}{16}$	$6\frac{1}{2}$	20	20,000	350°
Powered microsonde, PMS-A, Special	$5\frac{1}{16}$	$6\frac{1}{2}$	16	20,000	400°
Microlaterolog					
Powered microlaterolog sonde PML-A	$5\frac{1}{16}$	$6\frac{1}{2}$	16	20,000	250°
Powered microlaterolog sonde PML-B	$5\frac{1}{16}$	$6\frac{1}{2}$	20	20,000	250°
Surface exploration					
Core hole sonde	$2\frac{1}{4}$	$4\frac{1}{2}$	10	20,000	350°

a Determined by drill pipe I.D.
b Absolute minimum.

Service	Tool O.D., in.	Hole Size, in. Min.	Hole Size, in. Max.	Max. psi	Max. Temp.°F
Radioactivity logging					
Gamma ray or gamma ray-neutron with Geiger-Müller GR detector	$3\frac{5}{8}$	$6\frac{3}{4}$	14	15,000	275°
Gamma-ray or Gamma ray-neutron with Scintillation GR detector					
Type F	$3\frac{5}{8}$	$6\frac{3}{4}$	14	20,000	300°
Type H	$3\frac{3}{8}$	$6\frac{3}{4}$	14	20,000	400°
Midget gamma ray or Neutron	$1\frac{11}{16}$	2 tbg.	10	12,000	350°
Chlorine log	$3\frac{5}{8}$	5	12	20,000	275°
Gamma gamma PGT-A	$3\frac{5}{8}$	$4\frac{3}{4}$	14	20,000	300°
Directional survey					
Photoclinometer	$3\frac{3}{8}$	6	—	15,000	250°
Continuous directional	$3\frac{5}{8}$	6	—	20,000	350°
Continuous Dipmeter					
Poteclinometer	$5\frac{1}{4}$	$6\frac{1}{2}$	16	20,000	350°
Section gage	$5\frac{9}{16}$	6	36	15,000	300°
Temperature					
Deep well thermometer DWT-B	$3\frac{7}{8}$	6	—	15,000	300°
Deep well thermometer DWT-S	$1\frac{11}{16}$	2 tbg.	—	15,000	340°
Deep well thermometer DWT-B, special	$3\frac{7}{8}$	6	—	15,000	400°
Sonic logging					
With centralizer, Type B	$4\frac{1}{2}$	7	12	15,000	250°
With centralizer, Type C	$4\frac{1}{2}$	7	12	15,000	375°
Cement bond logging					
Type C	4	$4\frac{3}{4}$	$13\frac{3}{8}$	15,000	250°
Type CBT-A	$3\frac{3}{8}$	4	$13\frac{3}{8}$	20,000	375°
Lost circulation	5	$6\frac{1}{2}$	14	15,000	300°

Service	Tool O.D., in.	Hole Size, in. Min.	Hole Size, in. Max.	Max. psi	Max. Temp.°F
Sample taker					
CST-C	$5\frac{3}{8}$	$8\frac{1}{2}$	13^c	20,000	275^{od}
CST-U and V	$4\frac{3}{8}$	$6\frac{1}{8}$	$9\frac{7}{8}^c$	20,000	275^{od}
CST-W	$4\frac{3}{8}$	$4\frac{3}{4}^e$	$9\frac{7}{8}^c$	20,000	275^{od}
Formation Tester					
FTM-B	$6\frac{1}{4}$	$7\frac{7}{8}$	$12\frac{1}{4}$	20,000	250^{of}
FIM-A with 4-in. blocks and open hole pads	5.1	6	$10\frac{5}{8}$	20,000	250^{of}
FIM-A with 4-in. blocks and cased hole pads	4.4	$5\frac{1}{2}$ casing	10 casing	20,000	250^{of}
FIM-A with $5\frac{1}{4}$-in. blocks and open hole pads	6.25	$7\frac{3}{8}$	$12\frac{1}{4}$	20,000	250^{of}
FIM-A with $5\frac{1}{4}$-in. blocks and cased hole pads	5.65	$6\frac{5}{8}$ casing	$11\frac{3}{4}$ casing	20,000	250^{of}
FTS-B and D	4	$7\frac{7}{8}$	$12\frac{1}{4}$	20,000	340°
FTS-C	5	$7\frac{7}{8}$	$12\frac{1}{4}$	10,000	340°
FSA	4	$5\frac{1}{2}$ casing	12 casing	20,000	340°

[c] Larger sizes possible with special fasteners and centralizers.
[d] May go to 350°F with special powder and igniter.
[e] Absolute minimum with short bullet.
[f] May go to 340°F with special powder.

Appendix C

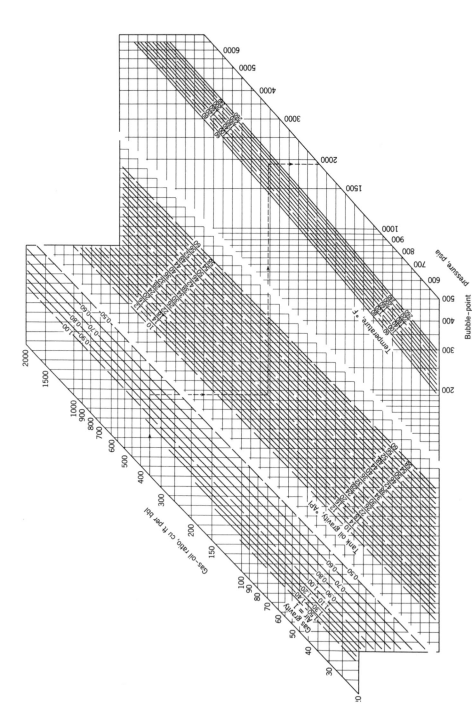

Fig. C-1. Gas solubility as a function of pressure, temperature, gas gravity, and oil gravity. (Copyright 1947 by California Research Corporation. Reprinted by permission.)

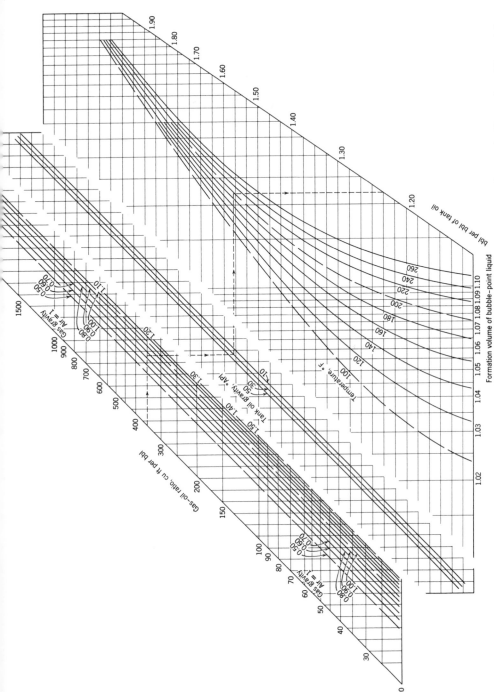

Fig. C-2. Oil-formation volume factor as a function of gas solubility, temperature, gas gravity, and oil gravity. (Copyright 1947 by California Research Corporation. Reprinted by permission.)

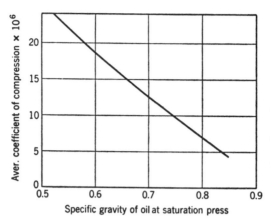

Fig. C-3. Average coefficient of compression as a function of oil gravity at the saturation pressure. (Reproduced by permission from John C. Calhoun, Jr., *Fundamentals of Reservoir Engineering*, revised edition. Copyright 1953 by University of Oklahoma Press.)

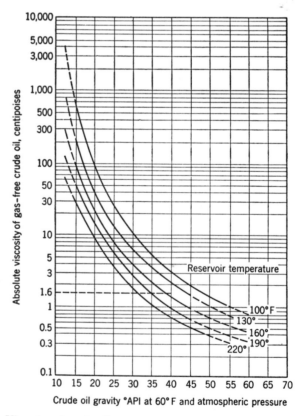

Fig. C-4. Viscosity of crude oil at one atmosphere pressure. (After Beal, courtesy of the AIME.)

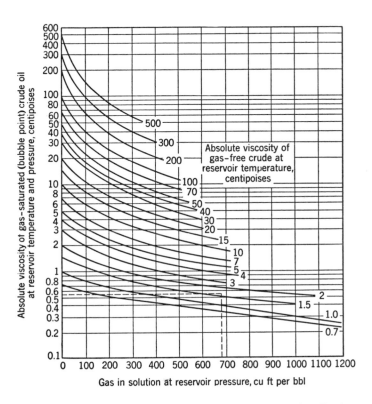

Fig. C-5. Viscosity of crude oil at reservoir conditions. (After Beal, courtesy of the AIME.)

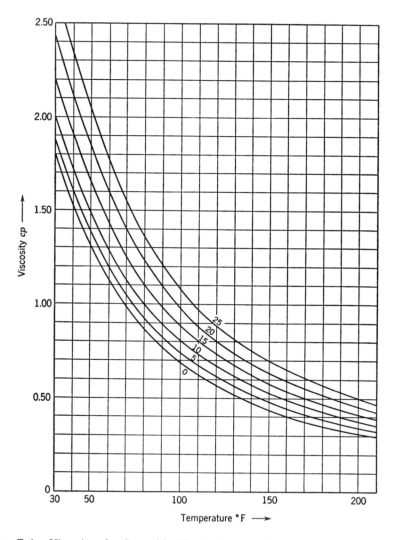

Fig. C-6. Viscosity of sodium chloride solutions as a function of temperature for solutions containing 0, 5, 10, 15, 20, and 25 g of sodium chloride per 100 g of water. (Reproduced by permission from Emil J. Burcik, *Properties of Petroleum Reservoir Fluids.* Copyright 1957 by John Wiley and Sons, Inc.)

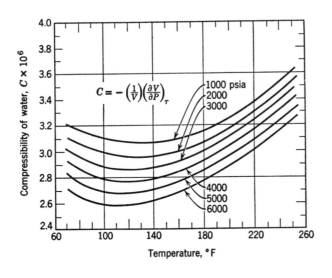

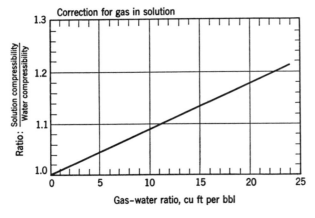

Fig. C-7. Effect of dissolved gas on the compressibility of water. (Reproduced by permission from Dodson and Standing, API Drilling and Production Practice, 1944.)

Appendix D

Pipe Capacities

INTERNAL UPSET DRILL PIPE

Size, in. Outside Diameter	Inside Diameter	Weight per Foot	Linear Feet per Barrel
$2\frac{3}{8}$	1.815	6.65	312.50
$2\frac{7}{8}$	2.151	10.40	222.22
$3\frac{1}{2}$	2.764	13.30	134.77
$3\frac{1}{2}$	2.602	15.50	151.68
4	3.340	14.00	92.31
$4\frac{1}{2}$	3.826	16.60	70.32
$4\frac{1}{2}$	3.640	20.00	77.66
5	4.276	19.50	56.17
$5\frac{1}{2}$	4.778	21.90	45.04
$5\frac{1}{2}$	4.670	24.70	47.20

TUBING

Nominal	Size, in. Outside Diameter	Inside Diameter	Linear Feet per Barrel
1	1.315	1.049	934.5
$1\frac{1}{4}$	1.660	1.380	504.5
$1\frac{1}{2}$	1.900	1.610	396.8
2	2.375	2.041	246.9
2	2.375	1.995	258.3
$2\frac{1}{2}$	2.875	2.441	172.7
3	3.500	3.068	109.4
3	3.500	2.992	114.9
3	3.500	2.922	120.6
$3\frac{1}{2}$	4.000	3.548	81.8
$3\frac{1}{2}$	4.000	3.476	85.1
4	4.500	3.958	65.7

Index

Index